Samantha King.

EXPLOSION INVESTIGATION

THE FORENSIC SCIENCE SOCIETY

A Series of Monographs

A BIBLIOGRAPHY ON ETHYL ALCOHOL FOR FORENSIC SCIENCE AND MEDICINE AND THE LAW
by R. Holleyhead

EXPLOSION INVESTIGATION
by H. J. Yallop

Editors

P. H. Whitehead
B.Sc., Ph.D., F.R.I.C.

W. A. Harland
M.D., Ph.D., F.R.C.Path., F.R.C.P.

EXPLOSION INVESTIGATION

by

H. J. YALLOP
O.B.E., M.A., B.Sc., C.Chem., F.R.I.C.

with a foreword by

S. S. KIND
B.Sc., M.Phil., F.I.Biol.

Published by

THE FORENSIC SCIENCE SOCIETY
AND
SCOTTISH ACADEMIC PRESS

Published by

The Forensic Science Society
Clarke House
18A, Mount Parade
Harrogate HG1 1BX
England

and

Scottish Academic Press Limited
33 Montgomery Street
Edinburgh EH7 5JX
Scotland

ISBN 0 9502425 5 1
ISSN 0143 0254

Printed in Great Britain by
Clark-Constable Ltd, Edinburgh

CONTENTS

v

FOREWORD

The Forensic Science Society was inaugurated in 1959 with the object of facilitating and encouraging discourse by both the spoken and written words amongst forensic scientists and members of the associated professions, law medicine and the police. The Society has met with considerable success in achieving these aims, firstly by the holding of bi-annual symposia on specific forensic topics, which are treated from a multidisciplinary viewpoint, together with smaller meetings treating rather more specialised subjects. In addition, the Journal of the Society, now in its 21st year of publication, has made a major contribution to the dissemination of information in the forensic sciences throughout the world. However, for some time, the Council of the Society has felt the need for monographs to be produced on various topics of particular interest to the forensic scientist. This book is one in this series of monographs.

The information and expertise contained here is the result of wide reading and long experience. It is the distillation of a career in the investigation of explosion incidents and in the subsequent presentation of the findings to a variety of judicial bodies.

The book is the first of its kind in the English language and, as such, it will be invaluable for the inexperienced and experienced specialist alike; the first will find an invaluable textbook and the second will find, at the very least, an excellent complement to his own expertise by providing fresh slants on old problems. Books such as this improve the quality of life both by helping to bring the bomber to account in terrorist outrages and by improving safety design by determining the causes of accidental explosions. It is to be hoped that it reaches as wide a responsible public as possible.

Specialists are, in general, unrenowned for their facility with the pen. Fifteen years as a scientific editor has left me with little confidence that things will improve in the foreseeable future but books such as this cause a hope to remain. Surrounded by the sea of jargon which assails us from every quarter it is refreshing to encounter one of the few scientific writers who follow Rickman's dictum of 1836:

> '... the direct purpose, and therefore the first
> merit, of writing, is to be easily read by all.'

John Rickman would have no complaint with John Yallop.

S S Kind
President
The Forensic Science Society

PREFACE

The identification of the causes of explosions is one of the oldest branches of forensic science. Isolated investigations are on record from a comparatively early date. These range from an observation by the Duke of York, after an attempt to assassinate King George III in 1800, that a slug which he extracted from the plaster of a pillar had been fired because it smelt of powder, to various more scientific investigations of accidents with government explosives made by Sir Frederick Abel later in the nineteenth century.

Systematic study of the subject in the United Kingdom dates from 1871. In that year an explosion occurred at the Patent Gun Cotton Company's factory at Stowmarket. An enquiry was conducted by Captain V. D. Majendie (later Colonel Sir Vivian Majendie, K.C.B.) who was the official Home Office Inspector. He decided that it would be necessary to enlist the services of a qualified chemist and obtained those of Dr. A. Dupre, F.R.S. Dr. Dupre carried out various chemical investigations into the cause of the explosion and gave expert evidence at the coroner's court.

The association continued and by 1873 Dr. Dupre had become the Chemical Adviser to the Home Office Explosives Department and was concerned in the investigation of many accidental explosions. He also extended his work to the criminal field and rendered considerable assistance to the police at the time of the Fenian outrages in the early 1880's.

Dr. Dupre remained in active practice until his death in 1907 when his sons, P. V. and F. H. Dupre, succeeded him in the consultancy. In 1923, for reasons of public policy, it was thought to be inappropriate that this service should continue to be undertaken by a private consultancy. On 1 April of that year the work was transferred to a newly formed Home Office section of the War Office Research Department at Woolwich Arsenal. Continuity, however, was ensured by appointing Mr. F. H. Dupre to take charge.

The Home Office branch continued with the duties of advising H.M. Inspectors of Explosives and with providing a forensic science service for the police. It retained its identity through many governmental reshufflings of ministries and still continues its work as a branch of the Royal Armament Research and Development Establishment.

It will be seen, therefore, that the systematic investigation of the causes of explosions by H.M. Inspectors of Explosives and the Woolwich Laboratory has a continuous history since 1871. This is sixteen years before the publication of the first Sherlock Holmes story, twenty two years before the first publication of Hans Gross's classic work *Handbuch für Untersuchungsrichter*, thirty nine years before the foundation of Edmund Locard's Institute of Criminalistics, and sixty four years before the foundation of the Metropolitan Police Laboratory in London.

Some forty years ago it was a common practice for authors of scientific books to express, in the preface, the hope that the book would fulfil a long felt need. This fashion appears to have died out. Whether the omission is an indication that present day authors doubt whether they are fulfilling a need, may be debatable. It is more likely that a new book is, almost inevitably, one further addition to a plethora of previous works already published on the subject.

Although the subject of explosion investigation is one of relative antiquity, and although many accounts of individual investigations and techniques have been published, no attempt appears to have been made hitherto to bring this body of knowledge together. I hope, therefore, that I can justly express the wish that this book will fulfil a long felt need. The book must, of necessity, be somewhat in the nature of a pioneering work. I should, therefore, be very pleased to receive constructive criticisms from all those who take part in the investigation of explosions, in the hope that the deficiencies of the first edition may be made good in a second. May I also express the hope that I will be spared the modern cult of public castigation for minor errors and omissions by critics who have lacked the resolution to write a book themselves.

One of the problems of forensic science is that the facilities may range from elaborate laboratories to observations in the field with no equipment at all. This situation and its consequences has been succinctly described by E. B. Hensel (1):

Forensic Science is at best a lonely trade, standing unique in the law enforcement field in that its practitioners cannot look for guidance and assistance from their police and lawyer associates. They can only get help from others of their own kind, and their nearest colleague may be thousands of miles away in another country. Books and periodicals are the only ready source of forensic information to the man in Singaradja, Zihuatanejo, or the Seychelles. He has no other specialist with whom he can consult.

If we delete the simple tests from the textbooks or confine our periodical contributions to esoteric methodology and elaborate instrumentation, we are not being fair to our occasional colleagues in the hinterland. . . .

Every publishing forensic scientist should pause now and then as he drafts another ponderous paper designed to impress his peers. Let him remember his less fortunate colleague in a remote place who has little equipment and a problem on his hands. However forensically untrained, these men need all the help they can get from us. Our books and periodical articles can give it to them.

A great deal can be done in explosion investigation by simple observation on the scene with no more elaborate equipment than a notebook and pencil, a measuring tape, and a camera. Eventually, however, some form of laboratory work will be needed. For this part of the investigation I have described, as far as possible, simple methods which do not require elaborate and costly apparatus and facilities. Apart from their ready applicability such methods have the merit of being more likely to be comprehensible to police and lawyer associates and, above all, to members of a jury.

None of this is to say that more elaborate methods are to be despised. The investigator should always be ready to consider the use of whatever technique is most likely to give an adequate answer to the problem in hand. It is not, however, always possible to use the ideal method and the choice of a technique must often be a compromise between what one would like, what is available, where it is, and the urgency for an answer of some sort.

In acquiring the necessary knowledge to write a scientific book, the author must of necessity be beholden to many people. This book is no exception and I gladly acknowledge my indebtedness to all those from whom I have acquired knowledge whilst at the same time absolving them from any responsibility for the use I have made of it. In particular, I am indebted to various members of Her Majesty's

Inspectors of Explosives, a number of my fellow-members of the Forensic Science Society and to fellow-representatives at the United Nations Group of Experts on Explosives. Above all, I am indebted to my former colleagues of the Royal Armament Research and Development Establishment. Rather than cause unwitting offence by the omission of a name I prefer to quote none but to express my grateful thanks to all those, of whatever rank, with whom I worked in that Establishment. Finally, I must thank all those, whether professional or amateur, who have subjected me to cross-examination in the courts. Their questions have often served to provoke fresh and valuable thought on many aspects of explosion investigation.

Chapter 1

INTRODUCTION

THE SCOPE OF THIS BOOK

This book is intended as a practical handbook for explosion investigators; that is, those who are called upon to make an investigation
with the object of identifying the cause of an explosion. There is a
number of aspects of the science and technology of explosives which
this book does not set out to encompass. It is not intended as a source
of instruction in the science of explosives, because it is presumed that
an investigator will always have an adequate grounding in the subject. Since, however, it is hoped that the book will prove of value to
lawyers, policemen, and others who will be associated with explosion
investigations, a chapter on the basics of explosives has been added.
More detailed treatments will be found in various standard works. A
selection of these is listed as References 2 to 10 inclusive.

The science and technology of explosives is a very large subject
and a comprehensive treatise would occupy many volumes. In this
book only such aspects as are relevant to explosion investigation are
considered. It will be found, therefore, that while some aspects, such
as chemical analysis and damage effects, are discussed in some depth,
others, such as the hydrodynamic theory of detonation and manufacturing techniques, are barely mentioned. It must be emphasised,
moreover, that it is a book on the subject of identifying the causes of
explosions. This does not include either the field or laboratory work
required in dealing with live explosive devices, either manufactured
or home-made. Some knowledge of this field is, however, important
background information for an explosion investigator, who is presumed to have studied some of the published books on the subject
(References 11 to 15 inclusive.)

Finally, this book does not deal with nuclear explosions. These
have not hitherto required the attention of the explosion investigator
and there seems little immediate prospect that they will do so.

The explosion investigator can be called upon to attempt to identify

1

the cause of many types of explosion. These can conveniently be classified as follows:—

ACCIDENTAL EXPLOSIONS

1. *Accidents in manufacture, transport and storage*

1.1. *Accidents with recognised explosives*

The essence of all explosives is that they are chemical compounds or mixtures in which much energy is stored and that this energy can be released quickly. In normal use some mechanism is used that will release it at a predetermined time in order to perform useful work. It is necessarily inherent in such a system that the energy may inadvertently be released at some other time, thus causing an accidental explosion. The possibility of such accidental explosions is an ever-present hazard in the manufacture, transport, and storage of explosives. Many precautions are taken to guard against such occurrences and the explosives industry the world over nowadays has a very good safety record. Nevertheless carelessness and the unforeseen mean that accidental explosions do occur, even in this carefully regulated field. These occurrences vary from comparatively trivial incidents in manufacturing processes, in which the safety precautions ensure that damage is restricted, to major disaster such as that at Brescia, Italy in 1769, when some 80,000 kg of gunpowder exploded, and that at Halifax, Nova Scotia in 1917, which involved 2,350,000 kg of high-explosive in the form of a ship's cargo of ammunition.

1.2. *Accidents with substances which are not recognised explosives but which are known to possess explosive properties*

There is a number of industrial products which, while not manufactured with a view to using them as explosives, nevertheless are capable of exploding. This is an unwanted and hazardous feature against which precautions have to be taken. Examples of such materials are ammonium nitrate fertilizers containing organic matter and some organic peroxides. Accidental explosions can and do occur from time to time with such materials.

1.3. *Accidents with substances not hitherto known to possess explosive properties*

Any chemical compound or mixture which is capable of decomposing with evolution of energy is potentially explosive. It does not follow, however, that any such material will necessarily possess explosive properties and so this possibility is usually ignored. From time to time accidents occur in which compounds or mixtures, hitherto believed not to be capable of explosion, do in fact explode. These incidents range from minor ones in chemical laboratories to major disasters such as that in Oppau, Germany, in 1921, when 4,000,000 kg of an ammonium nitrate mixture exploded.

1.4. Accidents with substances made by home experimenters

Explosives appear to exercise a fascination for many people, especially juveniles, perhaps because the ability to cause an explosion gives a sense of power. As a result, despite legislation designed to protect the public by prohibiting the manufacture of explosives except under authorised conditions, many instances occur of experimenters making explosives in private houses, garden sheds, and other unsuitable premises. The knowledge possessed by the experimenter is usually fragmentary and safety precautions are almost invariably non-existent. Their activities frequently come to the notice of the police and neighbours by an explosion from which the experimenter may or may not escape uninjured. The experiments usually run on well-worn lines either by the mixing of readily available oxidants with fuels or by the synthesis of nitroglycerine. A wide variety of other substances is, however, also found in cases of this type.

While most such cases involve experimenters a few involve small-scale illicit manufacture either for commercial sale or for criminal purposes.

2. Accidents occurring during the use of explosives

2.1. Accidents with explosives

All those who have to handle explosives in mining, quarrying, agriculture, civil engineering, and other activities in which blasting operations are carried out should be trained for their work. Familiarity, however, is liable to breed contempt, with a consequent relaxation of safety precautions. There is, therefore, a history of accidents among users of explosives. Often these are relatively minor explosions with, however, above-average chance of fatal injuries being inflicted.

2.2. Accidents with explosive devices

There are a great many devices for all kinds of purposes which depend for their operation on explosives. These include military munitions, sporting ammunition, industrial actuator cartridges, air-craft and spacecraft actuator devices, entertainment industry effects, explosive toys and fireworks. All are manufactured to be safe and reliable, in some cases reliability of a very high order indeed. Nevertheless some defective products will inevitably reach the hands of users and no manufacturer can guard against careless handling, disregard of instructions or wilful misuse. In consequence, accidents with high explosive devices can and do occur.

3. Accidental occurrences

3.1. Dusts

Any combustible material in sufficiently finely divided form can form a suspension in air, or dust cloud. If the correct proportions of dust and air are present, the cloud will be explosive and can be set off by spark or flame. The classic example of this is in flour milling, an industry in which many dust explosions have occurred.

3.2. Gases

Many gases are capable of forming explosive mixtures with air. Any accidental leak of such substances may, therefore, lead to an explosion. Gases in common use which can form such explosive mixtures include hydrogen, liquefied petroleum gases such as butane and propane, acetylene and the various gaseous mixtures supplied for industrial and domestic heating systems. Explosions of this type have produced effects varying from the very minor to the demolition of complete buildings.

3.3. Vapours

Many volatile organic liquids can evaporate and produce explosive mixtures with air. These include such materials as petrol, alcohol, paint thinners and some industrial solvents. The effects produced have a similar range to that for gas/air mixtures.

3.4. The unsuspected presence of explosives

There is a long history of accidental explosions caused by the unsuspected presence of explosives. Many of these accidents have given rise to serious injuries. Familiar examples are the presence of explosives or detonators in domestic coal supplies and in war souvenirs believed to have been empty. Perhaps the most striking of all such occurrences (1935)* was that of 25 July 1935 at Waverley, Nova Scotia, where a disused explosives factory was being made safe by firing small charges of explosive on the sites of old buildings and drainage ditches where nitroglycerine might have been present. Four shots had been fired on the shore of a lake and no evidence of nitroglycerine was observed. It was decided, however, to fire another shot near the lake where there was evidence that nitroglycerine might have flowed from a building which had last been in use prior to 1910. A detonation occurred leaving a crater 45 m long, 15 m wide and 8 m deep. It was estimated that about 8000 kg of nitroglycerine must have been present in the ground.

3.5. *Mechanical explosions*

The term explosion is usually reserved for the effects produced when there is a sudden release of energy stored by chemical means in a compound or mixture of the type described as an explosive. Somewhat similar effects can, however, also be observed when there is the sudden release of energy stored by physical means. Occurrences of this kind are referred to as mechanical explosions and include such things as the bursting of boilers and pressure vessels generally and the bursting of tyres.

At first sight it would seem that deliberate explosions would not require the services of an explosion investigator to identify the cause since this must be known. For the most part this is so. There are, however, some classes of deliberate explosion where the cause is not known to those who have a need to know and where the only possible way of finding out is by investigation. These explosions can conveniently be classified as follows:

DELIBERATE EXPLOSIONS

1. *Amateur experiments*

As was pointed out above, explosives have a fascination for some people and ill-considered experimentation takes place. The experimenters usually wish to test the effects of their products and carry out trials, often with little regard for the safety of themselves or others. The attention of the police having been aroused by the explosion, they arrive at the scene only to find that the experimenter has gone and the services of an explosion investigator are needed to attempt to determine what has happened.

* See References (p. 262) for source

2. Bomb attacks in the furtherance of private or political ends

2.1. Attacks against persons

While direct attacks are not unknown, almost all attacks of this kind are made with explosive infernal machines; *i.e.* lethal devices designed to go off when the intended victim is present but the attacker is not. The long history of such devices shows that they have mostly been time bombs or booby traps, but the range is as wide as perverted human ingenuity and misapplied science can make it. The classic example is the attempt to blow up King James and the Parliament of Great Britain on 5 November 1605, familiarly known as the Gunpowder Plot. Another famous case is the attempt to blow up Hitler in 1944. Other familiar examples are the explosive parcel and letter bombs which have been widely used in recent decades for both private and political aims.

2.2 Attacks against property

Here again the main agent for attack is the explosive infernal machine, though the charges are usually larger, sometimes much larger than those used against persons. Attacks of this type have been numerous and world wide, ranging from single acts of private revenge to para military operations such as those carried out by dissident political groups. Incendiary infernal machines are also used in this type of activity.

2.3 Aircraft sabotage

A recent development in bomb attacks is that against aircraft. It is inevitably an attack both upon property and persons. It is even more marked than other forms of attack on property for the callous indifference to whether the consequences fall on persons wholly innocent from any participation in the cause it is aimed to further. This form of explosion is particularly difficult to investigate since by its very nature the evidence is scattered over a wide area.

2.4 Suicide

Throughout history people have taken their own lives by a wide variety of means. A fairly common technique since the introduction of firearms is for the victim to shoot himself. A less usual, but not unknown, method is to use high explosives. There is for example a long history of suicide by the detonation of a blasting cartridge placed in the mouth. Other methods are on record.

3. *Breaking offences by criminals*

3.1 *Attacks on premises*

The application of explosives in the furtherance of breaking offences has been widespread for more than a century. One such application is to use explosives in order to gain entry to a premises believed to contain desirable articles. Attacks have been mounted on doors, windows, gates, walls, roofs and floors. Attempts have even been made to open explosives magazines by this method, but this carries the hazard that the explosion may set off the contents of the building, as one criminal found to his cost—he was standing within the crater radius

3.2. *Attacks on security containers*

Another aspect of breaking offences with explosives is their use to open security containers. This essentially comprises attacks on safes and strongrooms. For many years this form of activity has involved a competition between the designers of safes and the attackers. Despite improvements in design, it may safely be predicted that there is little likelihood that security containers will become so unrewarding a target that this field of work will disappear for the explosion investigator.

THE EXPLOSION INVESTIGATOR

THE ROLE OF THE INVESTIGATOR

When an explosion occurs which calls for investigation, the explosion investigator will find that he is not the only person involved. All have their contribution to make and the explosion investigator must not attempt to do things which are properly the responsibility of others, nor they his. The exact number of people involved will vary from case to case. There are, however, many different tasks to be undertaken and the people performing them can conveniently be described as follows.

1. *The person in charge of the enquiry*

Three types of person can fill this role. Where there are civil or criminal proceedings in a court of law, then the responsibility for the enquiry rests on the judge, magistrate, coroner or other member of the judiciary appointed as president of the court concerned. He may or may not be assisted by a jury in deciding matters of fact. At an earlier stage, and exclusively in cases not giving rise to court proceedings, a police officer will normally be in charge of the enquiry. In some cases some other person will be specially designated to conduct an enquiry. Thus, in the United Kingdom the Explosives Act 1875 empowers the Secretary of State to direct an enquiry to be made by a Government inspector into the cause of accidents arising from explosions in certain defined circumstances. The exact functions of this person will vary according to the legal system in force but essentially he will be concerned with all aspects of the occurrence and not just with what exploded and why.

2. *Police officers*

In almost every case of an explosion calling for an investigation, police officers will be involved. They are likely to be the first persons called to the scene and will be involved in public safety, crowd control, preservation of the integrity of the scene and other activities. Police officers will also be responsible for identifying and interrogating witnesses and for various specialist duties such as photography and identification of fingerprints.

3. *'On-call' technical experts*

It is important that somebody with a knowledge of explosions and explosives should be available to be called to the scene at the earliest possible moment. This role is often filled by the explosion investigator but in some places, such as the London area, it has been found more satisfactory to appoint specialist explosives officers for this task. This person has two essential tasks to perform: (i) as far as may be possible, to render the scene safe from further explosion hazard, and (ii) to use his specialist knowledge to ensure, again as far as may be possible, that all relevant evidence is preserved.

4. *The explosion investigator*

The task of the explosion investigator, who may or may not also be the on-call expert, is to determine what caused the explosion.

5. *Other experts*

According to the nature of the occurrence, a number of forensic scientists and other experts may also be involved. Pathologists and biologists may be needed to consider injuries to persons. Physicists and chemists may be needed to consider a wide range of materials such as paint flakes, glass fragments and safe ballast. Other specialists who may be involved include vehicle examiners, structural engineers and fire brigade officers.

6. Witnesses to fact

Any explosion enquiry will involve some witnesses of fact. There will be those directly involved, who may be able to give evidence of the explosion itself. Others may have knowledge of relevant attendant circumstances and others, less directly concerned, of such matters as the whereabouts of persons suspected of unlawful activities.

7. Lawyers

Lawyers will be concerned in many explosions enquiries. They perform two main functions. The first is to act as the person responsible for marshalling and presenting the evidence. The second is to represent the interests of a party, whether individual or organisation, involved in the occurrence.

This delineates the function of the explosion investigator and shows how it fits in with the responsibilities of others. He must, of course, work closely with them and carry out his investigation with due regard to their needs. He will receive information which may be of value in interpreting his observations from police officers, the on-call expert, other experts and witnesses to fact. He will be required to provide information to the person responsible for the enquiry, police officers and lawyers.

THE QUALIFICATIONS OF THE INVESTIGATOR

An explosion investigator must be suitably qualified. Explosion investigation is not a task which can successfully be undertaken as a part-time sideline by policemen, general forensic scientists, academic chemists or military personnel. It is essential that, if an explosion investigator is to be regarded as an expert, he should as a minimum possess the following qualifications:

1. He must know how to investigate an explosion

This may sound obvious but many people have tried to investigate explosions with very inadequate ideas of how to set about the task.

It is hoped that this book will prove helpful to those who wish to learn.

2. *He must have an adequate academic qualification*

Probably the best basis is a university degree or its equivalent in chemistry with its consequent subsidiary knowledge of physics and mathematics, supplemented with some knowledge of engineering and statistical analysis. Other variants of full professional knowledge in these subjects also form satisfactory bases. Professional status of this type, though desirable, is not absolutely essential and, as in other scientific disciplines, relevant experience can be an adequate substitute for some measure of formal academic training. There is little doubt, however, that, rightly or wrongly, the opinion of the man who possesses formal academic qualifications is likely to be accepted with more readiness than that of the man who does not.

3. *He must have a very broad based knowledge of explosives*

Some explosives scientists have an extremely detailed and highly authoritative knowledge of a particular branch of the subject. This sort of background is not a satisfactory one for an explosion investigator. The reason is that the explosion investigator will be confronted with cases in which the explosive may be domestic or foreign, commercial or military, solid, liquid or gaseous, manufactured or home made, initiatory, propellent, detonative or pyrotechnic, which may or may not be incorporated in devices which in themselves contain mechanisms of a similar wide range of origins. It is vital, therefore, that the explosion investigator should have a knowledge of explosives which embraces all these aspects.

4. *He must have experience in the field and of the practical handling of explosives*

Explosion investigation is not an armchair exercise. Theoretical approaches have their part in the whole investigation but to have attended and worked on many scenes of explosions is essential experience for an investigator. He should also have much practical experience in the handling of explosives. In particular, he should have seen and heard all types of explosive and explosive device functioning. Such experience is an invaluable foundation for evaluating the likely causes of observed effects.

5. *He must have command of adequate laboratory facilities*

Almost all explosion investigations involve the physical examination of exhibits and many involve chemical and other examinations in addition. In addition, tests on explosives and trial explosions may have to be undertaken. It is not feasible for any explosion investigator to have a laboratory fully equipped for the complete range of investigations he may need to undertake. It is essential, however, that he should be able to gain access to such facilities as required. Provided he has arranged adequate access, his own laboratory need only be relatively simple.

6. *He must be able to convey his findings to laymen*

The explosion investigator will, from time to time, need to convey his findings, his knowledge and his experience to fellow scientists. In addition, he will constantly be required to convey his findings to laymen. It is vital, therefore, that he should possess the attribute essential to all forensic scientists of appreciating what a policeman, lawyer, or other layman wants to know and then of being able to convey the information in clear language.

THE INVESTIGATOR AND THE LAW

The explosion investigator is not a lawyer and it is not part of his duties to usurp the lawyer's function. Nevertheless, there are certain aspects of law with which the investigator should make himself familiar. While it is desirable for him to be conversant with the explosives legislation of his own country, especially that regulating manufacture, transport, and storage, as well as international transport regulations, it is vital that he should be fully aware of two matters in particular.

The first of these is that he must have a working knowledge of the law in respect of those who may have statutory duties and interests in the explosion to be investigated. Thus in the United Kingdom, H.M. Inspectors of Explosives are concerned with explosions on premises licensed by themselves, H.M. Inspectors of Factories with explosions in factories, and the Ministry of Fuel and Power with explosions in coal mines. Likewise, the police have responsibilities in connection with explosions where crime may be involved and, in England, the Coroner where a fatality has occurred. In many cases these interests are multiple so that, for example, a fatality caused by an explosion in a factory would involve H.M. Inspectors of Explosives, H.M. Inspectors of Factories, the police, and the Coroner, at least. The explosion investigator will have been called in by someone concerned, probably the police, possibly one of the others mentioned or perhaps by an aggrieved party or an insurance company. It is essential that he should be aware of the rights and duties of everyone involved and should ensure that his actions are consistent with them. Secondly, he should always bear in mind that the results of his investigation may have to be presented in a court of law. He should ensure, therefore, that he is conversant with the rules governing evidence and the collection of exhibits, and conduct his investigation with due regard for them.

Chapter 2

FUNDAMENTALS OF EXPLOSIVES

WHAT IS AN EXPLOSIVE?

Explosion is a word in common, everyday use. It is one of those words of which we all know the meaning until we try to define it, when it appears to be less obvious. It is best defined by stating the three factors which are necessary and sufficient for the existence of a state of explosion. These are:

1. That gas is released.
2. That energy is released.
3. That 1 and 2 are released very rapidly.

The effect of these three in combination is that high pressure gas is produced suddenly and it is the effect of this on the surroundings that is described as an explosion. That all three factors are necessary to create an explosion becomes apparent if they are considered two at a time. A coal fire releases gas and energy but, because it does not do so very rapidly, there is no explosion. Gas is released very rapidly when the valve of a compressed gas cylinder is opened but since there is no release of energy there is no explosion. A thermite heating charge releases energy very rapidly but since there is no production of gas there is no explosion.

It follows from this that an explosive is a substance which is capable of producing the three requirements of an explosion. For a substance to act as an explosive there is, however, a further requirement, making four in all:

1. It must be capable of producing gas.
2. It must be capable of producing energy.
3. 1 and 2 must occur very rapidly.
4. 1, 2 and 3 must be self-sustaining; that is, they must continue throughout the mass of the explosive when started at any point within it.

13

These four properties constitute those required for a substance to be an explosive. No others are necessary. If an explosive is to be of practical use, however, one other is essential, and many others may be desirable in explosives for particular applications. The essential property is that the explosive is not spontaneously explosive, *i.e.* it will only explode when caused to do so. Other properties which may be desirable for particular applications include the ability to withstand high or low temperatures, the ability to withstand rough handling and the capability of being moulded or alternatively of retaining a predetermined shape.

PYROTECHNICS

The term explosives is usually extended to embrace a further group of substances, namely pyrotechnics. There are several reasons for this. Some pyrotechnic devices incorporate recognised explosives such as gunpowder. Many pyrotechnic compositions are capable of producing explosions, particularly if misused. Most pyrotechnic compositions require similar safety precautions in manufacture, transport, storage and use to those required for explosives.

The extent of the field of pyrotechnics is one for which there is no agreed definition. There are a great many substances, such as the majority of firework compositions, which are generally accepted as being pyrotechnic substances. There does not appear, however, to be complete agreement on such topics as the range of effects which are included in the term 'pyrotechnic effect' nor of the extent, if any, to which a pyrotechnic composition should, like an explosive, function independently of atmospheric oxygen. A reasonable working definition is that a pyrotechnic substance must function by non detonative, self sustaining, energy producing, chemical reactions and that the effects produced should include heat, light, sound, gas or smoke or any combination of these.

Just as the term explosive is extended to cover certain substances which are not strictly explosives, so the term explosion is conveniently extended to cover certain phenomena which, although not produced by explosives, have essentially the same characteristics. These are known as mechanical explosions. They occur in some instances when the pressure of a compressed gas exceeds the structural strength of its container, which then bursts. If the consequent release of high pressure gas is rapid enough it produces blast effects similar to that of a conventional explosion. The only essential difference between a mechanical explosive and a conventional one is that, whereas the energy of the latter is derived from chemical reactions, that of the former is derived from the kinetic energy of the compressed gas. Other phenomena, not involving explosives but which produce explosive effects, include thermal explosions, which occur when a liquid comes into contact with another at a temperature significantly above the boiling-point of one of them, chemical explosions, in which rapid chemical reactions occur with the production of heat and gaseous products, and electrical explosions, in which a sudden heating occurs owing to an electric spark.

THE CONSTITUTION OF EXPLOSIVES

Explosives depend for their effects upon chemical reactions which produce energy and gaseous products. In theory, any chemical reaction which fulfils these two requirements could form the basis for an explosive. In practice, however, the vast majority of explosives depend on two reactions, the oxidation of hydrogen:

$$2H_2 + O_2 \rightarrow 2H_2O \uparrow$$

and the oxidation of carbon:

$$C + O_2 \rightarrow CO_2 \uparrow$$

which can also be expressed as a two stage reaction:

$$2C + O_2 \rightarrow 2CO \uparrow$$
$$2CO + O_2 \rightarrow 2CO_2 \uparrow$$

Both these reactions are very familiar in everyday life, forming as they do the essential basis of much domestic heating, whether by the burning of oil, gas or solid fuels. Such processes rely on the air for their supply of oxygen and, hence, the speed with which energy is produced depends on the speed with which this can be brought into contact with the fuel. This mechanism is too slow for the production of explosive effects, except in the case of a preformed gas/air mixture, and so other techniques have to be used. There are two basic ones:

(1) The first technique of doing this is to make a mechanical mixture of a compound which will decompose to release oxygen, with carbon or substances containing carbon, hydrogen or other fuel. A number of sources of oxygen (oxidants) are available. These include

nitrates, nitrites, chlorates, perchlorates, permanganates, chromates, and dichromates. Fuels can be carbon, a wide range of compounds containing carbon and hydrogen, metals, and other substances. The classic explosive of this kind is gunpowder, the original and only explosive available until well into the nineteenth century. Gunpowder consists of a mixture of potassium nitrate (saltpetre), carbon (charcoal) and sulphur. The proportions have varied down the years and still differ according to the purpose for which the gunpowder is to be used, but a common formulation is 75 potassium nitrate, 15 carbon and 10 sulphur. Although the essential effect of producing energy is accomplished by the oxidation of the carbon, the overall reaction is complex. An equation which is believed to represent the reactions is:

$$10S + 30C + 20\,KNO_3 \rightarrow 14CO_2 + 10\,CO + 10N_2 +$$
$$6\,K_2CO_3 + 3\,K_2S_3 + K_2SO_4$$

It will be seen that more than 50% by weight of the products are solids, which means that gunpowder is less effective as an explosive than it might be. It shares this characteristic with many other of the explosives made by mixing an oxidant with a fuel. An exception is liquid oxygen explosive (LOX) which is made by absorbing liquid oxygen on to carbon and which can achieve, in theory, the production of nothing but gaseous carbon dioxide.

(2) A drawback of the mixture type explosives is that, even if the constituents are finely ground, there are, on the atomic scale of proportions, relatively large lumps of oxidant and of fuel. Thus considerable mixing has to occur in the explosion process before the chemical reactions can fully take place. The relative slowness resulting does not matter for some applications. More rapid reactions can be achieved from an explosive made by having the oxidant and fuel incorporated into a single compound, both then being present in every molecule. This is the basis of many explosives, including many well-known ones such as nitroglycerine and TNT.

However, not all compounds containing carbon, hydrogen, and oxygen are explosives. Thus methyl alcohol:

        H
        |
  H—C—O—H
        |
        H

is not explosive. The reason for this is that the oxygen is already linked to carbon and hydrogen so that as much energy would have to be put in to disrupt the molecule as would be derived from the formation of water or carbon dioxide from the individual atoms so produced. In order to produce a net release of energy it is necessary for the oxygen to be present in a form in which it is linked to some atom other than carbon or hydrogen. This is effected by the use of one or more of the following groupings:

nitro $-NO_2$
nitroso $-NO$
nitrate $-ONO_2$
nitramine $>NNO_2$

This principle is illustrated in the formulae of some well known explosives:

TNT
(2, 4, 6-trinitrotoluene)

RDX
(cyclotrimethylene trinitramine)

$$CH_3 \qquad NO_2$$
$$N$$
$$|$$
$$C$$

Tetryl
(2, 4, 6-trinitrophenylmethyl $O_2N{-}C \qquad C{-}NO_2$
nitramine)
$$HC \qquad CH$$
$$C$$
$$|$$
$$NO_2$$

$$H_2C{-}O{-}NO_2$$
Nitroglycerine $HC{-}O{-}NO_2$
$$H_2C{-}O{-}NO_2$$

Apart from compounds containing carbon, hydrogen, and suitably linked nitrogen, there are some others which possess explosive properties since they contain combinations of atoms which ensure that disruption produces energy and gaseous products. These include some of the azides (containing the grouping $-N_3$), acetylenes and acetylides (containing the grouping $-C{\equiv}C-$) and some peroxides (containing the grouping $-O{-}O-$).

THE CLASSIFICATION OF EXPLOSIVES

Although all explosives are alike in that they are capable of producing gas and energy very quickly, they are not all alike in their explosive behaviour. It is possible, therefore, to select explosives to achieve different results. Thus, an explosive which is suitable for propelling a bullet from a gun is useless for breaking boulders in a quarry, and, conversely, a boulder breaking explosive would shatter a gun instead of propelling a bullet. In practice it is found convenient to divide explosives into two broad classes, deflagrating explosives and detonating explosives. This classification is not absolute since some deflagrating explosives can, in some circumstances, behave as detonating explosives and detonating explosives can, under some circumstances, behave as deflagrating explosives. Nevertheless it is a practical and convenient classification.

Deflagrating explosives include gunpowder, cartridge propellents, pyrotechnic compositions, and similar materials. These substances behave differently according to whether or not they are in a container. When ignited in the open, intense heat is produced but there is normally no explosion. If, however, they are ignited in a closed container the pressure rises owing to the production of hot gases. This pressure rise, in turn, causes an increased rate of chemical reaction and so an accelerating reaction is produced. As a result an explosion occurs. The time taken by the whole process is of the order of a few thousandths of a second which, by explosion standards, is relatively slow. Deflagrating explosives are used in applications where a comparatively slow pushing action is required, such as in weapon cartridges and rockets or in pyrotechnics where the effects desired are heat, light, etc., but where blast effects are to be avoided.

Detonating explosives include military high explosives such as TNT and industrial blasting explosives such as gelignites. In small quantities these explosives will burn quietly if ignited. If, however, they are initiated by a powerful shock, a detonation is induced. This consists of a supersonic shock wave which travels through the explosive causing it to explode. The energy of the explosion reinforces the shock-wave which thus becomes self sustaining. Once initiated, this type of explosive will, in general, sustain the detonation whether confined or not. The speed with which the detonation traverses the explosive is characteristic of the explosive, though affected by other parameters, namely the density, diameter, and nature of confinement of the charge. Since these speeds (detonation velocities) mostly lie in the range 2,000 to 9,000 ms^{-1} it will be seen that the time taken by the whole process is of the order of a few millionths of a second, some thousand times faster than for deflagrating explosives. Detonating explosives are, therefore, used in applications where shattering effects are required, such as blasting operations and for the filling of military shells and bombs.

Detonating explosives are usually referred to as high explosives. Deflagrating explosives were formerly referred to as low explosives but, for no particular reason, this convenient term has tended to drop out of favour.

Another useful classification is that of primary and secondary explosives. In all practical applications it is necessary to cause the explosives to explode at a predetermined time. This is done by the application of a stimulus consisting of energy in the form of a mechanical blow, heat, flame, spark, friction or any other suitable means. Many explosives, high explosives in particular, require a large stimulus which, although convenient for safety in reducing the risks of accidental explosion, is inconvenient in practical application. These difficulties are overcome by the use of a small charge of an explosive which is easily set off and acts as the source of initiation of the main charge. In this way only explosives which are relatively difficult to set off and so relatively safe to handle need to be used for main charges in large quantities, whereas the more easily set off and, hence, more dangerous explosives are used in small quantities and can be incorporated in devices designed to ensure safety. Easily set off explosives of this type are designated primary explosives and those more difficult to set off secondary explosives.

Since the difference between primary and secondary explosives is one of degree and not of kind, there is no agreed demarcation between them. Well known explosives generally accepted as primary, however, include mercury fulminate, lead azide, lead styphnate and compositions containing them. Secondary explosives include military high explosives such as RDX and TNT and industrial blasting explosives such as gelignites and gun propellents. In practical applications, primary explosives are used in initiating devices such as detonators for setting off blasting explosives, fuzes for setting off shells, bombs and other military munitions, and percussion caps for igniting the propellent charge in cartridges.

THE ASSESSMENT OF EXPLOSIVE PROPERTIES

In order to determine whether a material is an explosive and, if so, for what purposes it is suitable, its explosive properties must be determined. A multitude of methods of determining the many explosive properties has been devised. Some relate directly to a product, whether an explosive substance or an article containing an explosive substance, while others set out to measure fundamental properties of the explosive. In the latter case, attempts have been made, mainly in the last 50 years, to make the measurements more 'scientific'. The result has all too often been to produce results with a misleading air of accuracy which are further and further removed from the problems of safety in handling and design for use, which are the only justification for the assessments attempted.

Although there are many properties of explosives which must be assessed, they can be conveniently grouped under four headings, namely sensitivity, stability, explosive effects and 'in use' effects. A brief description of the main properties encompassed by these four groups, together with the methods used to assess them, follows.

SENSITIVITY

Much confusion has been and is caused by the existence of the two words sensitivity and sensitiveness. They relate to two rather similar properties of explosives, namely the ease of initiation and the propagating ability. In some circles it is customary to use sensitivity to mean the former and sensitiveness to mean the latter, in others the converse obtains and in yet others the words are used synonymously. In everyday English the two words are synonymous and the confusion has arisen from attempts to force them not to be synonyms for scientific purposes, instead of coining new and more suitable words to describe the concepts involved. Throughout this book the word sensitivity, qualified where necessary, will be used to cover this branch of the subject.

There are five main forms of sensitivity:

1. *Sensitivity to impact*

This represents the ease, or otherwise, with which an explosive can be set off by a blow. The method of assessment is, almost invariably, a falling-weight test in which, by more or less elaborate means, a weight is dropped on to a sample of the explosive and the height required to cause explosion is measured. Various forms of apparatus are in use but, although all are basically similar, the results are not strictly comparable from one to another. The results are expressed as relative to that for a standard explosive, nowadays usually RDX, but should, like the results of most explosives tests, be regarded as indicative only.

2. *Sensitivity to friction*

This represents the ease with which an explosive can be set off by friction. The classic method is to spread a sample of explosive on a flat plate and strike it a glancing blow with a hammer. By varying the weight of the hammer and the materials, both of the hammer head and the plate, and observing the incidence of explosions, it is possible to arrive at an estimate of the probability of an explosion. In particular, it is possible to assess the effects produced by materials likely to be encountered in manufacturing processes.

Various pieces of apparatus have been devised to replace this manual test, many based on the pendulum principle. So far, however, no one method has won universal acceptance.

3. *Sensitivity to static discharge*

This represents the ease with which an explosive can be set off by an electrostatic spark. The method of determining it is to subject samples of the explosive to single discharges and to determine the maximum energy of the spark to which it can be subjected without being ignited.

4. *Sensitivity to heat*

This represents the ease with which an explosive can be set off by heat. Two aspects are usually considered. The first is the temperature of ignition. Many pieces of apparatus have been devised for measuring this but all are basically similar in providing a method of heating a sample of explosive and observing the temperature at which it explodes. The second aspect is inflammability, that is the ease with which an explosive can be ignited by flame. Some ignite readily and burn fiercely while others will only burn if an outside source of heat is applied continuously.

5. *Sensitivity to shock*

This represents the ease with which an explosive can be set off by shock from another explosive charge. The classic technique is the gap test in which a donor charge is separated from a receptor charge. The donor charge is detonated and in various experiments the gap is found which is just sufficient to cause the receptor charge not to go off. The gap may be an air one or filled with various substances. In other variants of this test the shock is induced by detonators of various strengths or mechanically by projectiles such as rifle bullets.

Stability

1. *Chemical stability*

Explosives range from those which are chemically so unstable as to explode spontaneously to those which remain unchanged indefinately. A large number of tests, over 40, have been devised for measuring this property, one of the best known being the Abel Heat Test. All are based on the same principle, namely to accelerate any potential decomposition by heating a sample at a predetermined temperature and observing by chemical or physical means the evolution of gaseous reaction products.

2. *Physical stability*

Explosives for practical use must, if they contain more than one component, be physically stable since separation of one component from the other could lead to a hazardous condition. Separation is a function of both time and temperature and so the normal procedure is to store a sample of explosive at an elevated temperature and observe whether any physical separation of the components occurs. Nitroglycerine can exude from badly made gelignites under pressure. Further tests have, therefore, been devised for these materials, in which samples are subjected to standard compressive forces and any exudation observed.

Explosive Effects

1. *Detonation velocity*

The velocity of propagation of a detonation wave through an explosive is directly measured in cgs units and is thus capable of precise determination. There are three basic techniques in use. The first is the classic method of Dautriche in which the velocity is determined by comparison with that of a standard detonating fuse which, however, must itself be evaluated by some other method. This method is obsolescent but some find it convenient by virtue of the simplicity of the apparatus required. The second method is to observe the movement of the detonation wave directly, by means of one of various forms of high speed camera. The third method exploits the fact that the detonation wave is electrically conducting and its passage may be observed by means of electrical detectors coupled to elaborate electronic equipment.

2. *Brisance*

Brisance is a term which is undeservedly out of favour but is of great value to users of explosives and particularly to explosion investigators. Essentially it is the shattering power of the explosive and attempts have been made to devise an apparatus to measure it without any marked success. It is, however, approximately linearly related to detonation pressure which is itself related to the density (ρ) and the detonation velocity (D) of the explosive:

$$p = f(\rho D^2)$$

It will be found in practice that the product ρD^2 makes an adequate substitute for brisance.

3. *Power or strength*

This is a measure of the amount of energy released by an explosive on detonation and hence of its ability to do useful work. The two main methods in use for measuring this are the lead block or Tranzl test and the ballistic mortar or pendulum. In the former, a small charge is detonated in a hole in a block of lead and the increase in volume of the hole is compared with that produced by a standard explosive. In the latter a small charge is detonated in a freely suspended mortar and its movement is compared with that produced by a standard explosive.

4. *The effect of ignition*

On ignition some explosives will burn quietly whereas others explode or even detonate. A range of tests has, therefore, been devised in which samples are ignited, either in closed or in open containers, and the behaviour observed directly or by instrumental methods.

5. *Communication*

It is important to know, in a given package containing a number of similar explosive charges or explosive devices, whether the accidental explosion of one will or will not cause the remainder to go off. The process of determining this is known as communication testing. The basic principle is to cause one charge or article to explode by means of a realistic stimulus and then observe the results. Details of the procedures cannot be compressed into a short account since they are as many and as varied as are explosives and explosive devices.

IN USE EFFECTS

There is a wide variety of properties which explosives must, or must not, have if they are to be used for particular applications. Some of these are as follows:

1. *Water resistance*

Explosives differ widely in their resistance to penetration of water. A knowledge of water resistance is, therefore, important in selecting an explosive for a particular purpose.

2. *Freezing resistance*

It is important for safety that explosives containing nitroglycerine should not freeze. Such explosives must, therefore, be tested for resistance to freezing to ensure that antifreeze additives are effective.

3. *Fume production*

It is essential that explosives for use in confined spaces should produce a minimum of toxic products. Tests are, therefore, carried out to identify and estimate the gases from explosives.

4. *Gallery tests*

Explosives for use in gassy or dusty coal mines must be designed to minimise the risk of igniting methane or coal dust/air mixtures. All such explosives are required to exhibit their failure to cause such ignitions when fired in a standard gallery. In the United Kingdom, explosives passing this test are designated as permitted explosives.

5. *Tests for undesirable characteristics*

Many explosive devices, such as fireworks, can exhibit undesirable characteristics in use. These characteristics are so varied that no comprehensive list can be formulated. The test procedure, therefore, is to cause a number of samples to function and to observe if there are any effects more hazardous than those hitherto regarded as acceptable in broadly similar products.

SOME COMMON EXPLOSIVES

The total number of explosives in use is very large, even if those used for the filling of explosive devices are excluded. A comprehensive list would fill a sizable volume. It is possible, however, to indicate the nature of the commoner ones most frequently encountered in explosion investigations.

1. *Nitroglycerine based industrial explosives*

Dynamite is the simplest of these, nitroglycerine being the only active ingredient. It should be noted, however, that in the United States the term dynamite is used to denote any blasting explosive containing nitroglycerine (Appendix N).

Gelignites are based on nitroglycerine gelatinised with nitrocellulose, various additional ingredients being used in individual compositions. Gelignites containing a high proportion of nitroglycerine are described as gelatines. Those containing ammonium nitrate are described as ammon gelignites. It should be noted, however, that, while manufacturers generally follow these conventions in referring to their products, they do not invariably do so and these must not be regarded as hard and fast rules.

2. *Ammonium nitrate based industrial explosives*

Industrial blasting explosives based on ammonium nitrate, excluding the ammon gelignites, fall into three types. Ammonium nitrate powders are usually based on ammonium nitrate and TNT. ANFO explosives are based on ammonium nitrate and fuel oil. Slurry explosives or slurry blasting agents are based on ammonium nitrate and water. Both of the latter two types are available as factory made products or as components which are mixed on site.

3. *Military blasting explosives*

These are mainly based on RDX and PETN (pentaerythritoltetranitrate). Other ingredients may also be encountered including nitroglycerine, TNT, and DNT (dinitrotoluene).

SOME COMMON EXPLOSIVE DEVICES

Explosive devices are even more numerous than explosives. A complete catalogue would not only be very extensive but would rapidly become out of date since new devices and new applications for explosives are constantly appearing. It is possible, however, to obtain a broad picture of this field by considering the main effects that explosive devices are designed to produce.

1. Devices for initiation or ignition

Detonators contain primary explosive and are used for initiating high explosives. They are usually operated mechanically, electrically or by flame and may function instantaneously or after a delay.

Igniters contain primary explosive or pyrotechnic composition and are used for igniting deflagrating explosives. They are usually operated mechanically, normally by percussion, electrically or by flame.

Fuzes are devices incorporating a detonator and are used for initiating detonation in munitions such as shells, bombs and mines or in similar contrivances. They can be very complex and may incorporate such features as safety and arming mechanisms, time-delays and proximity actuators.

Fuses are flexible tubes with an explosive core used for transmitting flame or detonation from one point to another. They range from a slow burning safety fuse, through faster burning fuses to a detonating fuse used primarily to transmit detonation from one high explosive charge to another. The word fuze is also used to denote this type of device but the normal convention is to use the words fuze and fuse in the senses given above.

2. Devices for propulsion

Cartridges for weapons are the devices used to propel projectiles from the barrels of firearms. They contain an igniter, often a percussion cap, and a propellent charge. They may contain one or more projectiles, which may be of plain metal or may contain tracer, incendiary or other compositions. A variant is the blank cartridge which contains no projectile and is used to produce a noise only.

Actuator cartridges, likewise, contain an igniter and a charge of propellent explosive. They are used to operate mechanisms and are widely distributed. The uses include such operations as the fixing of bolts into walls, aircraft ejector seat operation and cattle killing.

Rockets need no explanation and range from the simple display device to the sophisticated mechanisms used for interplanetary travel.

3. Devices to produce blast and fragments

Military munitions include a wide range of devices designed to produce blast and fragments. They are normally filled with high explosive and include such devices as shells, bombs, grenades and mines.

4. *Devices to produce pyrotechnic effects*

Owing to the spectacular nature of pyrotechnic effects, these find applications not only for serious purposes but also for entertainment. Thus, devices producing sounds include not only coast guard warning signals but also banger type fireworks. Devices producing visual effects include not only signalling flares but also display fireworks. Other products include gas producing devices, which are used for the emergency opening of aircraft doors, heat producing devices, which are used for welding and the emergency heating of tinned foods, and still others produce smoke and are used for signalling, drain testing, and other purposes.

5. *Devices producing other effects*

Since explosives are a form of stored energy which can be released at will, they can be and are applied to a multitude of purposes including ones outside the range outlined above. An example of these is the shaped charge which is used for such diverse purposes as anti tank ammunition, aircraft emergency ejection equipment and the tapping of blast furnaces.

Chapter 3

THE APPROACH TO THE SCENE

IMMEDIATE ACTION

When an explosion occurs, various actions must be regarded as of immediate priority. Clearly any necessary fire fighting and rescue of injured persons comes into this category, but there are certain actions which are the province of the first explosives expert on the scene, whether he be a separate 'on call' expert or the explosion investigator. The first and most important of these actions is to consider whether there appears to be any danger of further explosion and to take steps accordingly. No exhaustive list of circumstances which might lead to further explosions can be drawn up and the expert must make a quick appraisal of each individual scene in the light of his knowledge and experience.

As a guide the following are examples of the type of circumstance which can give rise to further explosions:

1. If the explosion was caused by a solid or liquid (condensed) explosive, there is always the possibility that further unexploded material may be on the floor or other parts of the scene. There is the danger, therefore, that firemen, rescue workers and police officers may cause a second explosion by inadvertently setting off this explosive through treading on it or in some other way. The possibility that this hazard may be present will probably be obvious to policemen and others if the explosion has taken place where explosives are known to be present, such as an explosives factory, a magazine or a rail or road vehicle used for transporting explosives. It is less obvious and, therefore, more hazardous that live explosive may be found on the scene of other explosions such as blasting accidents and safe-breakings.

2. If an explosion has occurred in an explosives process building, or a magazine, or any other place where explosive devices are present, there is the possibility that sensitive devices may now be in such a position that very little disturbance could cause them to fall and

detonate. The potential danger is shown by an accident (1930) when a rubber-covered sample bottle containing 56 g of washed nitroglycerine fell on to a rubber covered floor. When the bottle hit the floor after a fall of 1·2 m it detonated and a hole 0·6 × 1·2 m was made in the floor.

3. Any explosion which causes structural damage is liable to generate a new explosion hazard by the accidental release of gas or vapour. Obvious examples are an explosion which severs a pipe supplying domestic gas or one which breaks the valve of a gas cylinder from which an explosive gas/air mixture can escape. Another example is the explosion which damages a container of a compressed, liquefied or dissolved fuel gas such as hydrogen, propane or acetylene respectively. Here again an explosive gas/air mixture can develop. A third example is the explosion which damages a container of a volatile fuel, such as petroleum, thus allowing an explosive vapour/air mixture to be formed.

4. Other forms of damage by an explosion can increase the probability of a subsequent further explosion by providing fresh sources of ignition. Any electrical equipment or wiring damaged by an explosion is liable to be in a precarious state and so a possible source of sparks.

5. When an explosion gives rise to a fire various possibilities for further explosions exist. The most obvious is that the fire will ignite further explosives on the site. Another possibility is that the fire will cause the disruption of containers of compressed, liquefied or dissolved fuel gas or of a volatile fuel, with the consequent formation and ignition of explosive gas or vapour/air mixtures. Fire can also generate explosive gas or vapour/air mixtures by the pyrolysis of organic materials. The compositions involved are somewhat indeterminate but, since organic materials are very common in the structure, fittings, and contents of buildings, the generation of such mixtures by fires is very common. A further source of second explosions caused by fires is the presence of closed metal containers which give rise to mechanical explosions by reason of the internal pressure generated by heat.

6. Another possibility for a second explosion arises when the first is due to an infernal machine. There are many instances in which saboteurs have placed a second infernal machine on the site with the express purpose of injuring or killing police, fire and rescue workers, military personnel and explosion investigators. The location and neutralisation of such devices is a task for specialists and, unless the explosion investigator has the necessary training, experience, and

equipment to undertake such work, he should on no account attempt it. Nor should he allow an attempt to be made by other laymen. In any circumstance in which the possibility of the presence of such a device is suspected the only proper course of action is to clear the area and await the arrival of an accredited bomb disposal team.

The first action which must be taken in these, or any similar circumstances, is to ensure that all persons are kept at a safe distance. This immediately raises the question of what is a safe distance. Unfortunately this is a question to which no satisfactory answer can be given. The obvious answer is to use a formula relating the weight of the explosive to the distance for a given overpressure on the threshhold of potential damage to persons, say 1 atmosphere. Whilst blast pressure and missile effects are determined to an important extent by the weight of explosive, other parameters must be considered. These include the nature of the explosive, the efficiency of the initiation, the construction of the building in which the explosion is expected to take place and the configuration of the surroundings. Others can assume importance in particular circumstances. To attempt, therefore, to find some simple rule would either produce one which would be liable to prove disastrously misleading or one which erred so far on the side of caution as to verge on the absurd. In any case the circumstances will call for a quick decision with no time for elaborate observations and calculations. The expert must, therefore, make a very quick appraisal and base his judgement of what is a safe distance on an instinctive estimate based on his experience. If his estimate is wrong he will inevitably be criticised, as is everyone who has to make vital decisions on the spur of the moment, usually by those who have had plenty of time and retrospective knowledge to formulate their criticisms and who are not themselves called upon to make such impromptu decisions or to face the hazards of the situations requiring them. If, however, the expert resists all attempts to suggest that this or that formula should have been used, and explains why not, he should have little difficulty in justifying the advice he gave.

Obviously there will be some exceptions to the rule that all persons must be kept at a safe distance. Fire fighters and rescue workers must, in the course of duty, take calculated risks. While the first explosives expert on the scene must not attempt to tell such people how to do their job, he would be failing in his responsibilities if he did not place at their disposal his specialist knowledge of the dangers involved.

Another immediate action which the expert can take is to consider whether there is any possibility of preventing a feared second explosion and, if so, to act accordingly. In this he can only be guided by the circumstances he finds. Some situations can be foreseen. If there has been an explosion which may have left further live explosive on the scene, he can locate, identify, and remove or mark it. If there is a source of gas or vapour, he may be able to devise a safe way of cutting off the supply or otherwise removing it. He can also make a critical examination for potential sources of ignition. If the explosion has produced a fire, then time becomes a critical element. It is sometimes possible, however, after quick observation and questioning, to devise a method for the rapid removal of a source of danger. It must be remembered, however, that the prevention of a second explosion is never worth the cost of a life: if there is any doubt on the feasibility of preventing it, it is far better for everyone to stand well clear and let the explosion occur.

Although safety of persons is the first priority, there is another aspect of immediate action which must be regarded as second only to this. It is vital that at the earliest possible moment the scene should be 'frozen', that is preserved in the immediate post explosion state. If this is not done, much valuable evidence can easily be lost. The greater the integrity of the scene the greater are the chances that the explosion investigation will be successful. It is, of course, inevitable that some disturbance of a scene will occur, since firemen and rescue workers must have first priority, but their activities should be kept to the minimum required to meet immediate needs. The more spectacular the explosion the more likely it is to attract high-ranking police or military officers or politicians. Such visits not only serve no useful purpose and hinder the investigations by virtue of the attentions expected, but are liable inadvertently also to destroy evidence when the VIPs and their retinue make a tour of inspection of the site. Any encroachments on to the site by anyone other than those directly working on the investigation should be tactfully but firmly resisted with, if necessary, a brief explanation of the need for the apparent discourtesy.

THE INVESTIGATOR'S EQUIPMENT

It is clear that the explosion investigator should have some equipment at the scene. It is manifestly impossible for this to encompass everything he will require for his investigation and so the field equipment must, therefore, be a compromise.

INDISPENSABLE ITEMS

1. *Materials for recording information*

These should include a notebook or pad for recording information and a sketch pad of adequate dimensions for making drawing plans. Items for use with these include pencils (or ballpoint pens) in several colours, a ruler and a measuring tape. It is also essential to include a camera. This may be supplemented by further cameras as desired since it may be convenient to have one loaded with colour and one with black and white film. Some investigators may wish to use a Polaroid camera for immediate record or to use a plate camera for producing high definition enlarged prints. It may be possible, however, to obtain the latter through the police or fire service.

2. *Materials for packaging exhibits*

It is certain that it will be necessary to remove some exhibits for further examination under laboratory conditions. In some instances this will include large quantities of debris which can only be transported in paper sacks, large cardboard boxes or other containers conveniently to hand. For all other items the investigator should provide himself with suitable packaging and labels. The most convenient for general use is a supply of plastic bags of a range of sizes. Polythene bags are normally suitable for this purpose but if it is important to preserve volatile materials nylon bags must be used. If sensitive explosives or devices containing them are collected as exhibits a further outer soft packing is needed, but this can normally be obtained on the scene in the form of a suitable box padded internally with crumpled paper or other locally available soft material. Provision should also be made for materials requiring specialist packing. This is a matter for compromise since not every conceivable circumstance can be catered for, but the investigator should give consideration to providing himself with plastic capsules or small papier mâché pots for loose initiatory composition and a supply of kieselguhr or other inert absorbent for nitroglycerine or other sensitive liquid explosives.

Additions to these two items of equipment are largely a matter for the individual investigator, bearing in mind his circumstances.

SOME POSSIBLY USEFUL ITEMS

1. *Sensitivity test equipment*

The distinguishing of very sensitive explosives in the field can be an aid to safety. A simple portable apparatus which will provide a sorting test is shown in figure 3.1. The sample consists of a few milligrams of the suspect material which, if liquid, is absorbed on to a piece of paper. If the top is given a blow with a $\frac{1}{2}$ kilogram hammer, then the sample will normally explode if it is an explosive more sensitive than PETN. If there is no explosion, the material is unlikely to be a sensitive explosive.

2. *Identification equipment*

At first sight it is an attractive proposition to have a field kit for the identification of explosives. Proposals have even been made for the identification of components suitable for use in explosive mixtures. The difficulty with such ideas is to know how far to go, since the only adequate solution, namely a complete mobile explosives laboratory, is not feasible. A number of proposals have been made in various countries from time to time for field identification kits for a limited range of explosives. Apart from the difficulties and hazards of manipulating chemicals in improvised surroundings there is a very real danger that a nil result may be interpreted as an absence of explosive. Such a result may, on the contrary, denote a dangerous explosive not catered for in the limited range of analyses available and hence an entirely false sense of security may be engendered. Consideration of the fundamental requirements shows that the only essential one to identify in the field is sensitive materials, such as nitroglycerine and primary explosives, so that suitable precautions may be taken. It is simpler and safer to concentrate on the single physical property of sensitivity, common to all explosives, than on a multitude of chemical properties. It is better, therefore, to use a simple sensitivity test such as that already described and leave chemical identifications until they can be carried out properly in the laboratory.

3. *Equipment for rendering a scene safe*

This is another area in which a compromise must be made between what may be desired to cover every circumstance and what it is practicable to carry. Investigators may, however, find one or more of

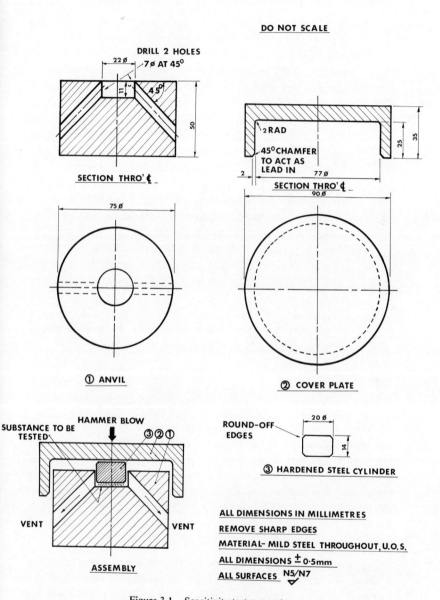

Figure 3.1   Sensitivity test apparatus

the following to be a worthwhile addition to their equipment:

(a) Solvents for the commoner explosives. These can usefully include diethylether, acetone, benzene and water.

(b) Nitroglycerine destroyer (*i.e.* liquid which can be used to destroy small quantities of nitroglycerine on site). It consists either of: sodium hydroxide 2%, water 23%, ethyl alcohol 50%, and acetone 25%; *or* 60% sodium sulphide solution 8%, ethyl alcohol 56%, acetone 14%, and water 22%. It should be remembered that these are slow acting and that care must be taken to ensure that they come into contact with all the nitroglycerine likely to be present.

(c) Special tools. These are a matter for experience and personal preference but may include such things as non ferrous probes for removing explosives from locks and portable lamps for the examination of crevices.

(d) Tools not likely to be readily available. These are also a matter for experience and personal preference. In cities it is usually possible to obtain the loan of or purchase any tools likely to be required. In rural areas this may be difficult or impossible and investigators likely to be working in such areas may find it expedient to provide themselves with a basic general tool kit supplemented by special items.

INFORMATION

All kinds of information will be recorded by the investigator during the course of his work but there are certain items which should be recorded as a matter of routine at the outset. This can at times appear to be fussy and time wasting but it will be found to save much time and frustration in the end. This type of information relates to two matters.

THE INCIDENT

Write down the time and date of the occurrence together with the address of the premises including the name and/or number of the building or part of building, street (if appropriate) and town or district.

PERSONS INVOLVED

Write down the name, address, and telephone number (if appropriate) of:

(i) The owner of the premises.

(ii) Any persons injured or dead.

(iii) The police officer in charge.

(iv) The fire officer in charge if fire fighters have been present.

(v) The chief representative of the gas, electricity or other public utility authorities if any such have been called to the scene.

(vi) The representative of any legal or insurance organization which may be involved.

THE INITIAL APPROACH TO THE SCENE

When the explosion investigator commences his investigation he can do no better than to follow the precedent of Sherlock Holmes (16):

> I had imagined that Sherlock Holmes would at once have hurried into the house and plunged into a study of the mystery. Nothing appeared to be further from his intention. With an air of nonchalance which, under the circumstances, seemed to me to border upon affectation, he lounged up and down the pavement, and gazed vacantly at the ground, the sky, the opposite houses and the line of railings. Having finished his scrutiny, he proceeded slowly down the path or rather down the fringe of grass which flanked the path, keeping his eyes riveted to the ground.

Although this was written as long ago as 1887 it is thoroughly sound advice today for the explosion investigator. Before plunging into the detailed investigation at the seat of the explosion he should do four things.

SECURE GENERAL PHOTOGRAPHIC COVERAGE OF THE SCENE

This should be, as fully as possible, consistent with maintaining the integrity of the scene. Further detailed photography will follow later but it is important to record the initial configuration. It will become necessary to move debris and initial photographic coverage is the only means of ensuring the recording of the position and appearance of items whose significance may only become apparent at a later stage in the investigation.

DETERMINE THE AREA OF THE SCENE

It is important to determine quickly the area in which significant items may be found so that this can be safeguarded from disturbance until it can be properly searched. A simple rule is to walk out to the furthest piece of debris quickly found, add 50% to this distance, and safeguard the whole area within this radius of the seat of the explosion. It may be possible to reduce this in some instances. For example, if a blown out window is the only possible exit for fragments, then only a limited area need be safeguarded.

CLASSIFY THE INCIDENT

The type of incident should be determined as a preliminary to making a plan of action. For this purpose explosions can conveniently be divided into two types:

1. *Explosions where the essential nature is obvious*

In these cases the investigation will be a limited one designed to determine some specific point only. Consequently, the plan of action can be likewise limited. Thus, in a safebreaking, the investigation may be limited to identifying the explosive, the means of initiation and ancillary equipment. In a murder by infernal machine the nature and origin of the explosive and the construction of the device are of paramount interest. In an incident of a legitimate nature, say the ignition of a firework during manufacture, the cause of ignition becomes the primary object of the investigation.

2. *Explosions where the essential nature is not obvious*

In these cases the investigation may have to be very comprehensive and involve every type of observation discussed in the following chapters. Consequently, the plan of action will have to make provision for all of these. Explosions of this type include large disasters leading to the substantial demolition of a building or worse. They also include more limited situations of similar character, for example a room reduced to ruins by an explosion but in which no explosive is to be expected.

MAKE A PLAN OF ACTION

The plan of action will be peculiar to the particular incident and must, in a large measure, be based on the investigator's experience. It is best, in the interests of safety, to work from the periphery inwards but the order in which the parts of the investigation are carried out may have to be modified from the ideal. There may, for example, be pressure to re-open a public street or to resume work in an office and such requests should be complied with as far as possible without jeopardising the investigation. Rain or threatened rain may necessitate giving priority to the recovery of exhibits from open situations. The plan of action will also depend on whether the investigator is working alone or whether he has trained colleagues available to help. In the latter case it becomes possible to carry out several parts of the investigation simultaneously.

Chapter 4

OBSERVATION AND ASSESSMENT OF DAMAGE

THE IMPORTANCE OF DAMAGE

The identification of the cause of an explosion can be a matter of considerable difficulty. Unless the explosion has been deliberately staged, direct observation is seldom possible and, in general therefore, the investigator has to proceed by indirect methods. After an explosion any remaining portions of the explosive and any identifiable decomposition products will be widely scattered, may have a short life and often prove difficult to find and identify. The damage caused by the explosion is, however, readily available for study and is permanent. Examination of the damage is, therefore, the usual starting point of an investigation into the cause of an explosion.

TYPES OF EXPLOSIVE AND EXPLOSION DAMAGE

When considering damage caused by explosions, it is convenient to classify it in two ways. The explosive itself can be either condensed (*i.e.* a solid or a liquid) or dispersed (*i.e.* a gas or dust suspension). In either case the explosion can take the form of a detonation or of a deflagration. This gives rise to four types of explosion:

1. Deflagration in a condensed explosive.
2. Detonation in a condensed explosive.
3. Deflagration in a dispersed explosive.
4. Detonation in a dispersed explosive.

In order to appreciate the nature of damage effects produced, the course of detonation in a condensed explosive may be compared with that of a deflagration in a dispersed explosive. In the first there is the very rapid production of large quantities of high temperature gas in a very small space. This produces a very high, but very localised,

40

pressure rise which leads to a shock wave expanding spherically at a supersonic velocity of the order of 10^3 ms^{-1}. The pressure rise is followed by a rarefaction, thus producing a pressure time profile of the form shown in Figure 4.1. As the shock wave progresses the form

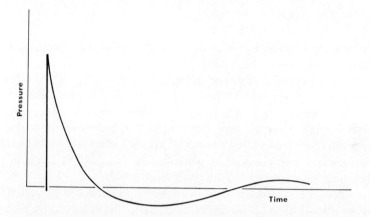

Fig. 4.1   Pressure/time profile of a blast-wave

of the overpressure changes, the amplitude decreases, and the length increases. Thus it has been shown (17) that, for a 1 kg charge of TNT, the peak pressure is approximately 10 atm and the duration of the positive overpressure is approximately 0·5 ms at a distance of 1 m from the charge, whereas at 10 m the values are 0·1 atm and 4 ms respectively. In considering damage to a target, two quantities are of importance. One is the initial, or peak, overpressure and the other is the positive impulse which is expressed as:

$$I^+ = \int_{t_0}^{t_1} p \ dt$$

where t_0 is the initial time and t_1 is the positive duration and is the time required for the overpressure to return to ambient. The ability to do damage depends on the relationship between the positive duration and the natural period of the fundamental mode of the target. Where the duration is less than the time taken to produce maximum deflection in the target, then the extent of the damage is determined by the positive impulse. When, however, the duration is much greater than the time taken to produce maximum deflection, the determining factor is the peak pressure. It will be seen, therefore, that the positive impulse is important near the seat of explosion and peak pressure farther away. A further quantity, which can assume importance in damage by shock waves from detonating condensed explosives, is the negative impulse:

$$I^- = \int_{t_1}^{t_2} p \, dt$$

where t_1 is as already defined and t_2 is the time at which the negative afterpressure returns to ambient.

In the case of a dispersed deflagrating explosive, it is necessary for the flame to travel a relatively large distance from the point of ignition until all the combustible mixture is consumed. This takes much longer than the time required for the detonation of a condensed explosive charge. The actual velocity of travel of the flame depends on several factors, in particular the nature of the flammable mixture and the extent to which turbulence occurs.

Cases are on record in which witnesses have watched deflagrations travel slowly through the air, but commonly the speeds range from a few ms^{-1} to about $100 \ ms^{-1}$. The rise in pressure is, therefore, much slower than is the case with the detonation of a condensed explosive and this results in a reasonably uniform pressure over an entire surface exposed to a blast.

The relative slowness of the deflagration of a dispersed explosive means that there is time for venting to affect the process. This may be an existing vent or ones created by the explosion, such as blown out windows. The result is that the peak pressure actually reached is less than that which would have been attained had the deflagration occurred in a wholly confined space.

As a result of these differences in mode of operation, it is possible to give qualitative descriptions of the general nature of the damage produced by the various types of explosion.

Deflagrations in condensed explosives tend to produce intense local heat with little or moderate blast depending on the nature of the explosive and its confinement. For example, in an accident, the ignition of some pyrotechnic composition spread to an open box of cordite. No great damage was done, but a man standing nearby was killed and severe, though superficial, charring made the body almost unrecognisable.

Detonations in condensed explosives tend to produce intense local damage and severe blast effects. As a result, whereas the deflagrating explosives tend to bend surrounding objects, detonating explosives cut them. Near the seat of a detonation even such materials as spring steel will be cut.

Deflagration in dispersed explosives will give a relatively uniform push to surrounding objects and hence tend to displace rather than shatter them. In this type of explosion it is possible for objects to be completely immersed in the explosive and in these circumstances they tend to escape relatively undamaged.

Detonations in dispersed explosives are rarely encountered and then normally only in an elongated, confined system such as a pipe line. They can, however, shatter the containing vessel with the projection of fragments.

VALUE TO BE ATTACHED TO DAMAGE OBSERVATIONS

It is possible to divide the types of damage observable into three divisions, with subdivisions. These are as follows:

1. Permanent distortion of objects:
    (a) Plastic deformation (*e.g.* bent pipes, bent metal roof members and dishing of metal plates).
    (b) Fracture (*e.g.* fragmented containers, splintered woodwork and broken glass).
    (c) Fragment attack (*e.g.* impact craters in metal surfaces and fragments embedded in persons and objects).
2. Displacement of objects:
    (a) Heavy objects (*e.g.* machine tools, motor vehicles, cookers and domestic equipment).
    (b) Light objects (*e.g.* cardboard boxes, fragments of building board and window curtains).
3. Flame and heat effects (*e.g.* scorch marks on paint work and melted nylon fabrics).

The reliability of these types of damage, as sources from which to make deductions, varies. Permanently distorted objects are on the whole reliable sources of information. In the case of plastic deformation, care must be taken to differentiate between distortions caused by the initial blast and any that may have been caused by subsequent collapse of a building.

In the case of fractures, similar care must be taken to eliminate the possibility that a particular piece of damage has been caused by fire-men. This can usually be done by observation, which will reveal tool marks, or by questioning. Evidence from fragment attack is normally unequivocal.

Evidence from the displacement of objects is less reliable since the effects observed can often be due to such causes as reflected blast waves and the activities of firemen and others. As a general rule, it may be assumed that the heavier the object the less likely it is that it will have been displaced by any force other than the initial blast wave. This distinction has long been recognised and is well illustrated in two observations made at the scene of an explosion in a rectangu-lar gunpowder drying building at Haverthwaite in 1898 (CXXVII):

> The distribution of the debris took, as usual, the form roughly
> of a cross, the arms of which were, speaking broadly, at right
> angles to the sides and end . . . but light debris, consisting
> of small bits of slate and splintered wood, was found in a
> continuous line for some 500 yards due east (*i.e.* with the wind).

The reliability of observations based on flame and heat effects is high in cases where the explosion has not been preceded or suc-ceeded by a fire. When a fire has occurred, then it must be assumed that this is the cause of the effects observed unless there is clear evidence that this is not the case. In this event the effects form a highly reliable source of information.

THE IMPORTANCE OF THE SITE OF THE EXPLOSION CENTRE

A vital step in any explosion investigation is to determine the ex-plosion centre. In many cases this will be quite obvious on casual inspection. Thus, in a safebreaking, it is often clear that the explosion was in the lock; in an attempted murder by letter bomb it is clear that the explosion was in the letter; and in a factory accident it is usually clear that the explosion was at a particular point in the machinery. There are many cases, however, where this is not so. Where there is substantial damage to a room, and particularly to a building, the centre of the explosion can be completely obscured; where there is an explosion of a dispersed explosive on any substantial scale the ex-plosion centre is seldom obvious.

The reason for determining the explosion centre lies in the deductions which can be made from it.

THE GENERAL TYPE OF EXPLOSIVE INVOLVED

When a charge of a condensed explosive explodes, the release of energy takes place in a small volume. The resultant blast and shock waves, therefore, expand from what is practically a point source. As they expand they attenuate, eventually dying away altogether. It follows, therefore, that with this type of explosion the region of maximum damage is near the explosion centre. There will, of course, be localised regions where, by reasons of reflections, focussing or other effects, greater damage will be noted than in an immediately adjacent region nearer the centre. Nevertheless, if an overall view is taken, the region of maximum damage is coincident with the explosion centre.

When a dispersed explosive is ignited the energy release is not confined to a virtual point source but takes place over the whole region occupied by the explosive. As the flame front progresses through the explosive it can be affected in several ways:

1. Dispersed explosives are generally mixtures and will normally be inhomogeneous in cases requiring investigation since, in most of these cases, the mixture will have been formed as the result of some accidental process. The gas or vapour is likely to form a layer, either at ceiling or at floor level depending on density. It also is liable to be dispersed throughout several rooms. As a result, some of the mixture will be outside the compositional limits within which an explosion is possible. Moreover, those regions containing mixtures lying within the explosion limits are liable to contain mixtures varying from those giving rise to the minimum pressure to those giving rise to the maximum pressure possible. It follows, therefore, that because of this the region of maximum damage may be remote from the explosion centre.

2. As the explosion progresses through the gas mixture it is liable to encounter items of furniture and to go through doorways. Both such circumstances increase the turbulence and this increases the speed of propagation of the explosion and hence the pressure. Since the encountering of obstacles in this way is progressive, the region of maximum damage is likely to be remote from the explosion centre.

3. If the appropriate configuration is present, the phenomenon of 'pressure piling' may occur. The ideal situation for this to occur is in a pipe but any relatively long narrow region, such as a corridor or

lift shaft, could give rise to it. If such a container is filled with an explosive gas mixture and ignited at one end, the explosion wave starts to travel along it. The pressure generated causes compression of the unconsumed gas ahead of the flame front and, in this higher pressure gas, the velocity and pressure is increased. The result is, therefore, an accelerating explosion which may become a detonation and which produces the maximum damage at the point furthest from the explosion centre.

It will be seen, therefore, that if the explosion centre is determined and its location compared with the region of maximum damage then, if the two coincide, it is likely that the explosion was due to a condensed explosive. If they do not, then it is likely that the explosion was due to a dispersed explosive.

The Existence of a Cased Charge

A condensed explosive charge may, or may not, be confined in some form of container. There are several possibilities. Detonating explosives will, in general, detonate whether or not they are confined in a container, such as a shell or bomb. Deflagrating explosives will not produce an effective explosion unless they are confined. The confinement would normally be a metal container but other materials can be effective, *e.g.* the stout cardboard used to fabricate maroons and mortar shells for pyrotechnic displays. In any case, there is the further possibility that the explosion was caused by an infernal machine built into some form of container. Thus, in many instances of explosion involving condensed explosives, there will be a container which will be fragmented by the explosion. These fragments will have diagnostic value and it is important to establish whether they exist and, if so, to recover them. Many are likely to be embedded in the ground or objects near the exposion centre, while those which have travelled further will have trajectories whose origin is at that spot. The establishment of the explosion centre is, therefore, of importance in the consideration of whether or not there was a cased charge and, if so, of its nature.

Optimum Sites for Chemically Detectable Residues

In many explosion investigations it is a matter of importance to determine the exact nature of the explosive. With dispersed explosives, particularly gaseous ones, this may be impossible and, where detectable materials can be found, their site does not necessarily bear a relationship to the explosion centre. With condensed explosives a different situation obtains and the sites at which chemically identifiable decomposition products and even traces of undecomposed explosive may be found are related to the explosion centre. Its location is, therefore, an important factor in the location of chemically identifiable residues.

THE CAUSE OF INITIATION

In the case of condensed explosives, the explosion centre is the point where the charge was located. In the case of dispersed explosives, the explosion centre is the point where the charge was ignited. In either case the explosion centre is the point where the means of initiation or ignition were situated. Its establishment, therefore, is a matter of vital importance in the investigation of the cause of the explosion.

THE DETERMINATION OF THE SITE OF THE EXPLOSION CENTRE

The method of determining the site of the explosion centre is to prepare a direction/damage diagram. This consists of a plan of the scene of the explosion, on which is marked the location of any damage which can confidently be ascribed to the explosion and which indicates the direction of travel of blast or fragments. The greater the number of such observations that can be put on the diagram the greater the reliability of the deductions that can be made from it. In general, an effort should be made to find a minimum of ten such observations and if more can be found so much the better.

No comprehensive list of features from which the direction of blast can be deduced is possible, since every object present could, in some circumstances, furnish such information. It is possible, however, to list some of the articles commonly found at scenes of explosion which have proved of value in this connection. They can conveniently be considered under the same headings as those already used to describe the value to be attached to damage observations.

PLASTIC DEFORMATION

This type of distortion can arise from two main causes. It can be primary, *i.e.* caused by the direct action of the pressure of the blast wave on the object. It can also be secondary, *i.e.* caused by the movement of some other object itself directly moved by the blast wave. Evidence based on primary plastic distortion is usually completely reliable. Evidence based on secondary plastic deformation is also usually reliable but, where the effect is due to the impact of another body, care must be taken to consider whether or not this would have been travelling in the direction of the blast.

There are three main types of observation in which this kind of distortion can indicate the direction of the blast:

1. *Bending of long metal objects*

(a) Pipes used for the conveyance of water or other services or used as electric conduit for the protection of electric wiring.

(b) Structural members, such as pillars, girders and roof trusses.

(c) Railings or other ornamental metal work.

(d) Nails, screws or bolts used to secure construction units, such as door frames, constructional panels and built-in furniture and fittings.

(e) Window frames.

(f) Furniture and storage racking.

(g) Appropriate parts of machinery, motor and rail vehicles and other engineering products.

2. *Dishing of metal plates*

(a) Containers, such as storage tins, jerricans, drums and tanks. No observations can, however, be made on such containers if filled with liquid, since the virtual incompressibility of liquids prevents distortion by blast. Thus domestic water tanks and central heating radiators are of no value for dishing observations.

(b) Metal doors.

(c) Metal clad equipment, such as cookers, refrigerators, washing machines and towel dispensers.

(d) Objects incorporating sheet metal in their construction, such as road vehicles and railway rolling stock.

(e) Metal sheet used as a constructional material in buildings.

3. *Movement of particulate objects*

Objects in the form of a heap of particulate material, such as sand, dry earth or a powder, will flow under the impact of a blast wave and so exhibit distortion which properly belongs to this type.

FRACTURE

1. *Structural elements of buildings*

(a) Walls made of stone, bricks or other building blocks, pre-fabricated panels and concrete or other materials.

(b) Woodwork, such as door frames, roof members and studding.

(c) Cladding panels, such as chipboard, hardboard and plasterboard.

(d) Brittle metal components, such as cast iron ornaments and inspection covers.

(e) Window glass. Double glazing can be of particular value since, at appropriate pressures, it is possible for one layer to be broken while the other remains intact, thus giving a clear indication of the direction of blast.

2. *Contents of buildings*

(a) Furniture of all types.

(b) Fittings of all types.

3. *Objects outside*

(a) Man-made objects, such as vehicles of all types, street furniture and fences.

(b) Natural objects, such as trees and rocks. It should be noted that the effect of blast on trees is complex owing to their wide variety. Thus, at Stowmarket in 1871, it was observed that trees between a severely damaged house and the explosion were undamaged, since they were able to bend to the blast.

FRAGMENT ATTACK

As with plastic distortion, this can be due either to primary fragments originating from the casing of the explosive charge or secondary fragments originating from other objects fragmented by the blast. While primary fragments will, in general, have travelled directly from the explosion centre, secondary fragments may not be so related and any observations based on them must, therefore, be weighted accordingly. Fragment attack may be of two kinds:

1. Surface attack in the form of dents and small craters. Where such evidence is found on a flat surface, the point of origin can only be deduced within broad limits. A closer identification can be made if

the surface is rounded, since this reduces the size of the possible region from which the fragments could have originated.

2. Penetrative attack in the form of elongated holes. Where such evidence is found, a reasonably accurate indication of the explosion centre can be made by projecting the lines of the holes backwards by means of stiff wires or strings. It may even be possible to arrive at an estimate of the size of the charge.

DISPLACEMENT OF OBJECTS

In general, the heavier a displaced object the more probable it is that its movement is due to the effect of the blast and not to human disturbance, reflected blast waves or wind.

1. *Heavy objects*

(a) Manufacture: objects such as machinery, bogies, heavy items of raw materials and partly finished products.

(b) Transport: objects such as vehicles and cased products.

(c) Storage: objects such as cased products and freight containers.

(d) Sale: objects such as heavy furniture, showroom fittings, safes and filing cabinets.

(e) Domestic use: objects such as cookers, washing machines and heavy items, such as furniture.

2. *Light objects*

These are so numerous in modern industrial society that there is little point in making any list. All are of potential significance but in practice it is found that few can be used as clear evidence of the direction of a blast wave.

FLAME AND HEAT EFFECTS

In the case of flame and heat effects, information about direction can be deduced even from objects which have been moved, provided that their original orientation can be determined. These effects can be conveniently divided into two kinds:

1. *Melting*

In general, the contact between the hot gases in the blast-wave and surrounding objects is so transient that little heat transfer occurs. However, metal surfaces close to the explosion centre can exhibit the phenomenon of gas wash, that is a scouring action with partial melting of the surface layers resulting in a characteristic rippled surface. Some melting may also be observed on the surface of objects made from plastics.

2. *Decomposition*

With some surfaces there is sufficient heat transfer from the blast wave for some chemical decomposition to take place and this may result in an observable effect. Charring of organic materials can occur, but this is often due to other causes, such as burning gases and fire subsequent to the explosion. Such evidence must, therefore, be appraised very carefully before it is decided that it is indicative of blast direction. Painted surfaces can sometimes provide evidence since heat can cause change of colour due to changes in the pigment or the binder or both.

PREPARATION OF A DIRECTION/DAMAGE DIAGRAM

The preparation of a direction/damage diagram is best illustrated by an actual example (Figure 4.2). It was prepared in connection with an explosion, subsequently determined as being of town gas/air, on 16 May 1968 at Ronan Point in Canning Town, London. It relates to a flat on the eighteenth floor of the building and shows features observable in the part of the flat remaining after the explosion. The part of the flat marked 'missing' disappeared on the partial collapse of the building and was not, therefore (except for feature 18), available for investigation. The nature of the nineteen points marked was as follows:

1. The metal guard rail to the balcony was bent outwards as a whole from its supports.

2. The kitchen window which formed the inner wall of the balcony was broken and part of it was found approximately 100 m to the east of the building. The part found was identified by the site foreman carpenter as being part of a kitchen window. Since all kitchen windows except that of the particular flat were still in position, this exhibit was positively identified as being from point 2.

3. Under the kitchen window and running for its whole length there was a built-in fitting having a one-piece top. This was raised upwards towards the window. Relatively large horizontal objects of this kind can behave in several ways when subjected to blast. If the blast wave has free access to both top and bottom surfaces, pressures

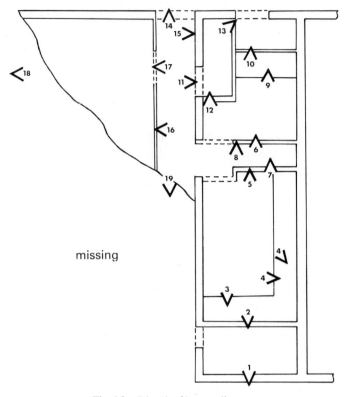

Fig. 4.2   Direction/damage diagram

on these will be equalised and there will be a tendency for horizontal movement only. If however, as in this case, the underside is protected from blast, the wave will travel over the top surface. If the dimensions of the object are comparable with the wavelength of the blast then, at a certain moment of the traverse, the positive pressure in the front of the wave will be exerting a downward pressure, while the negative pressure behind this will bend the object. The nature of this turning movement indicates the direction of travel of the blast.

4. A refrigerator was situated against the wall and near to the window. The front and the side of this remote from the window were dished in a manner typical of that produced by blast.

5. The wall which separated the kitchen from the bathroom was in the form of a cupboard constructed of two light partitions. The rear of this cupboard was partitioned off to form a services duct for

water and soil pipes. The main portion contained a hot water tank, equipped with electric immersion heater and header tank, supported on a wooden shelf. The bottom of the cupboard contained the gas meter but was otherwise empty. The gas main went through the front left hand side of the cupboard.

The cupboard was severely damaged in the explosion and was also subjected to the effects of fire from the burning gas emerging from the standpipe serving the cooker. In consequence, the first impression of this area was one of considerable confusion. A detailed study, however, showed that a number of features indicative of blast direction could be identified.

The two main walls of the cupboard were damaged in a different way from each other. The wall nearer the kitchen was completely disintegrated and pieces of it were found scattered within the kitchen. The positions in which such light debris is found are not usually significant in determining blast direction, especially in an enclosed space such as this where a complex system of direct and reflected blast and rarefaction waves must have developed. The fact that this wall was disintegrated could, however, be considered in conjunction with the fact that the other wall was relatively little damaged. This indicated that the primary blast was more intense on the kitchen side and, hence, that it was travelling from the kitchen towards the bathroom.

6. Further examination of the wooden frame of the wall on the bathroom side showed that one of the vertical members had been fractured in a manner which could only occur if it were bent towards the bathroom and that the nails securing it had come out. Since the members to which it had been nailed were not displaced, it was clear that the force causing the withdrawal of the nails had been in the direction of the bathroom.

7. The feed pipe of the water tank was bent towards the bathroom.

8. The rising gas main was slightly out of vertical and bowed. The bowing occurred over a distance of 0.6 m near the middle of the pipe and was directed away from the kitchen. In order to assess the significance of this, the corresponding pipes were examined in other flats. None was found to be distorted in this manner and it could be concluded, therefore, that this was a blast effect.

9. The bath was fitted along the wall and was boarded in with a laconite panel on wooden supports. The panel was shattered and the supports forced under the bath.

10. The bathroom wall adjacent to the bath formed the back of a services cupboard and carried a number of electric conduit pipes. The wall was fractured and these pipes were bowed away from the bathroom.

11. The door to the store had disappeared. Three observations, however, established that it had been blown inwards. Screws which had secured the frame of the door were found to be bent towards the inside, and the hinges of the door, recovered from inside, were found to be distorted in a manner which was shown experimentally to have been possible only if the door had been forced inwards. The door was missing since a fire developed in the store and only its metallic fittings were recovered.

12. The walls of the store were made of prefabricated panels. The short wall between the store and the bathroom had pivoted roughly about its vertical axis. This effect could be produced by blast from either side. It was observed, however, that the panel was constrained by steel pins at one side. The observed movement of the panel, with this constraint, could be explained only if the initial movement was towards the store from the bathroom.

13. The back wall of the store was cracked and displaced and indicated blast travelling through the store towards the service cupboard.

14. The front door of the flat was shattered and the fragments blown out into the corridor. Screws which had secured the door frame were found to be bent outwards.

15. Inside the front door a recess in the wall contained the electric meter and fuses. This recess had a steel cover which was found detached from its seating. It showed typical explosive blast dishing, indicating a pressure from the hall into the recess.

16. The panel forming the wall between the hall and bedroom was displaced bodily towards the bedroom.

17. The bedroom door was recovered intact in the bedroom. It had been blown off its supports and examination of the hinges confirmed that the door had, in fact, been blown into the bedroom.

18. One of the witnesses to the explosion, who was outside the building, reported that he saw a section of the building come outwards. He added that it was a section in which there was a window. A study of his evidence left little doubt that what he saw was the panel forming the bedroom wall.

19. The living room disappeared in the collapse of the building,

so that no study of possible blast damage could be made. However, part of the door to this room was recovered approximately 100 m to the east of the building, thus indicating that it was propelled outwards by a blast into the living room. Proof that the object found was part of this particular door depended on three facts: (a) the door was identified as a living-room door by the foreman carpenter; (b) all living-room doors on floors below were still in position; and (c) although the living-room doors from the upper flats were missing, the outer walls of these flats were still in position after the explosion. This would have prevented any of their living room doors from being blown eastwards.

Study of the direction/damage diagram clearly indicates that the origin of the primary blast was in the kitchen. A wave, starting from somewhere near the centre, moved outwards and blew out the window. In the other direction it passed through the bathroom and also through the hall and thence into the living room, bedroom, store and corridor.

The investigation during which this direction/damage diagram was prepared also provided two good illustrations of the care which must be exercised to avoid false deductions. The first concerns item 2, the fitment under the kitchen window. The top of this had been raised and the obvious explanation was that this was due to blast from underneath. This explanation, however, was in contradiction with the clear evidence of the direction of blast shown on the adjacent refrigerator. It became clear, therefore, that the correct explanation for the movement of the worktop was the other alternative, namely that it had been raised by a lifting force acting from above, as already described. The other illustration concerns the water tank which was situated in the cupboard between the kitchen and the bathroom. After the explosion the tank was found on the floor of the kitchen. This position was consistent with the fact that the wall nearer the kitchen had disintegrated, whereas the other had not. By this process the support for the shelf on which the tank rested would have been removed from the kitchen side only, thus causing it to tilt towards the kitchen and to drop the tank in this directiion. Normally, heavy objects such as this move, if at all, away from the explosion centre. This, however, is an example of an opposite movement due to special circumstances and illustrates the need for the care which must be exercised in deciding the significance of every observation at the scene of an explosion.

THE SIGNIFICANCE OF PRESSURES

A knowledge of the pressures produced by the explosion at various parts of the scene can be of value in various aspects of the investigation.

1. It has already been pointed out that, if the region of maximum damage and the explosion centre coincide, then it is likely that the explosion was due to a condensed explosive, whereas if they do not it is likely that the explosion was due to a dispersed explosive. The estimate of the region of maximum damage is a qualitative one, though none the less reliable for that. The observations can, however, be reinforced if the pressure profile in respect of the explosion centre can be determined.

2. If the direction/damage diagram indicates that the explosion was due to a charge of condensed explosive, then pressure/distance data can be used to furnish estimates of the weight of the charge.

3. Apart from their direct use to the explosion investigator, estimates of the pressure to which various parts of the scene were subjected can be of value to other interested parties. These are architects, structural engineers and others concerned in the design of buildings. They are interested in the pressures which gave rise to observed structural failures, particularly in new forms of constructional techniques, and also in the pressures generated in practical situations since these will be of importance in the design of future buildings.

THE DETERMINATION OF PRESSURES

1. *The theoretical approach*

It is possible to calculate the pressure exerted by an explosion on a structure. An apparently simple case is that of a dispersed explosive, say domestic gas/air, in a single room, where a calculation can be based on simple expansion. It is, however, necessary to assume the nature of the gas, but even if this is positively known it is also necessary to know the amount of gas present and its concentration in the gas/air mixtures. By making suitable assumptions, values for the pressure could be found ranging from negligible to a maximum of the order of 700 kNm^{-2}. In practice such a simple situation is not likely to occur. The gas or vapour will tend to form a more or less distinct layer, either near the ceiling or near the floor depending on its density. Several interconnecting rooms, passages, and other spaces are likely to contain quantities of explosive mixture. Both the original passage of gas through doorways and the subsequent passage of the explosion will increase the turbulence and hence the burning rate. Further turbulence can also arise from the passage of the gas and explosion past furniture; this is particularly pronounced when the explosive mixture is denser than air. A further complexity can arise if part of the structure acts as a pressure relief by blowing out at a pressure below the theoretical maximum.

With this considerable list of imponderables and the consequent assumptions, which may or may not be accurate but which have to be used in the calculations, estimates based on this approach are of very doubtful value. Indeed, results could be obtained with an entirely misleading and spurious air of accuracy. The position is essentially the same for the case of explosions due to condensed explosives. Formulae exist connecting charge-weight, distance and pressure and these can be applied with some success to uncomplicated situations. The circumstances in which the explosion investigator has to work are, however, often far from simple and, so here also, estimates of pressures based on purely theoretical calculations must be so hedged around with reservations as to be of doubtful value.

2. *Pressure determinations from plastic distortion*

A more reliable method of assessment of the pressures generated in a particular explosion is to use observations from the scene. From the study of some forms of damage, estimates can be made of the pressures actually generated at the particular points of observations.

One of the most useful forms of damage for pressure assessment is plastic distortion. In theory, any object showing plastic distortion can be used but, in practice, it is found that the determination is very much more convenient with some objects than with others. The principle on which pressure is assessed is to obtain a similar object as test piece and then determine the pressure which has to be applied to the test piece to produce a distortion similar to that observed in the original object. The actual technique employed in applying pressures to the test piece will vary according to the type of explosion under investigation and it is the practical considerations dictated by this and by the size of any particular distorted object which determine, to a large extent, which objects are chosen as pressure indicators.

The basis of all experimental techniques is to take the test piece, supported as necessary to simulate the original configuration, and then to apply to it a series of pressures. The distortion caused by each pressure should be recorded and the experiment continued until a distortion in excess of that observed in the original object has been obtained. A distortion/pressure graph can then be prepared and the pressure corresponding to the distortion of the original object can be read off.

In designing the experimental arrangements, it is essential that these should reproduce explosion conditions. Where relatively slow pressure application occurred, as in deflagrations and most explosions of dispersed explosives, non explosive forms of experimental pressure application may be found convenient. The technique must involve uniform surface loading which can most conveniently be applied pneumatically, by positive or negative pressure, or hydraulically. In some instances the application of a mechanical force may be possible. Normally a single test piece will suffice for the experiment.

No set method of experimental design can be laid down and the experimental procedure must be worked out for each individual case. Variations of some of the following techniques will, however, be found to be applicable to many instances.

2.1. *Elongated metal objects such as pipes*

The test piece can be supported in the same manner as the original, but turned so as to be horizontal. The piece is then loaded by placing sandbags on it, piled as high as may be necessary and uniformly dispersed along its length.

2.2. *Nails, screws and bolts used to secure door frames*

A similarly secured door frame is used as the test piece. A hydraul jack, equipped with pressure recorder, is then applied via a specially constructed head designed to fit the door frame and pressure applied until the door frame moves sufficiently to reproduce the distortion observed in the original. If the frame was secured to some detachable structural member then it is possible to turn the assembly into the horizontal direction and apply the sandbag loading technique. It should be noted that results from securing devices of this kind only indicate the minimum pressure which was exerted at the point under consideration.

2.3. Containers such as tins and drums

Various techniques can be applied to articles of this nature. If the pressure on the original was less than 1 atmosphere then a simple pneumatic procedure may be used. The tin is equipped with an outlet nozzle and its normal closure made airtight. The tin is then progressively evacuated and the distortion measured at various levels of pressure differential. If the pressure on the original was greater than 1 atmosphere then the pressure on the test piece must be applied externally either pneumatically or hydraulically. The test piece may be placed in a pressure vessel and measured pressures applied externally. A simple, but effective, method which can be used if an appropriate body of water, such as a deep lake or the sea, is conveniently situated, is to apply pressure hydraulically to a series of closed test pieces by sinking them in the water to a series of measured depths.

Penney et al. (18) have made a study of the collapse of empty 46 gal 16 bsw steel drums. They used both evacuation techniques and the subjection of drums to the blast wave from a nuclear explosion. They found that, although the pressure required to induce collapse in a drum varied considerably from drum to drum, the stronger the drum is against collapse the more it collapses when it does fail. They observed that the experimental results seemed to show that the pressure which caused collapse can be calculated, within a few per cent, as the sum of the pressure increase inside the drum caused by adiabatic collapse and a constant (in this case 8 lbf/in^2) representing the strength of the drum in the collapsed state. It is as if most of the work done by the collapsing pressure goes into plastic deformation of the drum rather than into kinetic energy of the drum walls.

2.4. Metal clad equipment

With this type of object the distortion which must be reproduced in the test piece will normally be dishing of a flat panel. This can be achieved by placing the test piece so that the panel to be distorted is horizontal. Vertical sheets are then added so that the test panel forms the bottom of an open topped box. Pressure is applied by filling the box progressively with water. If difficulty is experienced in devising a suitable waterproof seal round the edges of the test panel, dry sand can be used as an alternative filling.

Another approach is to apply the pressure pneumatically. The test piece is secured in a suitable stout metal rig so that the panel to be dished is situated to form one side of a box. A strong rubber bag of the correct size to fill the box is then inserted into it. Air is pumped into the bag and the distortion of the panel on the test piece is observed at various pressure loadings.

2.5. *Sheet metal constructional panels*

Similar techniques to those described for metal clad equipment can be applied to sheet metal panels used in the construction of road vehicles, railway rolling stock and as panels in buildings. The actual experimental procedures, however, are liable to be complicated by the need for suitable handling equipment needed to manipulate heavy objects.

Where the explosion being investigated involves the detonation of a condensed explosive charge, the application of pressures to test pieces must be carried out explosively. Whereas, in experiments where mechanical loading can be used, a number of individual experiments may be carried out on a single test piece, in those where explosive loading must be used a single experiment is carried out on a number of test pieces. The technique is to set up, in an open situation free from possible pressure distortions due to reflections, a charge of an explosive whose blast characteristics are well known. Test pieces are then placed at distances at which known pressures will occur. After firing the charge the distortions in the test pieces are measured and the distortion/pressure graph prepared. From this the pressure corresponding to the observed distortion in the original object can be determined.

3. *Pressure determinations from fractures*

Where distortions are produced in the form of plastic distortions, the degree of bending can be measured and hence an estimate can be made of the pressure required to produce it. Where the distortions are in the form of fracture it is, in general, only possible to estimate the minimum pressure which occurred at the point in question. This is due to the fact that, while a certain minimum pressure was necessary to produce the observed fracture, it could also have been produced by pressures in excess of this.

The techniques used in assessing the minimum pressures required to produce observed fractures are essentially the same as those already described in the preceding section. They are easier to carry out since, in cases where non-explosive loading is deemed to be appropriate, it is only necessary to continue to increase the pressure until failure occurs.

There is one aspect of pressure determination from fractures which forms a special case: the breakage of glass windows. The reason why it is a special case derives from the fact that the great majority of explosions requiring investigation occur in urban environments and in such places there are many windows. Within the damage zone of even a small explosion there can be a hundred panes of glass and, with larger explosions, the number can rise to thousands. With such a large number of potential observations, therefore, there is the possibility of improving the reliability of the deductions.

The main parameters which determine the pressure at which a pane of glass will break are the area, the ratio of height to width and the thickness. Other features, such as the rate of pressure loading, atmospheric corrosion, surface abrasion and pre-straining, can also contribute. Mainstone has made a valuable study of the subject and has published (19) a series of graphical diagrams. These can be used to determine the breaking pressure for a pane of glass from a knowledge of its area, height to width ratio and thickness. There are separate diagrams for single sheet glass panes, single plate glass panes and bonded double glazing units of sheet glass. It is possible, therefore, to consider all windows in the area of the explosion and, by measuring the three parameters, use Mainstone's diagrams to determine the pressure required to break them. If a pane of glass is broken, it can be deduced that the pressure at that point exceeded the determined breaking pressure and, conversely, if it is unbroken then the pressure was below that value. In this way a large number of points denoting upper- and lower-pressure limits can be plotted on a plan of the area and pressure profiles constructed.

This technique is laborious and time-consuming and will seldom be justified. A simpler approach is to select a few locations where some panes are broken and some remain unbroken. By examining a few of the unbroken panes in this region, an estimate of the maximum pressure can be made. Likewise, an estimate of the minimum pressure can be made from some of the broken panes. Each of these estimates will be subject to the margins of error introduced by the minor parameters mentioned above. Sometimes the estimated lower limit may exceed the estimated upper limit, but this can be taken as indicating that the values found are closely bracketing the true pressure at the location. From the information so devised it is possible to enter on a diagram of the area the estimates of the pressures at a series of locations. This confines this aspect of the investigation to no more determinations than appears justified in the particular circumstances.

An even simpler approach can be used for quick, on site, estimations. This is less precise than the methods already described but will often be found to be sufficiently accurate for the purposes of the investigation. It depends on the fact that the pressures required to break many commonly occurring window panes are not widely divergent. Provided that windows made from very small or very large sheets of glass or ones made from unusual types of glass are ignored, then it is a reasonable approximation to take the average pressure required to break panes of glass as being 7 kNm^{-2}. On the scene, therefore, this pressure can be assumed for any location where about half the panes of glass are intact and half broken. It must be emphasised that this is only an approximation, but it must also be emphasised that the imponderables at any explosion scene are such that any more accurate determination is seldom justified.

4. *Pressure determination from other observations*

The explosion investigator should never neglect any source of data which may help him in his work. He should always be alert, since valuable information can come from quite unexpected sources. An example both of this and of other sources of pressure determination occurred during the investigation of an explosion of a magazine near Rome in 1891 (1891). An astronomical observatory was situated about 3500 m from the magazine. The barometer at the observatory was observed to have shown a rise of $11 \cdot 4$ mm followed by a rarefaction of $8 \cdot 8$ mm. A second rise of $11 \cdot 7$ mm, followed by a rarefaction of $4 \cdot 4$ mm, was also observed and, in addition, a third rise of $1 \cdot 5$ mm.

THE APPLICATION OF PRESSURE OBSERVATIONS

THE TYPE OF EXPLOSIVE

The application of pressure observations to the determination of the type of explosive is essentially an extension of the procedure already considered under the determination of the site of the explosion centre.

A diagram similar to the direction/damage diagram is prepared. On it are marked: (a) the explosion centre determined from the direction/ damage diagram; and (b) the location of the points at which pressures have been determined and the pressures found. If the pressure distribution is one in which the numerical values decrease with distance from the explosion centre then this observation would support the view that the explosion was due to a condensed explosive. If, however, pressures did not conform to a relatively regular pattern, and particularly if the region of highest pressure is situated away from the explosion centre, then this observation would support the view that the explosion was due to a dispersed explosive.

It must be very strongly emphasised, however, that drawing conclusions of any kind from pressure observations must be done with great care and after very careful consideration of the significance of the observed numerical values. The numerical value found for the pressure by any given observation will be correct within the limitations of the experimental errors of the method used to determine it. It does not necessarily follow, however, that this represents the pressure which would be found at the observed distance from the explosion centre in the case of an explosion in an infinite atmosphere. The pressures which are actually exerted on a particular object will have been amplified by reflections from its own or nearby surfaces and will have been attenuated by diffractions round openings and corners. Considerable local increases in pressures can be observed. For relatively low overpressures, say up to 50 kNm^{-2}, a reflection will double the overpressure at the reflecting surface. Within a building it is not difficult to find topographical features, such as corners, where several such reflections can superimpose their effects and produce pressures up to four times that in the incident blast wave.

It is essential, therefore, to consider carefully the topography of each location at which pressures have been determined. If the pressure has been derived from a dished metal surface and this was located in such a position that it was sideways on to the direction of travel of the blast wave, which itself had traversed an unimpeded path from the explosion centre, then the numerical value obtained can be accepted as a direct pressure measurement. In all other cases the numerical values must be interpreted in the light of the amplifications and attenuations which the topography indicates. For example, in the relatively simple instance of an explosion which occurred on a burning ground (1937) when explosive was placed on hot ground, it was observed that windows were broken at a greater distance than expected. It was observed, however, that the protective bank around part of the burning ground was concave in shape and it is thought that this served to focus the blast wave in particular directions.

THE CHARGE WEIGHT OF A CONDENSED EXPLOSIVE

As already noted, the breakage of glass windows is a special case of damage since there are often a great many observations which can be made at the scene. A simple method was described where locations could be identified at which a pressure of 7 kNm^{-2} would be assumed. The same reservations must be made as to the effect of the topography, but there are often so many locations to choose from that the selection of ones with uncomplicated topography and unobstructed lines of travel for the blast wave is not a difficult matter. For each such location, knowing the pressure and distance from the explosion centre, the weight of the explosive in the charge can be calculated.

The usual model describing the scaling laws of peak over-pressure, distance, and weight of explosive may be written as:

$$P=f(Z) \quad \text{and} \quad Z=\frac{S}{W}$$

where P is pressure, S is distance and W is weight of explosive. Z is known as the scaled distance. From experimental evidence, Cook (9) has quoted peak over-pressures from cylindrical charges of TNT as being given by

$$P=\frac{11 \cdot 34}{Z} - \frac{185 \cdot 9}{Z^2} + \frac{19210}{Z^3}$$

where the units are in atmospheres, centimetres, and grams (1 atmosphere $= 101 \cdot 3$ kNm^{-2}). This equation relates to pressures from charges fired above ground over smooth terrain. Pressures from a charge fired on the surface are equivalent to those from a larger weight charge fired in air. The factors for a weight on the surface vary from $1 \cdot 3$ W at high pressure (21,000 kNm^{-2}) to 2 W at 70 kNm^{-2}. The effect on the numerical value of altering the explosive from TNT is not great. For most high explosives the numerical values calculated for TNT are within 20% of those observed. Since the pressures correlate roughly with the power of an explosive, this can be used as a basis for a correcting factor for the calculated figure.

Some useful data calculated from Cook's equation are given in Appendix A. Table A.1 lists the blast pressures generated at a number of distances by a number of weights of explosives. The distances and weights have been chosen to represent the range of these parameters most likely to be encountered in explosion investigation. Also included in the Appendix is a graphical representation of the relationship between distance and charge-weight for a pressure of 7 kNm^{-2}.

In an explosion investigation the number of modifying factors present is such that it is doubtful whether any great refinement of calculation is justified. An estimate of the order of magnitude of the weight of the charge is normally the most that is required and this can be derived adequately from the simplest technique for glass damage assessment described above and Cook's equation. It is only necessary to measure the distances to a number of locations at which pressures of 7 kNm^{-2} can be presumed to have occurred and the corresponding charge weights can be read directly from the graph in Appendix A. It will normally be found that several estimates obtained in this way will be in reasonable agreement. In this case, the mean of these can be taken as the charge weight. If there is a wide disparity between the estimates or one or more is markedly different from the rest, then the topography of each location must be considered and value judgements made in an endeavour to produce the most probably correct estimated charge weight.

THE PHENOMENON OF FRAGMENTATION

The property most obviously associated with explosions is blast. Another important one is fragmentation, the property of producing relatively small pieces of material, fragments, and projecting them.

Fragments can conveniently be classified as of two types, primary and secondary. Primary fragments are defined as being derived from the explosive device, while secondary fragments are defined as being derived by blast from surrounding objects. The production of primary fragments may be an intended part of the design of an explosive device, as is the case with many military munitions such as grenades, shrapnel shell and anti-personnel contrivances generally. Fragmentation effects may also be found as a design feature in home-made devices, where more or less sophisticated copies of their military counterparts have frequently been recorded. It may be taken as a general rule that where any explosive device incorporates features which indicate that it is designed to project fragments over a large solid angle, then it is probably intended for anti-personnel use. Directed fragment projection may also indicate an anti-personnel design, but devices incorporating this feature are also used for the penetration of materials such as armour and other metal plate. The general principle of all such devices is that the explosive charge is confined in a metal, usually steel, case which breaks up as the result of the explosion into pieces of predetermined size and these are projected outwards either generally or in specific directions.

Many other explosive devices which are not intended for anti-personnel use nevertheless produce primary fragments. This arises from the fact that, although the main effect aimed at is blast, there is in many cases fragment projection as a secondary effect since the explosive charge is contained in a metal case. There are two main reasons for the use of metal cases in explosive devices designed primarily for blast and not for fragmentation effects. The first is to provide confinement. This is essential if a deflagrating explosive is to produce adequate blast. Detonating explosives will, in general, function without confinement. However, with relatively small charges as used in many devices, confinement in a dense material causes the velocity of propagation to increase to a value nearer the theoretical maximum. This in turn increases the brisance and hence the intensity of the blast. In consequence, small charges of this type are frequently confined in metal. The second reason for the use of metal cases is that it is an easily worked material which at the same time has the necessary strength to withstand rough handling and the stresses imposed by warfare.

Primary fragments are not produced exclusively by explosive charges in metal cases. The material of any container will be reduced to fragments and these will be projected. Some, being combustible, will be consumed by the hot gases and will never be recoverable for study. Others, deriving from very brittle materials, will be so small that they too will not be recoverable. Others, however, will survive and with more or less trouble can be found and examined.

All primary fragments so far referred to derive from the immediate charge casing. However, all explosive devices contain components in addition to the casing, ranging from simple igniferous fuses to sophisticated and elaborate timing mechanisms. These components, being situated close to the charge, may be dismembered by the explosion and projected as individual fragments. It is convenient, therefore, to regard any fragments which originate from the explosive device as being primary and not just those which are parts of the explosive charge casing.

Secondary fragments can be of any material, since they originate from objects shattered by the blast. While not so informative as primary fragments, there are circumstances in which useful information can be derived from them. For example, fragments of aircraft fuselage produced by an explosion can be distinguished from those due to the break up of a gas turbine. The potential significance of secondary fragments should not, therefore, be overlooked by the investigator.

INFORMATION FROM FRAGMENTS
DIRECT IDENTIFICATIONS FROM FRAGMENTS

It is a cardinal principle of explosion investigation that as many primary fragments as possible should be recovered for examination. The primary fragments so gathered fall into two types, those which have features which give a positive indication as to the device from which they originated and those that do not. The examination of the latter type will be discussed in the next section.

Sometimes sufficient fragments can be recovered to make it possible to reconstruct virtually the whole of the device. Thus, when a youth was killed by an explosion of a chlorate mixture, it was found that the metal case which he had filled with the mixture had broken up into a few fragments and these had remained in the room in which he had been experimenting. On collecting these, it was found possible to reassemble them to show that they derived from an inert aerial practice bomb of the 1939–45 period which he had clearly been filling with his mixture. Reconstructions of this kind are completely convincing and of great evidential value in any subsequent proceedings in a court of law.

Even when a substantial reconstruction is not possible it may be found that one or more of the primary fragments exhibits features from which the identity of the original device, or some part of it, can be unequivocally deduced. In view of the multitude of manufactured explosive devices in existence and the almost limitless possibilities for home-made ones, it is not feasible to make a complete list of diagnostic features of this kind. It is possible, however, to indicate the general nature of the commoner ones. The investigator must build on this basis from his general explosives background and steadily widening experience.

1. *Fragments derived from the charge casing*

Fragments derived from the charge casing can exhibit four types of diagnostic feature which can lead to the identification of the original. These are:

1.1. *The shape*

Even small fragments can retain portions of the original shape of the object which are sufficient to identify it. Many fragmentation grenades have segmented surfaces and individual segments which can be recovered may sometimes be identified as being part of a particular model of grenade. Explosions involving gas cylinders can result in fragments bearing characteristic contours from the neck or base. Another feature which can be found on fragments, particularly from home-made bombs, is screw threads. Even quite small sections of a screw thread are sufficient for the identification of the thread form and pitch.

1.2. *Paint*

The metal cases of most manufactured explosive devices are painted and this paint will be found on fragments. The simplest feature of this paint for examination is the colour, which may be characteristic, though care must be taken to consider whether the colour may have been changed by heat effects in the explosion. More elaborate examinations can include layer analysis and, if it seems justified, a full chemical analysis.

.1.3. *Markings*

Many explosive devices, particularly military ones, bear identification markings. So also do other industrial products, such as gas cylinders and aerosol cans, which may be involved in an explosion either by reason of the properties of their contents or because they have been used as the casing of a home-made device. Even a few characters from such a marking preserved on a fragment can lead to the identification of the original object. Markings of this kind can be painted, engraved, embossed or indented either by casting, pressing or stamping. They can include colour-coded marks as well as letters and numbers denoting types, model numbers, lot numbers, and dates of manufacture or inspection. Sometimes the characters or language can indicate the country of origin.

1.4. *Material*

Fragments can readily be subdivided into metallic and non-metallic by inspection. The former can be further subdivided into ferromagnetic and non ferromagnetic with the aid of a magnet. While this knowledge will not generally be sufficient for positive identification of the original it can sometimes be indicative. The process can be carried further and a full analysis made, by a non destructive method such as electron microprobe if necessary, when a highly characteristic composition may be found.

2. *Fragments derived from an initiating mechanism*

Fragments derived from an initiating mechanism can most conveniently be considered according to their function:

2.1. *Detonator or igniter*

After an explosion there are seldom any recoverable and recognisable fragments of the end of the detonator which contained its explosive charge. Considerable portions of the other end, however, can often be found and these bear many diagnostic features. Electric detonators have wires of characteristic gauges covered with colour coded plastics insulation. The colour and material of the closing plug and the form of the crimping are likewise characteristic of the type and make of detonator and it should not be overlooked that crimps sometimes bear manufacturers' identification marks. Other features from which electric detonators can be identified include the design of the fuze head, the size and construction of the delay element if one is present, and the material, thickness and overall dimensions of the metal case.

Igniferous detonators are generally operated with safety fuse and portions of this may be found. The number, type, construction and sequence of the layers of windings on safety fuses vary greatly and may be used as a method of identification.

Mechanically operated detonators, such as those found in various kinds of military munitions, incorporate such features as strikers, protective shutters, and arming mechanisms. Any such pieces recovered can be highly characteristic.

2.2. *Operating mechanism*

There are a great many possible mechanisms which can be used to cause a detonator to function and all can give rise to fragments from which their nature can be deduced. Delay devices are frequently used and these can be mechanical, incorporating such mechanisms as clocks and creep wires, chemical, incorporating such mechanisms as permeable membranes and acid erosion, electrical, incorporating delay circuits and radio control, and a range of other types. Other mechanisms include a variety of switches used as anti-lift and anti-opening devices and as booby trap mechanisms. Auxiliary equipment can also be found. This includes wires and batteries, the latter in particular having many characteristic features of design, both of internal construction and outside colour and pattern.

3. *Fragments derived from an outer container*

Infernal machines are normally built into a container of some kind, both as a convenient method of housing the mechanism and, frequently, as a method of disguising the true nature of the object. Where explosions involve this type of device, therefore, fragments from the container may be found. Such fragments can often be used to identify the nature of the original container. This information can be of value in the checking of witnesses' accounts, in the detection of possible suspects and in the conviction of the actual criminal.

It is apparent from the foregoing that the number of diagnostic features of fragments, which can lead to the positive identification of the object from which they derived, is enormous. It is not feasible, therefore, for the explosion investigator to make a comprehensive list of them. What he can and should do is:

(a) Have a record of details of items commonly found in the type of case he is frequently called upon to investigate. This record can be in the form of written data and photographs supplemented, if possible, with a collection of actual objects. The latter may be live or inert according to the investigator's personal circumstances in respect of storage.

(b) Make sure he knows where to turn to for further information. This should include, as a minimum, a list of the commercial explosives manufacturers in his own country, or, where there are none, the country or countries from which explosives for domestic use are imported, a contact in the ammunition inspectorate or equivalent military body which has comprehensive dealings with military explosive items and his national explosives regulatory authority.

(c) To have studied the literature on improvised devices, such as References 11 to 15 inclusive, so as to be able to recognise the significance of fragments derived from these with the same facility as for those derived from their professional counterparts.

THE IDENTIFICATION OF FRAGMENTS

Apart from fragments bearing obvious distinctive features, such as those discussed, a search of the scene of an explosion frequently results in the finding of other fragments which do not have such features. Their general context may suggest that they are associated with the explosion but it may be necessary, both for the investigation and for purposes of subsequent proceedings in a court of law or at an enquiry, to provide further evidence of their origin. It is convenient to consider various types of fragment separately.

1. *Metallic primary microfragments*

These fragments, which can vary in size from a maximum dimension of a few millimetres to microscopic dust, are produced by the effect of a detonation on the immediate casing surrounding the charge. They can be derived from a case in which the main charge is contained and also from the case of a detonator.

When the explosive charge detonates a shock wave is transmitted through the metal. When this shock reaches an impedance mismatch, such as the discontinuity represented by the outer surface, it is partially reflected. The reflected wave produces a region of intensified stress parallel to the surface and this results in failure. The surface layer, therefore, breaks away or spalls, producing small, relatively thin, fragments. These fragments are then projected through the various zones of the expanding blast wave. These zones include the outer shock front in which a pressure of the order of 50 GNm^{-2} may be reached in a microsecond. Behind this is a region of hot gases, in which chemical reactions are still taking place, at temperatures ranging from 2000° K downwards. These various conditions modify the surface features of the fragments and, since the conditions producing them are so extreme, these can be used as a means of establishing the origin of the fragments.

Six surface features can be identified on metallic primary microfragments (20):

(a) Cupping. The spall, as it separates from the main body, lies with its larger dimensions across the direction of movement of the shock front. In consequence, the edges are subjected to pressure and the fragment forms a shallow cup.

(b) Reflected cracks. When a number of fragments are available for examination, it may be possible to find places where natural cross sections have developed. Examination of these may reveal cracks parallel to the original surface arising from the failures leading to breakaway.

(c) Rolled edges. As the fragment moves through the gases the edges become rolled.

(d) Gas washing. Under the influence of the hot gases, surface melting and reforming occurs. This can result in various patterns such as dimpling, which has the appearance of a multitude of very shallow depressions, and flow patterns.

(e) Surface deposits. When hotter zones of the gaseous reaction complex pass over the surface of a fragment, foreign matter may be deposited and this has a characteristic appearance.

(f) Microcraters. Very small craters with diameters of the order of a micrometre may be formed. These may be due to bombardment by very small particles or to gas bubbles escaping from a layer of molten metal.

All these features are characteristic of explosively produced microfragments. Not all will be detectable on any given fragment but the presence of two or three provides sound evidence of its origin.

Further evidence may be obtained, if required, by metallographic examination, but this is unlikely to be necessary. Such features as surface recrystallisation and the presence of Dieter lines and Neuman twinning bands are characteristics of explosively produced fragments.

2. Non-metallic primary microfragments

When an explosive charge is encased in a non-metallic material, fragments are seldom found. This arises from the fact that such materials tend to be combustible and are, therefore, entirely consumed in the hot gases of the blast wave, or to be brittle and this produces fragments of such microscopic size as to be impossible to recover. Occasionally, however, non-metallic primary microfragments of diagnostic value are produced from components of an explosive device. An example of this is glass fragments deriving from a bottle used to hold acid in a chlorate/acid delay mechanism. Such fragments tend to be rounded with many facets and do not exhibit the sharp edges found on fragments of glass produced by normal breakage, by impact, or by the breakage of windows by blast.

3. *Metallic secondary fragments*

The recognition of metallic secondary fragments can be of considerable importance in some investigations. This is especially so in aircraft crashes where explosive sabotage is suspected, since the extensive break-up which usually accompanies a crash may make it difficult to determine whether the suspicions are justified. A number of features characteristic of explosively-produced secondary fragments can be observed. Not all are exclusively produced by explosives (21), but the presence of several such features increases the probability that an explosion is the correct explanation. Another difficulty is that the characteristic features become less pronounced the further away the charge was from the metal which has been fragmented. The presence of fragments showing no evidence of explosive characteristics may indicate that there was, in fact, no explosive present or that the explosive charge was situated remotely from all metal surfaces or that the fragments found derived from metal remote from the charge. It is clear, therefore, that conclusions distinguishing between these possibilities can only be drawn after a careful and exhaustive search.

The characteristics which can be observed on metallic secondary fragments are of three types (22):

3.1. *Fractures*

1. *Reversing-Slant fractures.* In this type of fracture the material will fail for a short distance in a slant fracture. Failure will then continue in the same general direction but with the slope of the slant completely reversed. This effect can be repeated a number of times and produces a castellated effect. The frequency of the reversal has been found to be greatest nearest the explosion.

2. *Spike-Toothed fractures.* This type of fracture is characterised by a row of spiked teeth formed along an edge of the fragment.

3.2. *Surface effects*

1. *Pitting.* Metallic surfaces near an explosive charge become

pitted, *i.e.* marked with a larger or smaller number of small craters with raised rims. The general effect under magnification is reminiscent of a lunar landscape.

2. *Metal deposition.* Metal deposition, similar to that described as occurring on primary fragments, can also be observed in secondary fragments.

3. *Surface erosion.* Surface erosion due to gas washing can be observed on secondary fragments which have originated near the explosive charge.

3.3. *Shatter fragments*

Small fragments derived from metal near the explosion centre can exhibit certain features of shape characteristic of formation by explosive forces.

1. *Wire and rod fragments.* These are long thin fragments with length to thickness ratio in the range of 20:1 to 50:1. Their cross sections can be triangular or of parallelogram form.

2. *Curled fragments.* Curled fragments are basically similar to wire fragments but are curled into open spirals and helices or, occasionally, into tight spirals. They are readily distinguishable from engineering swarf by the lack of tool marks.

3. *Curved fragments.* These fragments, initially flat pieces, are curved round smoothly with a small radius of curvature.

4. *Spall fragments.* These are cup-shaped pieces as described under primary fragments.

5. *Fissured fragments.* Fragments can be found which are penetrated by a considerable number of open, roughly parallel cracks. Many run through the thickness of the metal.

DIRECTION EFFECTS SHOWN BY FRAGMENTS

The damage caused by primary fragments can sometimes be used to determine the direction in which the fragment was travelling. This knowledge can then be applied to deduce the position of the explosive charge and possibly an estimate of its size. There are three types of fragment damage which can be used in this way.

1. *Penetration*

When a fragment penetrates completely through a thick layer of a material or through two or more adjacent thin layers, its path can be traced. It is possible then to extrapolate the path backwards to indicate the line on which the explosive charge lay. Where several such observations can be made, cross bearings can be taken and the position of the charge determined reasonably precisely. The extrapolation may be done according to circumstances by passing wires (20) or strings through the holes or by optical sighting.

2. *Gougemarks*

When an explosive charge is situated near a surface, primary fragments will strike the surface at a glancing angle and produce gougemarks in the surface. If these are extrapolated backwards they will meet approximately at a point which is the ground zero of the charge in respect of the surface.

3. *Pitting*

When an explosive charge is situated at some distance from a surface, primary fragments will strike the surface approximately normally. The surface will, therefore, be marked with a number of small craters of more or less well-defined form according to the nature of the surface. Any surfaces of this kind found in an investigation can be used to locate the position of the charge. This will have been on a line normal to the surface. It must be emphasised, however, that this will be only an approximate observation and that the combined observations from several such surfaces would be needed to locate the charge position with any degree of precision.

PENETRATION BY FRAGMENTS

Where fragments have penetrated into an object and the fragment can be recovered for examination it is possible to estimate the velocity with which the fragment was moving. The higher this is the more probable it is that it was initiated by an explosion and if values of the order of 10^3 ms^{-1} are found no other explanation is probable. The depth of penetration can be found from the formula (23):

$$\text{Penetration} = K\left(\frac{MV^n}{A}\right)$$

where M = mass of the fragment (lbs);
         V = its striking velocity (ft/sec);
         A = its striking area (sq. in);

n = an exponent which is 1 for wood, steel and concrete and is 0 for soft plastic materials like wax; and

K = a coefficient that depends on the material out of which the object struck consists.

The relative values of K are: steel 1·5; reinforced concrete 12; brickwork 13·5; massive concrete 15; broken stone 24; earth, sand, wood 30; and baled wool 40.

Various formulae have been suggested (24) for the penetration of fragments into earth media. Useful equations which are based on average values from experimental data are as follows:

Penetration into sand $Y/D = 0·01\ \gamma_s V_s$.
Penetration into soft rock $Y/D = 0·001\ \gamma_s V_s$.
Penetration into hard rock $Y/D = 0·0004\ \gamma_s V_s$.

where
Y = the depth of penetration in inches;
D = the diameter of the projectile in inches;
V_s = the striking velocity in ft/sec; and
γ_s = the effective ballistic density is given by:

$$\gamma_s = \frac{W}{\pi/6\ p_s D^3}$$

where
W = the weight of the projectile in pounds; and
ρ_s = the density of steel.

There is one circumstance in which unexpectedly deep penetrations can be observed to arise from secondary fragments. This is where the explosive is coupled to the target by water, as for example when an explosive charge is detonated in a water filled container. The transmission of the shock wave in these circumstances is such that the fragments of the walls of the container, although secondary, behave like primary ones. This phenomenon has long been known and was observed, for example, in an explosion at Montrose in 1880 when a small amount of dynamite was present in a kettle of water which was being heated. In the resultant explosion the missile-effect killed several men. At a much later date, the effect was exploited in coal-mining where it formed one aspect of the technique of pulsed-infusion shot-firing.

THE SIZE OF FRAGMENTS

It was pointed out in Chapter 2 that the property of explosives usually called brisance is an expression of their shattering power. It follows, therefore, that the brisance of an explosive is reflected in the degree of shattering of any confining metal case and hence of the size of the fragments produced. Since the brisance is related to the product ρD^2, there is a connection between detonation velocity and fragment size. It has frequently been observed that, for a given design of confining case, the higher the detonation velocity of the explosive the smaller the fragments into which it is broken.

Although this observation is qualitative it can at times be of value in explosion investigation. An obvious example is where the case of some standard military munition, such as one of the classic fragmentation hand grenades, has been refilled with some explosive other than that normally used. If examination of the recorded fragments shows that they are much larger or much smaller than those produced by the functioning of the normally filled device, this observation can be regarded as indicative of the use of an explosive other than that normally used as the filling. Even with non standard metal containers the experienced investigator can derive an indication of the brisance of the explosive filling by comparing the size of the fragments recovered with the size he would expect in the light of his background knowledge and experience. If the two are not consistent he should be alerted to the possibility that the explosive was other than that which the general circumstances might, at first sight, suggest.

CRATERS

When an explosion takes place near to a surface, whether above, on or below it, a depression is produced which is usually described as a crater. A crater or craters found on the ground surface at the scene of an explosion are of potential use in several ways to the investigator.

The size of the crater produced by an explosive charge depends on three major factors. The first of these is the location of the charge in relation to the ground. If a charge is placed sufficiently deeply beneath the ground then the weight of the earth will prevent any manifestation on the surface. With less weight than the critical one a crater will be formed which becomes shallower and wider the nearer the charge is to the surface. A charge on the surface produces a relatively wide, shallow crater. Charges above the surface produce shallower, narrower craters than those produced by similar charges on the surface, and, above a critical height, no crater at all.

The second important factor in the formation of craters is the nature of the ground. Since the crater is formed by the action of the blast a soft soil will be displaced more readily than a hard rocky one and the crater in it will therefore be larger. A charge which will produce a sizeable depression in sandy ground may do little more than crack a concrete surface.

The third important factor in determining the size of the crater is the type of explosive involved. Thus, if a charge is well below ground, a low brisance explosive may produce a larger crater than will the corresponding weight of a high brisance explosive. On the surface, however, the effect is reversed and a low brisance explosive may detonate, leaving little or nothing to be seen on the surfaces with which it was in contact.

A formula which expresses the behaviour of high brisance explosives on the surface is:

$$v = kW^{1.14}$$

where v is the volume of the crater, W is the weight of explosive, and k is a constant. When v is measured in cubic feet and W in pounds, $k = 0.4$.

A simpler alternative is:

$$d^3 = 16W$$

where d is the diameter of the crater in metres and W is the weight of the charge in kilograms. Although these are simplified formulae and take no account of the ground, they work reasonably well except in the case of small charges and can be used to calculate the approximate weight of the charge from the crater dimensions. Estimates of the charge weight obtained in this way can be used for two purposes by the investigator. The first is as a check on other observational methods of estimation, such as glass breaking. The second is as a check on non observational methods of estimation, such as stores records. These should, of course, provide an accurate statement of what was present but may not always be kept as meticulously as they should. Thus, in an investigation of an explosion at Trimley Marsh in 1900 (CXLIV), a crater was found having dimensions which could not be reconciled with the amount of explosive supposed to have been present.

Another piece of information which can sometimes be derived from examination of a crater is the physical size and shape of the charge. This can be particularly apparent when a small charge of detonating explosive is set off in contact with a hard surface such as concrete or stone. Thus, in an explosion in London in 1968, an infernal machine was set off on concrete. It incorporated a cartridge of industrial blasting explosive which left a clear imprint on the surface. Measurement of the imprint was used as a basis for a calculation of the weight of explosive in the cartridge and this was found to agree with estimates based on observations of broken windows.

Craters can also be used as a source of fragments. If the explosive charge was cased, some of the fragments from this will have been driven downwards. If the crater is a shallow one in a hard surface, these fragments will ricochet and be lost. If, however, the crater has been formed in earth or other soft material, the fragments will have penetrated into the floor of the crater. Therefore, after physical examination and recording of the crater and the collection of any samples required for chemical tests, the crater should be dug out and the earth examined, in a laboratory if necessary, for primary fragments.

Another use for craters is to determine whether the explosion was due to a single charge or to several. This is a simple matter of searching the site to establish whether there is more than one crater. Thus, at the scene of an explosion at an explosives factory (1954) which entirely wrecked a cartridging shop, it was established that three bogies should have been present in the building. The two operators were killed, but examination of the scene showed that there were three craters from which it was possible to fix the positions of the bogies at the time of the explosion.

GROUND VIBRATIONS

Ground vibrations generated by explosions have been a subject of interest for many years since the damage caused to buildings by them must be considered carefully when blasting operations are planned. The effects are primarily dependent on the weight of the charge and its distance from the building. Other factors involved are the coupling of the charge to the ground, discontinuities in the ground and the coupling of the ground to the building. It is now generally accepted that the peak particle velocity of the vibration is the best criterion for assessing the potential of a vibration to cause damage to a structure. This quantity may be calculated from the relation:

$$V = 2\pi f a$$

where f is the frequency of the vibration in Hz, a is the amplitude in mm and V is the particle velocity in mm sec^{-1}.

The particle velocity can be linked to the charge weight and distance by a formula proposed by the United States Bureau of Mines:

$$V = K\left(\frac{D}{\sqrt{E}}\right) - B$$

where V is the particle velocity per second, D is the distance from the charge and E is the weight of the explosive charge. K and B are constants which have to be determined instrumentally for a given site. It has been found however (3) that blasting operations can safely be undertaken if the value of $D/\sqrt{E}$ is greater than 23 when D is in metres and E is in kilograms. It is possible, therefore, to construct an approximate relationship:

$$E = \left(\frac{D}{23}\right)^2$$

where E is the explosive charge weight in kilograms and D is the distance in metres to the building next beyond the furthest to show damage by ground vibrations. Since this formula is based on safe blasting practice, it would considerably underestimate the charge weight. A formula specifically for the damage threshold which has been proposed (25) is:

$$\frac{E^{\frac{1}{3}}}{d} = 0.1$$

where E is the explosive charge weight in lb and d is the minimum distance in feet at which ground vibrations will cause damage. Even this gives values which are more conservative than some which are laid down for regulatory purposes. The formula is, however, based on a considerable body of experimental work and can, therefore, be used by the investigator as a further method of estimating the weight of the explosive charge in cases where suitable observations can be made.

Chapter 5

IDENTIFICATION OF THE EXPLOSIVE

TYPES OF SITUATION

When the explosion investigator reaches that part of his work in which he attempts to identify the explosive responsible, he will be confronted with one of several situations. Since these require somewhat different procedures it is convenient to discuss them separately. The first situation is that in which an appreciable sample of the explosive can be recovered for examination. The identification can then be made by more or less straightforward chemical analysis. The second situation is that in which a condensed explosive has left no visible sample for recovery. In this case, microscopic fragments of the explosive or its residues must be located and identified by appropriate means. Frequently, only some of the components can be found and, therefore, only the general class of explosive identified. The third situation is that in which a dispersed explosive was involved. In such circumstances the residues are often purely gaseous and will have dispersed long before the investigator reaches the scene.

The investigator also has two other situations to consider, both of which arise if initial attempts to identify the explosive fail. The failure may be due to the fact that there are negligible identifiable fragments or residues of explosive to be found. In this case the investigator must proceed by one or more of the possible deductive investigation techniques. An alternative reason for the failure is that nothing has been identified because the explosion was a mechanical one. Proving that an explosion was mechanical and not chemical can be very difficult and may rest largely on a balance of probabilities. Nevertheless, there are investigational procedures which can go a long way towards establishing that an explosion was in fact due to mechanical causes.

IDENTIFICATION WHERE AN APPRECIABLE SAMPLE CAN BE RECOVERED

LOCATION

Samples of explosive can be found after an explosion in a number of places, depending on the reason for their survival. When an explosive charge has been ineffectively initiated or when the explosion fails to propagate through the whole charge because of faulty assembly, charge geometry or for some other reason, a partial explosion occurs. Unconsumed explosive is then scattered around the scene, whether it be that of an accident or of a deliberate explosion. Where an attack has been made on a security container and the explosive charge has been packed into the lock, a partial explosion is not uncommon. Unconsumed explosive may then be found in the lock itself and in the mechanism chamber of the door.

Samples of explosive may also be found on the scene of a criminal explosion because they have been left there either deliberately or accidentally by the perpetrator. Explosive may be found in containers used to carry it to the scene. Small pieces which have been dropped in the course of manipulation may be scattered around. In the latter case, as with partial explosions, the samples may be mixed with a great deal of debris such as safe ballast or powdered plaster from a wall and may only be found during the course of a search carried out under laboratory conditions.

Another source of samples of explosive after an explosion is the perpetrator. They may be found on the person (in pockets, trouser turn-ups or handbag), in a car (on the floor, in the boot or within the door trim or other places of concealment) or in a house (in almost any situation).

A special case is an explosion in the laboratory or workshop of a home experimenter. In such cases explosives may be anywhere. Such experimenters are liable to keep explosives in unmarked test tubes, bottles or tins and sometimes in containers still bearing the label of some harmless commodity with which they were originally filled.

RECOGNITION

If it seems possible that appreciable samples of explosive may be present on the scene, the first step in their recovery is their recognition. There is no easy way of recognising portions of explosive and untrained persons must always be warned that everything at the scene of an explosion must be treated with care. Explosives cannot be recognised by colour because components of a variety of colours are used in explosive compositions and, also, because colouring matter is not infrequently added to explosives for a variety of reasons. Explosives cannot be recognised by form because they are made as liquids and as solids which may be powders or elastic, plastic or rigid solids of a wide range of shapes and sizes. Explosives cannot be recognised by smell because though some are odoriferous others are odourless and, in addition, some compositions made essentially of the latter contain odoriferous non-explosive components.

Although there are no general rules by which explosives can be recognised, there are a number of aids which can be used by the investigator to recognise materials as being possibly explosive and, therefore, to be recovered for laboratory examination.

1. *Experience*

A wide experience of examining and handling explosives can enable the investigator to recognise samples of many explosives with a considerable degree of certainty. It has been found possible on many occasions, in the course of the investigation of explosions caused by industrial gelignite type explosives, not only to identify correctly a material as being explosive but frequently to make accurate predictions of the actual composition and the name of the manufacturer.

2. *Context*

The investigator may frequently be able to use the context of the explosion as an aid to predicting what explosive may have been involved and, therefore, the appearance of any samples which may be present. This course of action will seldom be possible when the explosion has been caused by an infernal machine. It can, however, frequently be used when accidents occur during manufacture, transport, storage and use, and in criminal cases, such as safebreakings, where one particular class of explosive tends to be used.

3. *Fragments*

Where primary fragments from an explosive device can be recovered and where these indicate that the device was used with its normal filling, an immediate clue to the explosive is provided and hence of the appearance of any samples which may be recoverable.

4. *Wrappings*

In some cases, particularly attacks on security containers, explosives may have been removed from their wrappers and these, or portions of them, discarded. If sufficient of the wrapper can be recovered to make its recognition possible then this forms a valuable guide to the nature of the explosive used.

5. *Explosive vapour detectors*

There are available a number of portable explosive vapour detector devices commonly known as sniffers. One of these can be used to aid in the search for explosives and useful results can be obtained. It must be remembered, however, that all such devices have limitations as to the explosives detectable and the conditions in which even these can be detected. These limitations must be fully recognised when using a sniffer.

6. *Dogs*

The well known powers of dogs in using their acute sense of smell for various purposes, has led to attempts to train dogs to find explosives. Unfortunately, a realistic assessment of the powers of dogs in this connection has been obscured by exaggerated claims for success by over-enthusiastic dog lovers. It is clear, however, that some dogs have the capacity to detect some explosives and so, if a trained dog and handler are available, they may provide assistance in finding samples of suspected explosive.

RECOVERY

When a material suspected to be explosive is identified at a scene, it must be recovered for laboratory examination and analysis. In the case of a solid this is a straightforward matter of picking it up with a clean spatula or other suitable clean tool and transferring it to a clean container which is then sealed and labelled. Experience has shown that polythene bags make very satisfactory containers for this purpose. By reason of their cheapness a new one can be used for every sample, thus removing any possibility of cross contamination. They are readily sealed with an adhesive cellulose tape and the general nature of the contents can be checked independently of the label without breaking the seal.

Before recovering a sample in this way the investigator must be satisfied that the explosive is not a very sensitive one. Unless it is quite clear that a sensitive explosive is not involved, a small sample should be picked up on a paper spatula and tested for sensitivity. If the test establishes that it is sensitive the remainder of the sample should be transferred by means of the paper spatula to a capsule, papier mâché pot or other suitable container for removal. This container must itself be packed in an outer one and padded with shock absorbing material.

When the sample is a liquid, it should be absorbed onto kieselguhr or some other suitable inert material in a plastic bag or other container. If kieselguhr is not available, new cotton wool or clean sawdust may be used as a substitute.

Sometimes no sample of explosive will be found and the procedures for locating and identifying trace quantities described in a later section will have to be used. It is possible, however, that appreciable samples of explosive are actually present but are obscured by debris. It is important, therefore, to recover the entire debris from the seat of the explosion and subject it to a detailed search.

One type of scene presents special difficulties. This is the laboratory workshop of the home experimenter or other maker of improvised explosives. Explosives of almost all types have been found in such cases. Some, such as TNT and guncotton, are relatively safe to handle. Others are much more sensitive and include nitroglycerine which has usually been inadequately freed from acid, some chlorate mixtures, and recognised primary explosives such as mercury fulminate and lead azide. Home experimenters also tend to make extremely sensitive explosives such as chlorate/phosphorus mixtures and nitrogen triiodide as well as spontaneously explosive ones such as some chlorate/sulphur based compositions. The potential presence of such materials, coupled with a general lack of safety precautions, unreliable labelling and inadequate cleanliness, means that the investigator must approach such scenes with special care. The individual samples must be taken out one at a time and must be treated on their merits. Particular care must be taken in opening closed containers, remote control opening being improvised if necessary, since it is by no means unknown to find highly sensitive compositions stored in glass jars with tightly fitting rusted metal screw closures. The procedure in dealing with such a scene must be dictated by extreme caution and based on a very wide experience of the practical handling of explosives.

ANALYSIS

Many identification tests and analytical methods for explosives have been described and a comprehensive review of these would be far too extensive for inclusion in this book. A considerable number can be excluded, since they deal with explosives which the investigator is very unlikely to encounter. Tests and methods in this category are ones for explosive compounds which have been synthesised for evaluation but which have never been adopted for practical use, ones for explosives only used in small quantities for highly restricted limited applications and ones for obsolete explosives.

The methods described are, therefore, limited to ones of proven usefulness in the identification of those explosives which are in reasonably common use and therefore the ones which will generally be encountered by explosion investigators. In using them, however, the investigator or other analyst must bear in mind four provisos:

1. Many explosive compositions, particularly commercial ones, contain a relatively large number of ingredients. Some of these are present in very small proportions. The search for and identification of every minor ingredient which might be present in a given sample of an unknown explosive would be far too time consuming and costly to be practicable. Analytical methods tend, therefore, to concentrate on major components and this limitation must not be overlooked in the interpretation of the results.

2. There are a great many explosive formulations in current production throughout the world. Because of their number, the frequent introduction of new ones and commercial confidence, it is impossible to compile a comprehensive list. While, therefore, it is often possible to identify an explosive by analysis it does not necessarily follow that even a complete knowledge of the formulation of an unknown explosive will necessarily enable it to be identified to the exclusion of all other possibilities.

3. The identification of military explosives can present peculiar difficulties. While the identification of the components of a sample may be straightforward it may be impossible to state its origin since most military formulations are safeguarded for security reasons. It should be possible for a *bona fide* investigator to obtain at least some information on military compositions of the country of which he is a national, though even then the information may only be given on an undertaking to respect its confidentiality. The corresponding infor-

mation for other countries may be harder to obtain or, depending on political considerations, impossible.

4. Although the majority of cases handled by an investigator will involve familiar formulations, he must always be on the alert for the presence of the less common explosives and components. This was well illustrated by a case in which some home-made detonators came into the possession of the police in connection with a series of safe-breaking offences. Analysis of the filling showed that it was lead azide. Microscopic examination, however, showed that it was not one of the forms normally manufactured for use in detonators, nor that usually produced by home experimenters, but the highly unusual γ lead azide. Further enquiries established that it had reached the criminal fraternity by the unlikely procedure of being part of a small quantity synthesised experimentally in a government laboratory and supplied for research purposes to a university laboratory from where a portion had been stolen.

A further general point must be made. The analyst must never forget that his results will have to bear the searching scrutiny of a court of law. He must make sure, therefore, that he takes the normal precautions of a forensic science laboratory to ensure that his results are proof against proper criticism. To avoid tedious repetition in the descriptions of analytical methods which follow, it will be assumed that the analyst will take all the normal necessary precautions to preserve the integrity of his samples and all the necessary use of blanks and control samples to ensure the reliability of his results.

In considering the various tests and analytical methods, it is convenient to split them into six groups according to the nature of the explosive. These are: (1) industrial blasting explosives; (2) military high explosives; (3) propellents; (4) pyrotechnics; (5) initiating explosives; and (6) improvised explosives.

1. *Industrial blasting explosives*

1.1. *Spot tests*

Most industrial blasting explosives are either of the gelignite type based on nitroglycerine gelatinised with nitrocellulose, with or without the addition of ammonium nitrate, or are based on ammonium nitrate itself. Samples of such explosives may be analysed quantitatively as described below by a series of extractions and the qualitative and quantitative examination of the various extracts and residues.

This method is satisfactory with adequately sized, clean samples in good condition. The samples handled in a forensic laboratory, however, often fail to meet these requirements. Explosives in the hands of unauthorised persons are seldom stored under satisfactory conditions and tend to deteriorate. In particular, they tend to gain water by deliquescence of ammonium nitrate with consequent leaching out of water-soluble components. Recovered samples are often small, and hence unrepresentative, and may be contaminated with an unknown number of unknown materials in unknown concentrations. It has been found, therefore, that with some samples the normal quantitative method of analysis is liable to give misleading or unintelligible results.

It has been found, however, that even deteriorated samples generally still contain the actual ingredients originally present in the composition in spite of changes in their proportions due to the various causes already described. This observation forms the basis of the spot test method of analysis which consists of determining the presence or absence of as many as possible of the commonly used ingredients by simple chemical tests mainly done on a spot plate. The results are then compared with declared formulations and, in many cases, it will be found that there is only one explosive with the combination of ingredients identified. Where there are two or more, one further test can usually be devised which will distinguish between them. The reservations concerning interpretation set out in the section on quantitative analysis must, however, be considered.

The scheme of procedure is set out in Appendix B. It is not exhaustive, since manufacturers are always liable to use new components in their formulations or it may be wished to extend it to a country whose explosives industry uses some different ingredients. Tests for these substances can, however, be added as and when required.

1.2. *Quantitative analysis*

The general procedure for the quantitative analysis of industrial blasting explosives is based on the principle of extracting various groups of constituents with appropriate solvents and then treating each extract as a separate analytical problem. The full, quantitative analysis of an industrial blasting explosive can be a very lengthy operation. For purposes of identification, however, a complete analysis is seldom necessary and the procedure described in Appendix C will normally be found fully adequate for the purposes of explosion investigation.

The first part of the procedure splits the sample quantitatively and successively into: (1) volatile matter; (2) components soluble in benzene or ether; (3) components soluble in water; (4) components soluble in hydrochloric acid; (5) components soluble in acetone; (6) components lost on ignition; and (7) the residue. These determinations, coupled with the identifications of the main components in each extract by means of spot tests (Appendix B) or thin layer chromatography (Appendix D) and examination under the microscope of the original sample and the residue, is often sufficient to give a satisfactory identification of the explosive. If the identification is still not unequivocal, the second part of the procedure can be used and quantitative determinations made of the main components present in the ether and the water extracts.

The results of the quantitative analysis are compared with manufacturers' declared formulations and an identification can normally be made. In making the identification, the investigator must not only bear in mind the possibility that the explosive may derive from some country whose formulations are not known to him but also two other points. The first is that he must allow for manufacturing tolerances. Coal mining explosives are usually rigidly controlled for reasons of safety and the compositional tolerances can be expected to be of the order of $\pm 1\%$ on the main constituents. Other explosives have wider tolerances but they will usually be found to be within about $\pm 2\%$ of the figures for the main constituents in declared formulations. The second point is that, although the manufacture of industrial blasting explosives is normally subject to control, it is common practice to allow the manufacturers options in the inclusions of some components. It may be found, therefore, that the minor constituents of a particular named explosive may vary from time to time. The existence and nature of these options can usually be learned from the manufacturers.

It may appear from these reservations that the positive identification of an industrial blasting explosive is unlikely to be possible. This is not so. The identification is not solely a matter of chemical analysis (Chapter 13). When all the available data are used, it is normal to find that, in most cases, the identification can be made beyond reasonable doubt and in many with certainty. The investigator must, however, guard against too facile an assumption of identity on the one hand and an unhelpful scepticism which refuses to apply common sense on the other.

2. *Military high explosives*

The two main uses for military high explosives are as fillings for munitions and as demolition charges. The latter, many of which are the much publicised plastic explosives, have frequently been misappropriated and used for criminal purposes. Munitions and explosives extracted from them have likewise been used in this way and have also been involved in many accidents.

Although the number of different devices containing military high explosives is very large, the number of explosives is not. Many explosives have been proposed and used in limited quantities. These range from straightforward compounds such as trinitroanisole to a composition used in Imperial Austria which consisted of a mixture of ammonium nitrate and dried stable manure. The historical tendency has been for such materials to be discarded and for military high explosives to be based on a limited number of well tried compounds. In consequence, the military high explosives encountered by the investigator are likely to have one or more of the following 10 materials as the major constituents:

1. Aluminium, flake or powder.
2. Ammonium nitrate.
3. HMX (cyclotetramethylene tetranitramine).
4. Nitrocellulose.
5. Nitroglycerine.
6. Nitroguanidine.
7. PETN (pentaerythritol tetranitrate).
8. RDX (cyclotrimethylene trinitramine).
9. Tetryl (2, 4, 6-trinitrophenylmethylnitramine).
10. TNT (2, 4, 6-trinitrotoluene).

Preliminary information on the constituents can be conveniently obtained by using the appropriate spot tests from the series described in Appendix B. These will indicate the presence of ammonium nitrate, TNT, nitroglycerine, RDX, HMX and aluminium. It should be noted that the test for TNT also gives a red colour with Tetryl, but the two may be distinguished since the reds are different. It should also be noted that the thymol/sulphuric acid test for RDX gives a green colour with nitrates, as mentioned in Appendix B. This means that the green colour is produced with ammonium nitrate and with PETN.

For further identification a useful method is thin layer chromatography. Various applications of this technique to explosives analysis have been described and used. Appendix D sets out a scheme of analysis for the identification of the main military high explosives based on that described in Reference 26.

The identification of the unknown with the control in these circumstances, should satisfy most requirements. If, however, it is thought desirable to obtain further information, infra-red spectroscopy can be convenient. Two approaches may be used. Spectrograms can be made on the original sample and compared with a sample of the postulated explosive, if a sample is available. Alternatively, the original sample may be split into its components by means of extraction with suitable solvents and the spectrograms of the individual component compared with those of known explosives.

3. *Propellents*

Propellents are principally used for propelling missiles and, in this connection, are employed either in the chamber of a gun or in the motor of a rocket. In order to achieve the necessary degree of accuracy in the projection of the missile (external ballistics) it is essential that the burning of the propellent (internal ballistics) should occur in a known and highly reproducible manner. One important parameter in internal ballistics, as in all explosives performance, is the amount of energy liberated and this depends on the chemical composition. Another is the rate of burning.

The rate of burning of a propellent is affected by several factors. It depends markedly on the pressure and as a first approximation can be regarded as obeying Vieille's Law:

$$R = ap^n$$

where R is the rate of burning, p is the pressure, a is a constant and n is an exponent known as the pressure index.

Another factor which determines the burning characteristics is the initial temperature of the charge. This has a relatively minor but, nevertheless, not unimportant effect when the whole range of possible terrestrial ambient conditions is considered.

A third factor which controls the rate of burning derives from Piobert's Law, which states that propellent burning proceeds by successive layers with the burning front always parallel to the initial surface. Piobert's Law has important consequences in forensic science for it is upon this that the design of propellent grains depends and the design provides the most important single feature for the recognition of propellents.

Propellent grains can be designed to have a decreasing burning rate (degressive), or a constant burning rate, or an increasing burning rate (progressive). All may be illustrated by considering a basically cylindrical form. If the grain is a solid cylinder then the burning will proceed from the surface inwards so that the unconsumed propellent remains cylindrical but with a decreasing radius. The surface area of the propellent, therefore, gradually decreases and in consequence the mass burning rate also decreases.

If the propellent grain is made in the form of an annulus instead of a solid cylinder, it will burn on both the outside and inside surfaces. In consequence, the degressive character of the outer surface is compensated by the progressive character of the inner surface and the overall effect is a grain of constant mass burning rate. If the cylinder is pierced by several channels, then the progressive burning in these predominates and the overall effect is a progressive mass burning rate.

Apart from the rate of burning of the propellent the internal ballistics also depend on the time taken for the burning to occur. This is controlled by the grain size and, therefore, provides another important diagnostic feature. The distance through which the burning travels, and hence the controlling factor in the burning time, is called the web thickness. In a sphere this is the radius, and in a plate or annulus half the thickness. The web thickness can vary from 0·25 mm for very fast burning small arms propellents, to the order of a metre for very large rockets.

In the identification of a propellent the first step is to record the physical characteristics of the grains. These can conveniently be recorded under the headings:— shape, size, and colour. Grain shapes can be classified as being one of six types.

1. Cords (cylinders whose length is many times the radius) which may be pierced with one or more perforations or be modified by slots.
2. Cylinders (cylinders whose length is only a few times the radius) which may be pierced with one or more perforations.
3. Circular flakes.

4. Straight edged flakes which may be in the form of any regular or irregular quadrilateral.
5. Spheres.
6. Irregular granules.

Grain sizes vary considerably as has been pointed out but the propellents most likely to be encountered by the explosion investigator are the smaller grained ones used in small arms and similar sized cartridges. The outside dimensions of most grains can be determined by careful measurement with a micrometer. The dimensions of perforations must be measured optically by a microscope and graticule or by a travelling microscope, if one is available.

The colour of propellent grains varies enormously and literally embraces the whole spectrum. It should be noted that some manufacturers indicate the difference between propellents of the same grain design but with slightly different compositions by the inclusion of a small proportion of brightly coloured grains.

The establishment of the physical characteristics of the grains of a propellent sample is of value in two ways. The experienced investigator will be able to make a reasonably reliable estimate of the purpose for which the propellent was designed. Thus, in firearms, the longer the barrel the longer the burning time of the propellent. Hence the greater the web thickness the longer the barrel of the weapon for which the propellent was designed and, to some extent, the greater its calibre. It must be emphasised that any such observations can only be tentative but, when made by someone with experience, they can be valuable pointers to the truth.

The second use to which the physical data can be put is to compare the sample with a reference collection or with a control. The physical characteristics of propellent grains are so varied that it will often be found that a given sample will match only one in an extensive reference collection. If form, dimensions, and colour all match, then the assumption of identity can be made with fair certainty.

Having considered the physical characteristics of a propellent sample, further diagnostic data may be derived from its composition. For this purpose propellents may conveniently be divided into blackpowder, nitrocellulose based propellents, and others.

Gunpowder can readily be distinguished by placing a grain in the depression of a spot-plate and adding 1 drop of water. On crushing with a glass rod, the grain will disintegrate and the potassium nitrate will dissolve in the water. The solution can be tested for nitrate and a fresh sample for sulphur by the tests described in Appendix B. If a small portion is ignited, a characteristic puff of white smoke is emitted and the residue can be subjected to the flame test for potassium. This identification is sufficiently positive for most purposes but if a more complete identification is necessary quantitative analysis can be carried out. A sample can be subjected to carbon disulphide extraction to determine the sulphur content, then to water extraction to determine the potassium nitrate content, and finally to ignition to determine the carbon content, the procedure being essentially as described in Appendix C. The nitrate in the water extract can be estimated by the procedure also described in Appendix C.

Nitrocellulose based propellents can be either single based, consisting essentially of nitrocellulose, double based, when the main constituents are nitrocellulose and nitroglycerine, or triple based, when the main constituents are nitrocellulose, nitroglycerine and TNT. These types may be readily distinguished by the spot tests described in Appendix B. Confirmation can be obtained by the use of the thin layer chromatographic tests described in Appendix D. The latter technique can also be used to identify nitroguanidine which is added to some ordnance propellents as a flash and smoke suppressant.

If further identification is necessary, tests for some of the minor ingredients can be carried out. Two types which may be considered are stabilisers such as diphenylamine and its derivatives and modifiers such as dibutyl and other phthalates. The identifications can be conveniently made by thin layer chromatography using a method such as that described in Appendix E. In making an identification of a propellent by comparison of the minor constituents, it must be remembered that diphenylamine decomposes at high temperatures and is transformed mainly into nitroderivatives such as those listed in Appendix E. Care must be taken, therefore, to consider whether there is any evidence to indicate whether a difference between two samples, or a sample and a control, are due to the original compositional differences or to decomposition of the stabiliser.

Another type of propellent which may be encountered by the investigator is the so-called composite type which consists primarily of ammonium perchlorate and an organic binder. The spot tests used for nitrocellulose based propellents will demonstrate the presence of ammonium and the paper chromatographic method described in Appendix F may be used to identify perchlorate.

4. *Pyrotechnics*

Pyrotechnic compositions are used for many purposes in a wide variety of devices but a great many of these are not likely to be encountered by the explosion investigator. The commonest type of case in which pyrotechnic compositions are found is that in which firework fillings have been misapplied to the production of infernal machines or other devices. The investigator is liable, therefore, to be confronted with the problem of identifying a sample of an unknown firework composition.

Since fireworks embrace a considerable number of different effects, it is found that there are a very large number of formulations on record. At first sight these formulations comprise a mass of unrelated data but they can in fact be systematised since almost all function on the same basic principles. The components in firework formulations can be classified under four headings as follows:

1. Oxidants.
2. Fuels.
3. Substances added to produce or enhance a particular effect.
4. Miscellaneous ingredients, usually present in small

TABLE 5.1
Common components of firework compositions arranged by functions

Oxidants	Fuels	Additional colouring agents	Special effects components	Miscellaneous components
Ammonium perchlorate	Aluminium	Basic copper carbonate	Gallic acid	Barium carbonate
Barium chlorate	Antimony	Copper oxychloride	Sodium salicylate	Barium fluoride
Barium nitrate	Antimony sulphide	Cryolite		Boric acid
Potassium chlorate	Carbon	Orpiment		Dextrine
Potassium nitrate	Iron	Paris green		Gunpowder
Potassium perchlorate	Magnesium	Sodium oxalate		Oils
Sodium nitrate	Resins	Strontium carbonate		Stearin
Strontium nitrate	Sulphur			
	Titanium			
	Woodmeal			

proportions, which perform such functions as binders, stabilisers, lubricants and combustion rate controllers.

Although a large number of oxidants and an even larger number of fuels exist, it has been found in practice that only a few can be used to produce satisfactory fireworks. In consequence, firework compositions are nearly all made from a limited list of components and in practice it will be found that few compositions contain ingredients other than those listed in Table 5.1.

In the analysis of a firework composition it is important to consider how comprehensive an analysis is required. For some purposes a complete quantitative analysis may be considered to be necessary, but in many cases it is sufficient to identify the material as being a firework composition of some general type with perhaps an identification of the major components. Since the analysis can conveniently be carried out in stages, it can be stopped at whatever stage is considered to have provided sufficient information for the particular case. The analytical procedure described is in three stages with subdivisions:

4.1. *Physical examination*

1. *Visual examination.* A portion of the sample should be examined under low magnification ($\times 10$) and the general appearance observed. If the material consists of black granules it is probably gunpowder. Normally, however, it will be a mixture and this will be quite apparent. An estimate can be made of the number of components and a provisional identification can be made of at least some of them. Table 5.2 shows the common components of fireworks compositions arranged according to their visual appearance. This should be supplemented, if possible, by a reference collection so that the investigator may familiarise himself with their appearance and so that comparative examinations can be made. For the latter purpose a comparison microscope will be found useful.

The components of many firework compositions are relatively coarse and it is often possible, with the aid of the microscope, fine tweezers and manipulative skill, to extract particles of individual components. These can then be subjected to further physical examination for characteristics of crystal form, refractive index, density and melting point, if appropriate, and may also be subjected to chemical examination.

TABLE 5.2
Common components of firework compositions
arranged by appearance

Appearance	Components
Red	Resin (red gum), orpiment
Yellow	Resins, sulphur
Green	Basic copper carbonate, Paris green
Blue	Copper oxychloride
Black	Antimony sulphide, carbon, gunpowder
Colourless crystals	Ammonium perchlorate, barium chlorate, barium nitrate, potassium chlorate, potassium nitrate, potassium perchlorate, sodium nitrate, strontium nitrate, cryolite, sodium oxalate, strontium carbonate, gallic acid, sodium salicylate, barium carbonate, barium fluoride, boric acid
Metallic	Aluminium, antimony, iron, magnesium, titanium
Characteristic	Woodmeal
Amorphous	Dextrine, oils, stearin

2. *Ignition test.* A portion of the sample should be ignited and its behaviour noted. If it burns with a bright colour, it is probably a composition for a star, coloured fire, lance, flare or similar device. The colour will be indicative of the component or components used to produce it. The following colours are produced by one or more of the substances indicated:

> red – strontium carbonate, strontium nitrate;
> yellow – cryolite, sodium oxalate;
> green – barium chlorate, barium nitrate;
> blue – basic copper carbonate, Paris green, copper oxychloride;
> white – gunpowder, antimony, orpiment;
> silver – aluminium.

Star compositions tend to be finer grained than those used for fires and are likely to contain accelerators such as carbon and sulphur. The coarser grained fire compositions are likely to contain retardants such as woodmeal.

If the test portion burns with a dullish effect it is likely to be a driver composition derived from a roman candle, rocket or other device where propulsion is required. Such compositions are based on gunpowder, usually with additional potassium nitrate and/or carbon and/or sulphur to produce the correct burning characteristics.

If the test portion burns with a bright flash it is likely to be a flash and sound unit composition. It will most probably consist of potassium perchlorate and aluminium, though other mixtures of a similar nature are sometimes used for this purpose.

If the test portion burns with a dullish flame together with sparkling effects it is likely to be a fountain composition. It will, therefore, most probably be based on gunpowder and/or its components or some of them, together with a metal powder.

It should be noted that pyrotechnic whistle compositions will only produce their characteristic noise when ignited in the firework. When ignited loose they produce an effect similar to a driver composition.

4.2. Chemical examination

1. *Spot tests.* A number of the spot and other tests quoted for use in the identification of components of other types of explosives are appropriate to firework compositions. A series of references to these together with some other relevant tests are listed in Appendix G. These may usefully be supplemented by spectrographic analysis for the major elements present.

2. *Group analysis.* The chemical information obtained from spot and other tests will often enable an adequate identification to be made. If, however, it is considered that further identification is necessary then a portion of the sample may be subjected to the chemical group analysis procedure for a mixture.

4.3. Quantitative analysis

Quantitative analysis may sometimes be necessary. This can arise, for example, if it is required to test whether or not a given sample may be indistinguishable from some particular composition. Owing to the large number of combinations of oxidant, fuel, effects and modifier components possible, even from such a restricted list as that in Table 5.1, it is advisable to design an analytical procedure for each individual case in the light of the information obtained from the previous physical and chemical tests. In this way the analytical procedure can be kept as simple as possible and avoid the unnecessary complications inherent in any scheme designed to be of general use. The designing of suitable analytical procedures is normally quite straightforward and may be based on the type of separation techniques used for industrial blasting explosives. There is, however, one particular difficulty which arises in the quantitative analysis of firework compositions. This stems from the presence of resins which are natural products consisting of complex mixtures. They tend, therefore, to be neither completely soluble nor completely insoluble in any solvent and also have a tendency to cause blockage of filters. These facts must be taken into account in the design of an analytical method and in the interpretation of its results.

As an example of the identification of a firework composition consider the red star composition: potassium chlorate 70; strontium carbonate 15; accaroid resin 10; dextrin 4; and charcoal 1.

The results of the various stages of the examination would be:

> 1.1 – white crystalline material, red resin, and black charcoal
> 1.2 – red star or flare composition
> 2.1 – chemical tests: potassium, strontium, chlorate, and car-
>   bonate
>   spectrogram: major elements, potassium, strontium, and
>   chlorine
> Conclusion – this is a star or flare composition containing potassium chlorate, strontium carbonate, red resin, and charcoal. Since it may be a star composition, dextrine may be present. (The alternative, potassium carbonate and strontium chlorate is not credible since it is not a viable pyrotechnic composition.)

Scheme of quantitative analysis:

Sample
  ↓
Extract with water → extract = potassium chlorate + dextrine
  ↓   ↓
Residue   add alcohol → white precipitate = dextrine
  ↓
Extract with dilute hydrochloric acid → extract = strontium
  ↓   carbonate
Residue
  ↓
Extract with alcohol → extract = resin
  ↓
Residue = charcoal

5. *Initiating explosives*

The initiating explosives produced by amateurs for experimental or criminal purposes are usually single primary explosives. Manufactured initiating explosives are normally mixtures containing a selection of materials from some of the following categories:

1. Primary explosives.
2. Oxidants.
3. Fuels.
4. Abrasives to increase sensitivity to friction.
5. Binders.
6. High explosives.
7. Miscellaneous ingredients for modifying the characteristics.

Many compounds have been proposed from time to time for use as primary explosives. Most of these have been found to be less than satisfactory and initiating compositions tend to be based on a few well tried compounds. Mercury fulminate has been in use as a primary explosive since the early nineteenth century, but its poor keeping qualities have caused a decline in its use in manufactured devices in recent decades. It is, however, still in favour with amateur experimenters. The two primary explosives most widely used are lead azide and lead styphnate. The latter is a poor initiating explosive which has the disadvantage of being very sensitive to electrostatic discharge. It is, however, also very sensitive to flame and is therefore used as an additive to other compositions to improve flame sensitivity. Lead azide is readily prepared by the reaction of sodium azide on a soluble lead salt, usually lead nitrate or lead acetate. This ease of preparation has caused it to be made by amateur experimenters. The usual product is a mixture of the α and β forms and these can readily be recognised under magnification by their respective prismatic and elongated crystals. Lead azide is very sensitive and, when in the form of large crystals, may explode spontaneously. This hazard can be avoided by careful control of the conditions of preparation and the product recognised under magnification as consisting entirely of small crystals of the α form. The method adopted for commercial preparations, however, is to precipitate the lead azide in the presence of dextrine. The product, dextrinated lead azide, contains about 5% dextrine and consists of rounded granules composed of small crystals. It can, therefore, be readily distinguished from the other types under magnification.

The first stage in the identification of a primary explosive is to check for the presence of these three substances. Some convenient tests are as follows:

1. *Mercury fulminate.* Add an equal amount of vanadium pentoxide to the sample on a spot plate and allow one drop of concentrated hydrochloric acid to run into the mixture. Mercury fulminate produces a violet colouration.

2. *Lead azide.* Add one drop of freshly prepared ferric chloride solution to the sample dissolved in saturated ammonium acetate solution. Azide produces a blood red colour which is discharged by hydrochloric acid. Thiocyanate also produces a red colour which is, however, not discharged by hydrochloric acid.

3. *Lead styphnate.* The presence of lead styphnate is indicated by its characteristic yellow-green colour.

In the event of positive results from these tests, confirmation may be obtained by means of the thin layer chromatographic method described in Appendix H.

Apart from these three primary explosives two others may be encountered:

Tetracene, 4-guanyl-1-(nitrosoaminoguanyl)-1-tetrazine, is a pale yellow, fluffy material which is completely insoluble in common organic solvents. It is soluble in concentrated hydrochloric acid, from which it may be precipitated by dilution with water or neutralisation of the acid. The precipitated crystals possess a very characteristic dendritic appearance.

Diazodinitrophenol forms bright yellow needles which are soluble in acetone, from which it may be precipitated by dilution with water. Unlike the other common primary explosives, diazodinitrophenol has an explosion temperature above its melting point, 157° C. It may, therefore, be characterised by this property but it is essential that the melting point test should be carried out with adequate precautions against the effects of an explosion since the material under test may not be diazodinitrophenol.

These tests, coupled with a visual examination under magnification, should establish whether the sample consists of a single primary explosive or an initiatory mixture. For many investigations this will provide an adequate identification. If a fuller analysis of an initiatory composition is required, the scheme set out in Appendix H may be used. This covers most of the main ingredients used in initiatory compositions but, as with other explosive formulations, the investigator must always be alert to the possibility of other substances being present and be prepared to amend the details of the method accordingly.

It must always be remembered that an important property of primary explosives and initiating compositions is to be sensitive to stimuli. They must, therefore, be handled in very small quantities and with the normal precautions for such highly sensitive materials. These include measures to eliminate electrostatic discharges such as the wearing of appropriate clothing, the use of safety glasses and safety screens, and the use of paper spatulas.

6. *Improvised explosives*

The maker of improvised explosives may adopt one of two approaches. There is, therefore, a dichotomy of analytical methods. The first approach is to synthesise an explosive compound. Since those who do this are not usually professional scientists, they are not well versed in tracing information in the more specialised scientific literature and tend, therefore, to use only readily-accessible sources. Explosives made by such people are, therefore, usually confined to a limited number of well known ones. The only primary explosives usually attempted are mercury fulminate and lead azide. The commonest secondary explosives found in such cases are nitroglycerine and nitrocellulose, though occasionally TNT, RDX, and Tetryl may be found. Procedures for the identification of all these have been described in the sections on military and primary explosives.

The second approach to the production of improvised explosives is to make an explosive mixture. The classic example is gunpowder and the identification of this has been described in the section on propellents. Gunpowder is, however, only the best known example of the class of explosive mixtures which all depend on the principle of containing oxidants and fuels which can react with the liberation of energy and gaseous products. The number of oxidants is considerable and the number of potential fuels is immense, since virtually any organic compound or naturally occurring organic material will serve the purpose. The problem, therefore, of identifying the components of an improvised explosive mixture is formidable and the only complete solution, as in the case of pyrotechnics, is to undertake a complete qualitative analysis. For this it is necessary to use not only one of the standard procedures for the identification of the components of a mixture of unknown inorganic salts, but also a corresponding procedure for the identification of organic compounds.

The investigator's problem in identifying the components of an improvised explosive mixture is, however, often very much simpler than the discussion above suggests. Such mixtures are, in practice, largely confined to variants on a few formulations which appear to be known worldwide to juveniles and anarchists. By far the most commonly used oxidants are sodium and potassium chlorates. Potassium and ammonium nitrates are sometimes used and, occasionally, potassium permanganate. The commonly occurring fuels are sugar, starch in the form of flour, sulphur and aluminium powder. A procedure for identifying the components of a mixture containing combinations of these substances is given in Appendix I. It must be emphasised, however, that the investigator should always be alert to the possible presence of one or more components other than the common ones. In consequence, he should use the procedure in Appendix I with an appreciation of its limitations and always be ready to carry out comprehensive analyses by such methods as appear most appropriate for the problem in hand.

One property must always be considered when handling improvised explosives, namely sensitivity. This has already been mentioned in connection with the procedures for collecting samples. All samples should be treated with great care and considered to exhibit the sensitivity of primary explosives until they are shown to be otherwise. One class of these mixtures presents particular problems in the laboratory and exhibit store. These are ones containing both chlorate and sulphur, which are not only dangerously sensitive but also can be spontaneously explosive. It is essential, therefore, initially to isolate all samples of improvised explosives. If any are found to contain both chlorate and sulphur it is highly advisable to destroy all but a small portion (1 g) to be retained against any necessity for further examination. This should be kept in suitable isolated conditions. The necessity for this course of action is unlikely to be questioned but its justification may be found in the long history of spontaneous explosions with these mixtures and the existence of legislation in many countries to restrict their use to limited, closely controlled conditions.

IDENTIFICATION WHERE NO APPRECIABLE SAMPLE CAN BE RECOVERED – CONDENSED EXPLOSIVES

LOCATION

When an explosive explodes, the resultant chemical species can be considered to be of three types. The first is gaseous decomposition products such as CO_2, CO, H_2O, CH_4, NH_3 etc. These are dispersed into the atmosphere and, by the time the investigation takes place, are no longer available for examination. The second type is solid decomposition products such as chloride and perchlorate from chlorate explosives, and potassium sulphate from gunpowder. These will adhere to surfaces surrounding the seat of the explosion and can sometimes be found in sufficient quantities to enable identification to be possible. The third type arises from the fact that, although in theory the molecules of an explosive are converted on explosion entirely into new species (*i.e.* decomposition products), in practice this is not invariably so even with detonating explosives. It seems probable that some of the explosive on the outside of the charge is physically dispersed by the shock wave without being initiated. This explosive adheres to surrounding surfaces and, as is the case with solid products, although present in microgram quantities and therefore invisible, can nevertheless be chemically identifiable.

In considering the locations where identifiable materials may be found, five parameters must be taken into account.

1. *The concentration*

The precise distribution in space of solid products and undecomposed explosive will be unique to any given charge. As a first approximation, however, they can be regarded as equally distributed and hence equally spread on the surface of a sphere. The amount c in grams of material on 1 cm² of surface will be:

$$c = \frac{10^{-4}W}{4\pi r^2}$$

where W is the total weight of distributed material in grams and r the distance from the charge in metres. It will be seen that the amount per unit area will decrease proportionally to the reciprocal of the square of the distance from the charge. It follows, therefore, that the distance beyond which concentrations will be below the limits of detection is relatively short. Thus, the search for detectable residues must be made close to the seat of the explosion.

2. *The fireball*

The inner zone in an explosion consists of hot incandescent gases and is known as the fireball. Any explosive which is projected undecomposed, but which adheres to a surface which is subsequently engulfed in the fireball, will be decomposed at this later stage. It follows, therefore, that a search for detectable residues will be fruitless if made at distances less than the fireball radius. A formula for fireball radius is:

$$r = w^{\frac{1}{3}}$$

where r is the radius in metres and w the weight of the charge in kilograms. Thus the approximate radii for 100 g, 1 kg and 10 kg charges are 0·5, 1 and 2 m respectively.

3. *The charge weight*

Some portions of explosive in some charges of detonating explosives escape initiation. The mechanism whereby this happens is not known but it is a matter of practical observation that the phenomenon exists. It is also a matter of practical observation that the larger the charge the less the likelihood, in general, of finding detectable undecomposed explosive on surrounding surfaces. The chances of success appear to be high with charges up to about 1 kg and very low with charges greater than about 10 kg.

4. *The nature of the surface*

No surfaces within the zone in which detectable residues and traces may be expected should be neglected. However, some materials are liable to retain explosive traces somewhat more readily than others. This fact may be used in assigning orders of priority in collection and examination. Surfaces can be tabulated in decreasing order of effectiveness of retention. In general, fabrics are more effective than wood and wood, in turn, is more effective than metal.

5. *The orientation of the surface*

The orientation of the receptor surface is important in determining the concentration of residues and traces deposited. In general, only surfaces which were approximately normal to the direction of travel of the blast wave will have received deposits in detectable amounts.

RECOVERY

The method of recovery of samples for examination for explosive residues and traces varies with the nature of the object on which they are deposited. Since it is best to carry out as much work as possible in the convenience of the laboratory, all small objects for examination should be collected, packed in sealed plastic bags, and sent to the laboratory complete. Removal to the laboratory need not necessarily be confined to small objects. It is advantageous where possible to transport, for example, a motor vehicle so that its examination can be carried out in an unhurried and comprehensive manner. It may also be convenient, on occasion, to transfer large quantities of debris to the laboratory for both physical and chemical examination. This may arise, for example, in a street explosion where it is required to reopen the street as soon as possible.

When the surfaces for examination form part of an immovable object, such as the wall of a building or the floor of a crater, samples must be taken from it. If the surface is a non-absorbent one this should be done by swabbing. The swabs should be of cotton wool damped with appropriate liquids. The most useful general technique is to swab first with diethyl ether and then with water. If RDX is suspected, swabbing with acetone may be advantageous. If the surface is an absorbent one, such as brick or concrete, the sample for examination must be obtained by scraping. For this purpose a convex hardened steel scraper, such as that sold under the name Surform, is invaluable.

The principles of recovering samples from articles returned to the laboratory for examination are the same as those for immovable objects, *i.e.* swabbing of non-absorbent surfaces and scraping of absorbent ones.

In the taking of samples and their subsequent examination, careful attention must be paid to the examination of control samples. This subject can conveniently be considered in two parts, controls of materials used in gathering samples and controls of the scene of the explosion.

The control procedure for the materials used in gathering samples follows the normal forensic science principles of using only materials of known integrity and confirming this by examining controls. It will be found advantageous in explosion investigation to use individual swabbing kits containing sealed packets of cotton wool, disposable tweezers, a bottle of ether from a tested source, ampoules of distilled water, new plastic bags, and new polythene gloves for wear when handling the contents (see also Chapter 9). The kits should have been assembled under controlled explosive-free conditions. After use the kit, still containing a portion of the cotton wool, the tweezers, some of the ether, and the water ampoules, should be returned to the laboratory and examined in parallel with the collected samples. Where a number of kits have been used, time may be saved by examining only those returned kits associated with samples which have given positive evidence of explosives traces or residues.

The gathering of controls from the scene of an explosion presents difficulties peculiar to this branch of forensic science. The essential purpose of any control from a scene is to ensure that the material identified is either foreign to the scene or is in significantly higher concentration than that already present. Thus, when examining a paint smear, it is possible to take a scraping immediately adjacent to the smear as a reliable guide to the chemical composition of the surface before the smear was made. In the case of an explosion, the distribution of traces and decomposition products is general and there are no adjacent surfaces which can be guaranteed as uncontaminated. Ideally, the only meaningful controls that could be taken would be from the affected surfaces immediately before the explosion. This can only be done in experimental explosions and is not a course of action open to the investigator. He must, therefore, proceed by less direct and, to an extent, less satisfactory methods.

When chemical examination gives positive results for undecomposed explosives such as nitroglycerine, RDX and TNT, there is little need of controls from the scene since even the most captious critic has difficulty in sustaining a convincing argument that these substances were already present. There are two exceptions to this. One is the obvious circumstance of an explosion in premises or other places where explosives were known to be present, in which case the finding of evidence for any of these will anyway not be significant. The other is the finding of traces of nitroglycerine on the hands of a suspect. Some medicinal tablets contain a small proportion of nitroglycerine and, if handled, these will leave detectable quantities of it on the skin. However, the explanation of the presence of nitroglycerine by this mechanism cannot carry conviction unless the person concerned is actually in possession of such tablets or has had them prescribed by a doctor.

The detection of the presence of explosives residues at a scene can be a much more controversial matter, since many of the chemical species involved could be present owing to other causes. Thus ammonium can arise from urine, faeces, fertilizers and electric batteries, nitrate from fertilisers, chlorate from weedkillers and chloride from sea spray and road salt. In the absence of a control from the specific scene before the explosion, three types of control can be considered.

The first is to take a control from a nearby surface. This is open to so many objections that it is doubtful whether it has any real value. It is quite impossible to say whether the chemical species present on or absent from this site were or were not present on or absent from the site of the explosion before it occurred. Nor can there be any certainty whether the chemical species present represent material previously present or material deposited by the explosion or a combination of both. A more useful approach is to examine controls from a number of similar sites in the same general area. Thus, if an explosion occurs on the doorstep of a house and there are other houses nearby, control swabs may be taken from their doorsteps. In interpreting the results of analysis of the swabs, due regard must be given to differences between the scene of the explosion and the control sites. Consideration must be given to such features as doorstep materials, paint, the presence or absence of shelter from rain and wind, the compass bearing, etc., and these must be recorded at the time of taking the samples.

A third possibility is to use as control a general knowledge of the background levels of the species of interest. This information can be gathered as a specific research programme or accumulated from data obtained from the examination of controls of the type already discussed.

ANALYSIS

A successful analytical technique for the identification of traces of explosive compounds in case materials must fulfil certain conditions. An important requirement is that it must be capable of identifying the desired substance in the presence of contaminants, since the explosive sample will always be contaminated. Sometimes the contaminants will be known ones and the analytical techniques can be adjusted accordingly. For example, a sample from a safeblowing in a butcher's shop is likely to contain fat. Often, however, the contamination will be 'general dirt' and hence the sample will contain unknown substances. Since it will normally be impractical to remove all the contaminants before analysis, it is important that the analytical method is one with which they will not interfere.

A technique which fulfils this requirement is thin layer chromatography, since it provides for both separation and identification. It is

advisable to use, initially, the method described in Appendix J which
will give positive results for the main explosives from a single experiment. Controls of the explosives must be run in parallel on the same
plate as the sample or samples. If a positive result is obtained it
should be confirmed by the use of the appropriate part of the more
specific method described in Appendix D.

Although thin layer chromatography provides for both separation
and identification, difficulties can be encountered when examining
samples derived by swabbing and scraping. Many surfaces at the
scene of an explosion will be covered with petroleum products such
as bitumastic paint and lubricating oil. Contamination with these
materials may be widespread since it may be on surfaces either
because it was there initially or by transfer from surface to surface
during the movement of debris by the blast or because the blast
scattered it from a container. Petroleum products tend to consist of a
very large number of individual compounds which, on a thin layer
chromatographic plate, exhibit a complete spectrum of Rf values.
Explosives present in a sample contaminated with petroleum products are liable, therefore, to become entrained in these with consequent distortions of their movement characteristics. Three techniques
can be used to overcome the difficulties presented by the presence of
multicomponent contaminants:

1. A solvent may be used which combines the maximum possible
solubility for the explosive with the minimum possible solubility for
the contaminant. Thus, *e.g.* where nitroglycerine may be present in
an oily sample, extraction may be carried out with methyl alcohol or
with acetic acid.

2. The technique of two-way elution may be used. The first elution
will separate the explosive from much of the contaminant and this
will allow reasonably undistorted movement in the second direction.
The first elution should not be carried to the full extent of the plate
so as to allow room for the addition of the explosive control sample
or samples before the second elution.

3. The controls may be made by mixing portions of the extract
with portions of the normal control samples of explosives. In this
way the control explosives will be subjected to the same distortions
on elution as those in the sample and both should, therefore, produce
the same uncharacteristic Rf value.

The examination of samples for explosive decomposition products
is more complex since both qualitative and quantitative aspects must

be considered. The first stage is to establish whether relevant chemical species, such as ammonium, sodium, nitrate, chloride and chlorate, are present at all. For this purpose the appropriate tests from Appendices B, F and I may be used but due consideration must be paid to possible contaminants which may interfere with the tests. Where necessary, steps must be taken to eliminate them or other tests suitable for the particular investigation must be substituted. If a positive result is obtained, the tests must also be carried out on control samples, preferably of the second type discussed above.

Three results may be obtained from examination of the control. There may be no indication of the particular chemical species, a slight indication or an undoubted positive reaction. In the event of the first of these, consideration must be given to the possibility that the controls are not representative of the site of the explosion. If there is no reasonable doubt that this is not the case then the chemical species found may be attributed to the explosive. In the event of the second result, similar considerations apply but with less certainty as to the validity of the conclusion. In the event of the third result, the obvious conclusion to be drawn is that the chemical species found is not due to the explosive. Such a conclusion must be resisted since it may derive from a source extraneous to the explosive, or from the explosive, or from both, and it is not possible to conclude that one of these deductions is correct and the others false.

In the event of a result of the second kind, further steps may be taken to enhance the validity of the conclusion drawn. The technique is to collect the sample suspected of containing explosive decomposition products and the various controls from equal areas of the surfaces swabbed or scraped. Each sample is then analysed quantitatively by any suitable method so that the concentration of the chemical species per unit area can be calculated. Standard statistical analysis can then be applied to test whether the concentration in the sample is significantly different from that in the controls.

Many of the spot and other tests listed in Appendices B and I are of only moderate sensitivity. This, however, can be an advantage. If the tests were very highly sensitive, positive results would be obtained for a wide range of chemical species from almost any surface which had not been chemically cleaned immediately prior to the examination. If such results were not to be exploited to mislead by the unscrupulous, every examination would have to be quantitative with a consequent considerable, unprofitable and unnecessary increase in the time required to carry out the investigation. The use of only moderately sensitive tests ensures that their qualitative results are in fact to some extent quantitative. This arises from the fact that they will not respond to slight background traces, but only to significant quantities of explosive decomposition products and to unusually high levels of contaminant, the presence of which can be reasonably readily accounted for.

The procedures described in this section can also be used to test for the presence of chemical species deriving from parts of an explosive device other than the main explosive charge. An obvious example is the electric battery used to actuate the firing device in some types of infernal machine. Both manganese dioxide and ammonium chloride are commonly used in the electrolyte. Appropriate tests are among those given in Appendix A.

IDENTIFICATION WHERE NO APPRECIABLE SAMPLE CAN BE RECOVERED – DISPERSED EXPLOSIVES

DUST EXPLOSIONS

Dust is formed in many industrial processes either as an end product or as a by-product, especially where grinding or sieving operations are involved. Both on account of the health hazards to operatives and the possibilities of explosions, care is normally taken to control the spread of dusts. Sometimes, however, dust control is not as adequate as it should be and, even when it is, accidental dispersal cannot be ruled out. In consequence, from time to time dust explosions do occur in industrial premises. Dust explosions in other places are rare but not unknown. Thus in 1970 (27) a man threw fine sawdust from a floor sander into an incinerator. An explosion ensued and the man was killed.

In theory any combustible material can generate a dust capable of forming an explosive mixture with air. In practice, however, not all combustible dusts are explosive, though a very wide range of materials exhibits this phenomenon as is shown by the diversity of the short list in Appendix K.

The identification of the material involved in a dust explosion is normally a simple matter since it will be obvious from the nature of the scene of the explosion *e.g.* flour in a flour mill, coal in a coal mine, etc. While such an identification is most likely to be correct, it should not be accepted until the investigation has established that there is no evidence that alternative dispersed phase materials, such as gas or petroleum vapour, were responsible. The possibilities can be illustrated by a diagram:

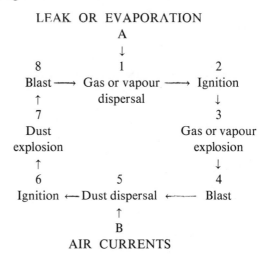

It will be seen that a dust explosion can result either from the path B-5-6-7 or from the path A-1-2-3-4-5-6-7. Similarly, a gas or vapour explosion could result either from the path A-1-2-3 or from the path B-5-6-7-8-1-2-3. When considering a dust explosion, the simple case is the path B-5-6-7. The alternative, which must be investigated, will depend on the presence or absence of A. If there is no evidence for the existence of a leak of gas or of evaporation capable of producing an explosive vapour/air mixture, then the alternative mechanism can be discounted and the explosive identified as the dust. If, however, there is evidence for either of these it is necessary to consider whether the cause of the dispersal is a leak or evaporation due to the blast from a dust explosion, 8, or whether it is due to some other cause, A. A decision on this matter will depend on the particular circumstances of each individual case and sometimes it will be found that no definite conclusion can be reached. The crux will be the nature of the leak or evaporation process. Thus, where gas has escaped from an opened tap or a vapour has spread from a source not in the room where the explosion occurred, there will be little doubt that the gas or vapour explosion has caused the dust explosion and not vice versa. Where, however, gas has escaped from a fractured pipe or vapour has spread from a fractured container, the most detailed consideration, including possibly metallographic examination, will be necessary in order to reach a decision on what was cause and what was effect.

Sometimes a positive identification of a dust will be necessary. This can arise if a definite confirmation is required in an apparently obvious case or if the explosion is apparently a dust one but the nature of the dust is not obvious. Unless there has been a subsequent intense fire, a search of the scene will almost certainly reveal traces of unconsumed dust on ledges and in crevices unaffected by the explosion. An initial examination of a sample can be made under the optical microscope, supplemented if necessary by the scanning electron microscope, for the resolution of characteristic surface features. This examination carried out with the aid of a standard reference work such as The Particle Atlas, together with appropriate chemical tests, should normally provide positive identification. If any doubt remains, specialists in the material of which the dust is suspected of being comprised should be consulted.

VAPOUR EXPLOSIONS

There are a great many substances which are capable of generating explosive vapour/air mixtures. This is illustrated by Appendix L, which lists those items in the list of inflammable liquids in the International Maritime Dangerous Goods Code for which explosion compositional limits are quoted. This list is far from comprehensive. With such a diversity of chemical species, it is advisable to carry out a preliminary survey in order to reduce the number to be considered in any particular case. A considerable reduction can be made by considering what are the possibilities. This may conveniently be done under three headings:

1. What substances which are capable of producing explosive vapour/air mixtures are known to have been present?

The answer to this question is obtained by questioning persons connected with the site of the explosion and the examination of debris. In the case of a chemical manufacturing plant, it will be necessary to consider all substances known to be used on the premises and list any that can give rise to explosive mixtures. Similar considerations apply to mixed storage depots, mixed load vehicles and mixed commodity retail premises. Domestic dwellings are simpler to deal with since the number of these substances used is very limited. The simplest case of all is the single product store or the single product user such as a motor vehicle filling station.

2. What substances which are capable of producing explosive vapour/air mixtures may have been present?

In addition to considering the substances known to have been present, it is necessary to consider whether there may have been others. Thus, in a large mixed storage depot where an explosion has affected only part, it is possible that a substance normally unconnected with this part may have been present inadvertently either by human error or by seepage of liquid or vapour.

3. What substances which are capable of producing explosive vapour/air mixtures should not have been present but the possibility of their presence cannot be discounted?

Clearly, at any given scene there will be a vast list of substances which should not have been present and it would be quite unreasonable to suppose that they may have been there. Thus, the majority of substances listed in Appendix L are so unlikely to be found in a domestic dwelling house that it would not be reasonable to suggest their presence on a particular occasion. Not all substances, however, which should not have been present at a particular scene can be so readily discounted. In spite of repeated safety warnings and regulations, the storage of motor spirit in unsuitable premises persists and, in the event of an explosion in a domestic dwelling house, for example, the explosion investigator should treat assertions that no motor spirit was present with an open mind. Another instance arises in cases where both fire and explosion have occurred. If, by reason of multiple initial burn points or for some other reason, the investigator has grounds for suspecting arson, he must be alert to the possibility of the presence of one of the inflammable liquids favoured by arsonists.

Having given consideration to these three possibilities, it should be possible for the investigator to make a short list of substances which will contain all those with any reasonable probability of having provided the explosive vapour/air mixture. In endeavouring to identify which of these was actually present, the investigator can proceed by direct and indirect methods.

The vapour involved in a vapour/air explosion will have been derived from a volatile liquid so that the direct method of identifying the vapour consists in recovering and identifying a sample of this liquid. The method of search for a sample is determined by the fact that, with normal ventilation, a concentration in the explosion range will, in general, only be attained if the liquid is spilled. This is not to say that containers should be ignored since these can have traces of liquid still in them. The main search, however, must be directed to the debris and structure of the building.

If a volatile liquid is spilled onto a non-absorbent surface, complete evaporation may occur before the explosion and will probably have occurred before the investigator reaches the scene. If, however, the spillage has been on an absorbent suface, some of the liquid will be absorbed and can frequently be found after the explosion and even after the almost inevitable fire. Such liquid samples must be searched for in the lower layers of the absorbent material or in absorbent material which has been protected by fall of debris. The initial detection of such liquid can be carried out with some form of vapour detector. However, experience has shown that, if no characteristic odour can be detected, then the chances of samples being present which are large enough to be identified by laboratory techniques is slight (28). The debris should, therefore, be examined using both eyes and nose, and anything bearing a smell of a volatile liquid should immediately be packed into a sealed impervious container for further examination. Glass jars and nylon (not polythene) bags are suitable containers for such exhibits. The subsequent examination of the sample may be carried out by any suitable technique. Where the sample is large, the liquid can be distilled from the absorbent and the sample subjected to standard chemical analysis for a mixture of unknown organic compounds. With small quantities different techniques must be used and it is convenient to use these for all samples. The two main ones are infrared spectroscopy and gas chromatography, the latter having been found to be particularly useful for the identification of petroleum hydrocarbons.

In carrying out sophisticated direct methods of identification the possibilities of indirect evidence should not be overlooked. During the course of the search through the debris, any containers or remains of containers found should be examined critically to determine whether they can be associated with liquids capable of producing explosive vapour/air mixtures. Diagnostic features include shape, size, material, and markings.

GAS EXPLOSIONS

The number of gases which can give rise to explosive mixtures with air is considerably less than the number of substances capable of producing explosive vapour/air mixtures. Nevertheless, the number is not inconsiderable as is shown by the list in Appendix M, which is not exhaustive. The first step, therefore, in identifying the gas involved in a gas explosion is to reduce the possibilities to the reasonable probabilities by considering the three questions used for the same purpose in investigating a vapour explosion.

The investigation continues to follow the same principles as for vapour explosions, in that the identification of the gas involved may be by direct or by indirect methods. The direct method is not likely to be effective owing to the unlikelihood of any sample being recoverable. While, in general, any unconsumed gas will have dispersed long before the investigator reaches the scene, some possibilities should not be overlooked. As with vapours the sense of smell should be used and lingering traces, which can be neither collected nor examined in the laboratory, may be identified in this way. Another possibility is that pockets of gas may have been trapped in a container. Thus, in one case, after an explosion a closed safe was found to be still filled with unconsumed town gas. The possibilities of gas identification afforded by the examination of the bodies of victims should not be overlooked and this subject is discussed in Chapter 8.

In most cases of gas explosions indirect methods of identification must be used. The essential principle is to demonstrate the presence of a source of gas. Where a piped gas, such as town gas, is present, this is overwhelmingly the most probable source of the explosive mixture. The whole system must be examined for defects which could give rise to leaks, care being taken to distinguish between defects which existed before the explosion and those resulting from the explosion. The possibility of a deliberately made leak in the course of a successful or unsuccessful suicide attempt should not be overlooked. Similar considerations apply to gas stored in cylinders or other containers, where consideration must be given to imperfectly closed or defective valves and accessories.

Apart from gas which is intended to be on the premises, gas may also arise from an accidental gas-forming process. A well known example of this is the gas formed by pyrolysis of organic materials in a fire. This can give rise to the explosions which often accompany fires. Other gas-producing processes are electrolysis and chemical reactions. Thus (1925) a man was cutting up scrap steel drums with an oxyacetylene torch. One drum contained sulphuric acid sludge which had reacted with the steel to produce hydrogen. The hydrogen/air mixture was ignited by the flame and the man was killed by the subsequent explosion. More recently (1969) a fire occurred in a laboratory building as magnesium powder was being sieved mechanically. As the fire did not respond to the carbon dioxide extinguishers available, another extinguisher, thought to be foam, was directed at the seat of the fire. It was, however, a water extinguisher, and the fire increased in intensity. This was immediately followed by an explosion, which removed the roof and the wall dividing the room from another laboratory. This second laboratory became involved and three more explosions occurred before the fire was brought under control.

DEDUCTIVE INVESTIGATION

By the application of one or other of the techniques described above, it should be possible to identify the explosive involved in an incident. Sometimes, however, this will not be so and another approach must be used, namely deductive investigation. This consists, in principle, of assuming the identity of the explosive and then considering whether the observed effects can be deduced from this assumption. There are three aspects of this technique.

1. *Performance observation*

The technique of performance observation consists in setting up a replica of the original situation, introducing an explosive charge of the size and nature assumed to have been present, causing it to explode and then observing the effects. The effects observed can be any of the forms of damage discussed in Chapter 4 and any chemical observations of the types discussed in this chapter. The use of a full replica of a situation is usually not practicable, owing principally to the cost and to a lesser extent to the time required for its assembly. The usual procedure is to select readily replicated and diagnostically significant portions of the original scene and use only these. Thus, in the investigation into the loss of the Comet aircraft G-ARCO (20) an experiment of this type was mounted on a pair of seats and a section of floor and wall of the passenger cabin, since this was judged to be the only significant area for observation.

Having carried out the experiment, the effects are compared with those produced by the original explosion. It is not normally practicable to carry out a sufficient number of tests to provide enough data for the application of the techniques of statistical analysis. Any conclusions may, therefore, be controversial but the application of normal commonsense will usually make it clear whether or not the proposed explosive charge is or is not consistent with the effects observed in the explosion under investigation.

2. *Performance assessment*

If it is not practicable to set up a performance observation experiment then performance assessment tests may be used. This technique consists of taking a sample of the postulated explosive and measuring its explosive performance by one or more of the standard techniques used for this purpose described in Chapter 2, or some other technique such as the Lidstone Cartridge Case Test (29). The explosive performance can then be assessed as comparable with some familiar explosive. The experienced investigator will then be able to assess whether a charge of this familiar explosive would be consistent with the effects observed at the scene of the explosion under investigation.

3. *Performance prediction*

Some deductive investigation can be carried out from purely theoretical considerations. The first step is to postulate any probable chemical equations representing the decomposition of the compound or mixture thought to have been present. The energetics of the equation(s) can then be calculated from bond energy data. If the reaction or reactions are not exothermic then they cannot have been responsible for the explosion and others must be considered. If, however, they are exothermic it is necessary to consider whether they are likely to have produced an explosive effect.

It was pointed out in Chapter 2 that the four requirements which must be met if a substance is to be classed as an explosive are:

1. That it must be capable of producing gas.
2. That it must be capable of producing energy.
3. That 1 and 2 must occur very rapidly.
4. That 1, 2 and 3 must be self-sustaining.

In order to assess whether a substance exhibiting these properties will be an effective explosive it is necessary to quantify them and assign limits for 1, 2 and 3. No effective explosion will occur if the gas volume is less than x mlg^{-1} or if the amount of energy is less than y Jg^{-1} or if the rate of evolution is less than z mls^{-1} or Js^{-1}. Any values given to x, y and z will be purely arbitrary and there appears to be no basis on which other than arbitrary and, therefore, controversial values can be assigned.

A way round this difficulty is to calculate the explosive power of the substance and compare this with measured power values. If the calculated value lies within the range of observed or calculated values for substances generally accepted as explosives, the substance under review can likewise be accepted as being explosive and an estimate of its likely effects made by comparison. If its calculated value lies below this range then it is unlikely to be capable of producing effective explosive effects.

One method of calculating the explosive power of a substance is by means of the 'characteristic product' developed by Berthelot (30).

If the explosion takes place at fairly low density then the pressure, volume, and temperature may be related by the equation:

$$\frac{PV}{T} = \frac{P_0 V_0}{273}$$

where P is the explosion pressure in atmospheres, T the absolute temperature, V the volume of the vessel in which the explosion takes place, V_0 the specific volume of gaseous products from unit weight of explosive calculated at O° C in 1kg^{-1} and P_0 the standard pressure. This equation may be transformed to:

$$PV = \frac{V_0 Q}{C} \times \frac{P_0}{273} + \frac{P_0 V_0 T_1}{273}$$

where Q is the quantity of heat liberated in Kcal kg^{-1} by the explosion of unit weight of explosive, C the sum of the mean specific heats of the products and T_1 the temperature of the explosive before initiation.

The expression:

$$\frac{V_0 Q}{C}$$

is Berthelot's characteristic product and may be used as a measure of the power of the explosive. In view, however, of the difficulty of obtaining reliable values for C the product V_0Q has often been used instead. Values for the product $V_0Q \times 10^{-3}$ range from 1,200 for blasting gelatine to about 200 for gunpowder.

Another variant on Berthelot's product is obtained by multiplying Q by the mechanical equivalent of heat to give the maximum quantity of work that can theoretically be done by unit weight of the explosive. This, expressed in kilogram metres per kilogram of explosive, gives values ranging from 600 for blasting-gelatine to 250 for gunpowder.

A simple method for substances containing only carbon, hydrogen, nitrogen, and oxygen (31) is to evaluate the expression:

$$P = \frac{\Sigma f_i x_i}{M}$$

where f_i is the frequency and x_i is the value in the table associated with the ith feature of the molecule and M is the molecular weight. P is the explosive power expressed as a percentage of TNT.

TABLE 5.3

Feature (f)	Value (x)	Feature (f)	Value (x)
C—NO$_2$	+9,134	C=O	+904
N—NO$_2$	+10,066	C—O	+2,019
O—NO$_2$	+10,887	O—H	−1,250
C—C	−199	N—H	−275
C=C	−993	C—N	+932
C—H	−364	benzene ring	+1,093

For dinitrotoluene the calculation would be as follows:

Feature	f	x	fx
C—NO$_2$	2	+9,137	+18,274
C—C	4	−199	−796
C=C	3	−993	−2,979
C—H	6	−364	−2,184
benzene ring	1	+1,093	+1,093

$$\Sigma fx = 13,408$$
$$M = 181$$
$$P = 74$$

As a guide, any substance giving a value of P less than about 50 is unlikely to be an effective explosive. The power of a mixture of explosives may be derived by calculating the power values of the individual components and then determining the value for the mixture by calculating the weighted mean.

It must be emphasised that no type of deductive investigation will give a positive identification of the explosive responsible for the explosion under investigation. This technique is only able to suggest which explosive or explosives could have been involved. It will, however, establish the fact that the explosive concerned must have been either some suggested one or one of essentially similar characteristics.

MECHANICAL EXPLOSIONS

If the various procedures described fail to produce a positive identification of an explosive then consideration must be given to the idea that the explosion is a mechanical one. The 'explosive' in such a case can be any gaseous substance, whether or not present with a liquid phase, whose pressure rises beyond the mechanical strength of its container. It follows that four conditions must obtain at the scene of a mechanical explosion:

1. The presence of a burst container.
2. Damage consistent with a pressure burst.
3. The absence of any identification of a chemical explosive.
4. The availability of a source of high pressure.

When a confined charge of a chemical explosive deflagrates or detonates, the container is subjected to sudden pressure considerably or very considerably in excess of its bursting strength. It is, therefore, fragmented and the size of the fragments will depend primarily on the brisance of the explosive. In the case of a mechanical explosion the rate of pressure rise is normally relatively slow. Moreover, the container is only subjected to a pressure which is equal to the minimum necessary to cause failure since on the attainment of that pressure the container bursts. Consequently, the container is merely split open or broken into only a few relatively large pieces. The observation of some object burst open in this manner is an important diagnostic feature which should alert the investigator to the possibility that a mechanical explosion may have occurred.

The pressures involved in mechanical explosions are low by explosion standards. The container which bursts will often be one which has not been designed to withstand high pressures and will consequently burst at a pressure of a few hundred kNm^{-2} or less. If a vessel designed to withstand high pressures is involved, pressures can be higher and may be in the MNm^{-2} range. The damage effects observed at the scene of a mechanical explosion are, therefore, of the types observed with deflagrating explosives rather than with detonating explosives. The damage can, however, be considerable. Thus, in one case the bursting of an incorrectly installed electric water heater resulted in the demolition of a substantial portion of a semi-detached house. Numerous fatal accidents have also occurred when motor vehicle tyres have burst owing to overinflation (32).

The nature of the material giving rise to the high pressure, the 'explosive', can conveniently be considered under two headings, *i.e.* materials which should have been present and materials which should not. In either case, the identification of the 'explosive' must involve the identification of the material itself and also of the reason why it was able to cause the explosion.

In dealing with materials which should have been present, their actual identification presents no problems. The reasons for their producing an unexpected effect can derive from the material or from the container. If the explosion has been caused by the material, then some mechanism must have been present to cause its pressure to rise above normal. This will have been a systems failure, leading to an excess pressure due to physical or chemical action. Physical causes include the failures or inadequacies of temperature control devices, pressure control devices, or pressure relief valves. Human errors at control panels and/or errors such as placing a sealed container in hot sunlight may also occur. A well known example of this type of explosion is the bursting of a pneumatic tyre or wheel which usually results in severe and often fatal injuries to the fitter. The pattern of such accidents is well established (31) and usually consists of:

1. A young person employed on fitting tyres after a minimum of instruction, probably of a very inadequate nature.
2. The absence of, or disregard of, safety cages or restraining devices.
3. An airline taken from a compressor without any form of pressure reducing valve, indicating gauge or remote control device.

The classic case is that of Karl Blom, in Sweden, who while inflating a tractor tyre, went to answer the telephone and left the compressed air hose attached. On his return he was in the process of uncoupling the hose when the tyre exploded. He was killed instantly and his body was projected against the ceiling with sufficient force as to leave a clearly defined imprint.

Chemical causes include the failure of devices controlling the addition of reactants in chemical manufacturing processes and human errors in using incorrect materials in such processes. A somewhat similar situation, which has been reported from time to time, occurs when pneumatic tyres have been filled from oxygen bottles. Lubricants or grease inside the tyre can then ignite spontaneously and the resultant rapid pressure rise will cause the tyre to burst.

If the explosion has been caused by the container, this will have been due to its ceasing to be capable of withstanding its design pressure. Failures of this type can arise from such causes as undetected flaws in manufacture, corrosion stress cracking and corrosion. For example, a cylinder filled with coal gas spontaneously exploded (1971) in a laboratory. Examination of the remains of the cylinder showed that it had failed owing to stress corrosion cracking from prolonged service with coal gas. Failures can also arise from the use of unsuitable containers. Thus, a man was seriously injured (1972) when a cylinder was being charged with compressed air. The cylinder was normally used for underwater diving but investigations showed that it was originally designed for use in one of the pneumatic systems on aircraft. The use of the particular aluminium alloy from which it was constructed had ceased ten years previously because of stress corrosion problems.

In the case of mechanical explosions involving materials which should not have been present, the cause of the explosion must be sought in a gas or heat generating process. Gas can be generated by the presence of a chemical impurity, for example a suitable metal in an acid environment or by a physical process such as electrolysis. Heat can likewise be generated by the presence of a chemical impurity leading to an exothermic reaction either directly or by catalysis. Thus, during the filling (1971) of a batch of cylinders with Entonox (50/50 nitrous oxide/oxygen) one of the cylinders burst thereby injuring a man operating the filling rig. The probable cause was the ignition of a slug of oil which had built up in the system and then been forced into the cylinder in question. The cylinder thereupon burst owing to the sudden overpressure.

In the mechanical explosions discussed above the container failure constitutes the initial indication of disaster. Such events may be termed primary mechanical explosions. Secondary mechanical explosions also occur. These arise if any closed container is involved in a fire so that after a period of time it will burst owing to the rise in internal pressure. Such explosions can form part of a sequence of progressively more hazardous occurrences if the container is filled with an inflammable gas or liquid. The initial fire will then give rise to the mechanical explosion which will be followed by a dispersed phase explosion of the gas/air or vapour/air mixture.

Confusion can arise if a mechanical explosion occurs in a situation where explosives are present. Proof that the explosion was a mechanical one will then depend on showing that the diagnostic features for a mechanical explosion are present and that those for explosion of the explosive are absent. An example of such a case is an explosion which occurred (1914) in a steam heated explosives mixing pan. The outlet pipe had become blocked and, since the bursting pressure of the pan jacket was 275 kNm^{-2} and the steam feed pressure was 482 kNm^{-2}, a mechanical explosion ensued. Investigation showed that the explosive had remained intact.

Sometimes a more difficult situation to interpret arises, in that a mechanical explosion acts as the initiatior of a chemical one. Such incidents are rare but not unknown, as is shown by the following case (1923) which occurred in the smoking-room of an hotel. A lighted paraffin lamp was placed upon a table immediately below an unlit, suspended petrol lamp. The reservoir of the petrol lamp was about 60 cm above the chimney of the paraffin lamp. About half an hour later there was a violent explosion. This wrecked furniture, blew the door across the hall, and blew out all the windows and a portion of the wall. It is clear that the heat from the paraffin lamp generated pressure in the petrol lamp until it burst. The petrol vapour then formed an explosive mixture with air which was initiated by the flame of the paraffin lamp.

THERMAL, CHEMICAL AND ELECTRICAL EXPLOSIONS

Another form of explosion which can occur with materials other than explosives is the thermal explosion. The contact of two liquids, when one is at a temperature significantly above the boiling point of the other, can lead to explosive vapour production. In experiments conducted by Wright (33) in which a column of water was dropped on to a pool of molten aluminium, peak pressures of the order of 20 MNm^{-2} were observed. A theoretical thermal interaction model for metal/water explosions has been developed by Board, Duffey, Farmer, and Poole (34) and it has been found that this successfully predicts the peak pressures observed.

An explosion akin to a thermal explosion can occur when a substance makes contact with a liquid with which it is highly reactive, with the production of heat and gaseous products. A familiar example is the reaction of metallic sodium with water. If a piece of sodium about 2 cm cube is projected on to water the resultant explosion sounds similar to the discharge of a 12 bore shotgun. A delayed action explosion can be achieved by wrapping the sodium in paper so that the reaction occurs only after the water has soaked through this wrapping.

The identification of the materials responsible for explosions of these types stems essentially from an examination of the circumstances. If no evidence of an explosive substance or of a mechanical explosion has been found, consideration can be given to the possibility of a thermal or similar explosion. If two liquids were present and one was at a temperature significantly above the boiling point of the other then the scene should be examined for any evidence of mechanical or systems failure or human error which could have led to contact between the two. The postulated contact must, of course, have occurred at the established explosion centre. Similar considerations apply to chemical explosions though here there is the added possibility of deliberate action either as an act of sabotage, a miguided expeiment or a misguided practical joke.

Another phenomenon which produces effects which are often reported as explosions is electric discharge. Sometimes accidental discharges occur in switchgear or other electrical installations which produce sufficient heating of the air or other dielectric to cause a sound wave with or without damage to the equipment. If the discharge occurs through a solid dielectric this may be vapourised and contribute to the effect. This principle is exploited in some explosives ignition devices which are accordingly designated exploding bridge-wire igniters.

Here again the identification of the 'explosives' can only be made by elimination and a study of the circumstances.

Chapter 6

CAUSES OF INITIATION

TYPES OF INITIATION

Apart from the mechanical, thermal, chemical, and electrical explosions discussed at the end of Chapter 5, there can be no explosion without an explosive. There will not, however, be an explosion even then unless it is initiated. It is an integral part, therefore, of the investigator's work not only to identify the explosive but also to identify what caused it to explode.

There are many possible mechanisms for the initiation of an explosion but all depend on the principle that energy must be transferred into the explosive. In considering possible mechanisms of initiation and the methods of identifying them it is, therefore, convenient to classify them according to the modes of energy input. These are as follows:

1. Explosively generated shock.
2. Mechanical effects.
3. Heat.
4. Sparks.
5. Chemical effects.
6. Miscellaneous mechanisms of energy input.

One further type of initiation should be added though it differs from the others in that energy of initiation is derived from internal sources. This is:

7. Spontaneous explosion.

In considering whether initiation has been caused by any particular effect the investigator has to establish the answers to three questions:

(a) Did the conditions for the particular type of effect exist?
(b) Could the effect have involved some or all of the explosive?
(c) Would the effect have been sufficient to have caused initiation?

Questions (a) and (b) can only be answered by a close examination of the scene of the explosion. No particular rules can be laid down since each occurrence is unique. Nevertheless, experience and a knowledge of the history of explosions can be of value in guiding the investigator. Sherlock Holmes said (16): '. . . I am generally able, by the help of my knowledge of the history of crime, to set them straight. There is a strong family resemblance about misdeeds, and if you have all the details of a thousand at your finger ends, it is odd if you can't unravel the thousand and first.' This certainly holds good for explosions whether criminal or accidental, but in following one part of the Sherlock Holmes method the investigator must never forget another (35): 'It is a capital mistake to theorise before one has data. Insensibly, one begins to twist facts to suit theories, instead of theories to suit facts.' While a knowledge of history is a valuable aid to the interpretation of observations it should never be used as a substitute for investigation.

The third question can be partly answered from a knowledge of the sensitivity properties of the explosive. If, for example, it is clear that a very sensitive material, such as a primary explosive, has been subjected to a heavy blow between hard surfaces then it can be confidently concluded that initiation occurred. In many cases, however, the matter will not be so obvious and it will be a matter of doubt whether the supposed stimulus would have been sufficient to have caused initiation. In such cases it will be necessary to carry out deductive investigations to test whether such a stimulus could have been effective.

When the investigator has succeeded in establishing a positive answer to all three questions, he should be on his guard against stopping his investigation into the cause of initiation at this point. An explosion produces a complex situation in which several possible mechanisms for initiation may be observable. It is essential to identify all of these and then to consider what evidence there may be to establish which was the primary cause of the explosion and which were caused by it, or were merely potential sources of initiation. This may not always be possible, as is illustrated by an explosion which occurred (1970) in a building on a firework factory. Several possible causes of ignition were identified. Smoking materials were found in the building, there was a failure to observe the normal precaution of wearing 'clean' shoes to exclude grit, and an oil filled electric radiator was found to be defective. A more complex case occurred in 1890

(XCIII). It was the procedure at a quarry to use a mixture of gunpowder and dry guncotton as the blasting explosive. The mixing was carried out in a stone built hut with a grit covered stone floor into which the employees entered still wearing their iron shod quarry boots. The hut was heated by an open coal fire and smoking was permitted. In such conditions an explosion was inevitable and, in due course, it occurred. The investigator in his report made the point that usually it is possible to deduce the cause of an initiation by a process of elimination. In this case, however, he said this was difficult since conditions gave rise to so many possible causes. In the event he made no attempt to assign a definite cause.

EXPLOSIVELY GENERATED SHOCK
DETONATORS

Detonators are the devices which are designed and made for the purpose of initiating detonating explosives. They are, therefore, the most probable cause of initiation in many cases. These include ones involving accidents with devices, such as grenades having high explosive fillings, accidents in blasting operations, infernal machines containing high explosives and attacks on security containers. In the latter two, the detonators involved may be manufactured devices, modified manufactured devices or home-made. Almost all types of detonator consist of a case, usually of metal, and a filling either wholly consisting of a primary explosive or of primary explosive and a base charge of a secondary explosive. The means of igniting the primary explosive may be a flame, either from a fuse or an electrically operated match head, or a mechanical blow from a striker or, in some specialised applications, a shock or an electric spark.

After the explosion, parts of the detonator may survive and be recognisable. The diagnostic features are described in Chapter 4. In addition, some chemical evidence may be found. The primary explosive most widely used in detonators is lead azide which decomposes on exploding into nitrogen and metallic lead. Some of the lead is deposited on the walls of the detonator tube and in consequence can be detected on fragments of the metal from that part adjacent to the primary explosive filling. The detection is best carried out by an electron microprobe, since this instrument provides not only the sensitivity required for the identification of the small quantities involved but is also non-destructive, thus preserving the exhibit for further examination and/or production in a court of law. If this instrument is not available, the thin layer chromatographic technique described in Appendix H or a spectrographic method may be used.

In instruction in blasting practice, or other practical use of blasting explosives, emphasis is rightly laid on the necessity of close contact between the detonator and the explosive. Unless close coupling is achieved there is the possibility of a misfire occurring. As the separation between the detonator and the explosive charge increases, the probability of a failure to achieve initiation increases until, beyond a distance of about 15 cm, no initiation will occur (36). As the separation increases the probability of a partial explosion also increases. An exceptional case occurs when a dimple headed detonator separated from an explosive charge is so positioned that the axis of the detonator points to the charge. The dimple head then acts as a shaped charge with a pronounced directional effect and with such a system it is possible to achieve initiation at separations up to about 60 cm (36). These facts are of importance in explosion investigation since they can account for observations of explosions which were expected to occur (*e.g.* infernal machines) but which did not and others which were not expected to occur (*e.g.* accidents) but which did.

SYMPATHETIC DETONATION

A detonator is a special case of the general phenomenon of sympathetic detonation. If an explosive charge (the donor) detonates then the shock wave is capable of initiating another charge (the acceptor) in the vicinity. Since two important parameters in this phenomenon are the weight of the donor charge and the distance separating it from the acceptor, formulae for the critical distance beyond which sympathetic detonation will not occur, are based on these two quantities. The usually accepted form is:

$$\frac{W}{L^3} = k$$

where W is the weight, L is the distance, and k is a constant. Robinson (23) suggests that the formula:

$$\frac{W}{L^{2.25}} = k$$

is a better fit of the available experimental data. The usefulness of such formulae is restricted by the fact that k is only a constant for any given donor and acceptor system and has different values for different explosives and conditions. Thus, with the data quoted by Robinson for two different blasting explosives when W is measured in kilograms and L in metres, the average values for k are 1·18 and 27 75 respectively. Van Dolah (37), using the L^3 form of the equation with W measured in lb and L in ft, quotes values of k derived from various sources ranging from 1·2 for an ammonium nitrate mixture to 11 for general high explosives. Other parameters which affect the value of k are the nature of the confinement, if any, of the donor and acceptor charges and the nature of the medium between them.

The problem confronting an explosion investigator when considering sympathetic detonation as a possible explanation of initiation, is whether the available donor charge could reasonably have been expected to have induced detonation in the explosive under consideration. One approach to a solution is to apply one of the formulae quoted with either an average value for k or the extreme values of k. If the observed distance is considerably in excess of that calculated, it is reasonable to assume that sympathetic detonation is not the correct explanation for the initiation. If the observed distance is comparable with or less than that calculated, then it is reasonable to assume that sympathetic detonation is at least a possible explanation of the initiation.

Another approach is to regard the minimum safety distances authorised for magazine separation as being the maximum distance for sympathetic detonation. Some representative figures are given in Table 6.1 for data from the United States (American Table of Distances for Storage of Explosives) and the United Kingdom (Guide to the Explosives Act) converted to metric units.

The column headed U.K.(z) gives the distance for explosives having a mass explosion risk with serious missile effect, the column headed U.K.(zz) gives the distance for explosives having a mass explosion risk with minor missile effect, and the column headed U.K. (mean) gives the mean of the figures in the previous two columns. It will be seen that, apart from the U.K. provision of a minimum distance of 9 m, the U.S. and U.K.(mean) values are in good agreement with each other. Using the L^3 formula these data give values for k of 0·28 and 0·13 for the U.S. and U.K.(mean) respectively.

TABLE 6.1

Weight (kg)	Distance (m)			
	U.S.	U.K.(z)	U.K.(zz)	U.K.(mean)
4·5	3	9	9	9
9	3	9	9	9
23	5	9	9	9
45	5	9	9	9
91	7	9	11	10
181	9	9	13	11
272	9	9	16	12
362	10	9	17	13
453	12	9	18	14

The United States has separate tables for recommended distances for use with ammonium nitrate and with insensitive blasting agents based on ammonium nitrate. These figures when used in the L^3 formula give values for k of 48·2 and 1·01 respectively. In using this information, or the formulae based on it, it must be remembered that it is primarily based on practical experience of accidental explosions in barricaded or mounded magazines. It represents, therefore, for relatively large quantities of explosive the combined possibilities of sympathetic detonation and initiation by missiles as modified by typical magazine structural features. Any attempt to apply it to other situations by making allowances for the ambient differences must be regarded as providing only indicative results.

A method of assessing the probability of sympathetic detonation in the case of TNT has been suggested by Kinney (38). His argument is as follows. The mean detonation distance can be defined as that distance at which there is a 50% probability that sympathetic detonation may occur. Observations show that this distance corresponds reasonably well to the radius of the crater formed in a surface explosion. The crater radius for a charge of TNT detonated on the surface may be found from the relation:

$$\frac{r_m}{W^{\frac{1}{3}}} = 1·0 \pm 0·05$$

where W is the explosive energy release expressed as pounds of TNT and r_m is the crater radius in feet.

For separation distances greater than the mean detonation distance, the probability of sympathetic detonation is reduced. Since, however, it has been observed that the standard deviation in the distance is of the order of 50% of the mean detonation distance, estimates of 'this probability can be made. Numerical data from which such estimates may be derived are given in Table 6.2.

TABLE 6.2

Ratio of actual deviation to standard deviation	Probability of occurrence	Odds against one
0·675	0·5	1
0·8	0·424	1·36
1·0	0·317	2·15
1·2	0·230	3·35
1·4	0·162	5·19
1·6	0·110	8·12
1·8	0·072	12·9
2·0	0·045	21·0
2·5	0·012	80
3·0	0·0027	370
3·5	0·00046	2,150
4·0	0·000063	15,770
5·0	$5·7 \times 10^{-7}$	$1·7 \times 10^6$
6·0	2×10^{-9}	5×10^8
7·0	$2·6 \times 10^{-12}$	$3·9 \times 10^{11}$

MECHANICAL EFFECTS

IMPACT

The initiation of explosives by impact can arise in very many circumstances. These can, however, be classified into three types. The first of these is the case where a stationary quantity of explosive is hit by a moving object. This can arise from such circumstances as an accidental blow with a tool or from some object falling on to the explosive or as part of the events in a transport accident. It may be accidental or deliberate impact from a bullet or as the result of some foolish action, as when (1891) three boys threw stones at a can of nitroglycerine on a tree stump. The resulting, inevitable, explosion killed all three.

The second type is the case where a moving quantity of explosive hits a stationary object. This can arise from a transport accident, the accidental dropping of a container of explosive or even in the course of careful handling. Thus (1925) a scientist who was conducting experiments to determine the detonation velocity of hydrazoic acid/

water mixtures, placed a bottle containing a quantity of the explosive into a box on the ground. An explosion occurred and he was killed.

The third type is the case where a quantity of explosive is crushed between two surfaces, usually metal. This can arise in such situations as between a spanner and nut in the course of adjustment of machinery, between moving parts of a machine or between a wheel and rail. Thus (1951), sludge from a settling pond, through which nitroglycerine wastings passed, was loaded on to a bogie. The next day when the bogie was moved there was an explosion. Evidence of detonation was found on both a wheel and the rail, and investigation showed that it was possible for nitroglycerine to have leaked on to the wheel.

It was pointed out in Chapter 2 that the assessment of impact sensitivity is, almost invariably, carried out on an impact machine. Various forms of apparatus are in use but, although all are basically similar, the results are not strictly comparable from one to another, even when of the same design. Fortunately, this difficulty need not hamper explosion investigation since, for investigational purposes, it is normally adequate to classify explosives into three broad categories in respect of this property.

1. *Sensitive explosives*

These comprise such materials as primary explosives, percussion cap compositions, toy pistol cap compositions and their amateur experimenter's equivalents.

2. *Explosives of normal sensitivity*

These comprise the majority of the well known secondary explosives such as RDX, PETN, TNT and explosives derived from them, nitrocellulose based explosives and nitroglycerine based industrial blasting explosives.

3. *Insensitive explosives*

These comprise such materials as dinitroaromatic compounds and ammonium nitrate based blasting agents such as ANFO and slurries.

There are, inevitably, borderline cases but these should be regarded as such, rather than attempting to force them into one category or another by defining the boundary with an accuracy which can only be spurious. If the investigation involves a material for which an impact sensitivity value is not available, a test on any impact apparatus will suffice to establish to which of the categories it belongs or whether it is on a borderline. For purposes of evidence in the case of an unfamiliar material, it is useful to select a well known explosive whose impact sensitivity very nearly corresponds to that of the one under investigation and then to describe the latter as having a sensitivity to impact comparable with that of the former. Such a statement will convey the essential truth and will be more intelligible than any attempt to give a more precise answer, which will inevitably include reservations on such matters as the differences produced by different pieces of apparatus and different operators.

In attempting to decide whether the observed circumstances would have been sufficient to cause the initiation of an explosive of the determined sensitivity, the investigator must compare them with the blow delivered in an impact apparatus. Where the explosive was subjected to an impact, a reasonably direct comparison can be made by comparing the energy delivered per unit area. Other cases are not so straightforward since similarity with the mechanics of an impact apparatus will be tenuous. In such cases it will be necessary to conduct experiments with the actual artefacts from the scene, or replicas, and determine experimentally whether or not the explosive could have been initiated.

FRICTION

The initiation of explosives by friction can arise in many circumstances. There are many operations in the course of the manufacture of explosives in which friction is involved. These include grinding, sieving, shovelling and almost any kind of movement of materials. The techniques are, of course, devised in the light of experience and scientific principles to eliminate any friction capable of initiating the explosive. It is possible, however, for an unforeseen circumstance to arise. For example (1946), a serious fire occurred in a fireworks factory when magnesium was being removed from an iron drum with a brass scoop. Normally a safe process, it became unsafe due to the presence of rust which causes magnesium to be very liable to frictional ignition.

Normally safe processes can also be unsafe due to the explosive becoming contaminated with grit. Such a cause may be very difficult to detect since the grit will probably have been dispersed in the explosion. Evidence may, however, remain as in a case (1895) in which fluted rollers showed recent evidence of scoring by a hard substance. Another reason for normally safe procedures to become dangerous is departures from the set procedure carried out by an operative, possibly in an attempt to speed up operations but in ignorance of the possible consequences. Thus (1972) a fire occurred during the mixing of a smoke composition. Although the finished product was regarded as non-explosive, it contained both an oxidant and a fuel and an incorrect sequence of addition of ingredients produced an intermediate composition which was liable to frictional ignition under the normally safe procedures. Apparently slight changes in technique can make significant changes in the probability of ignition due to friction. An explosion occurred (1971) in a brass rotary mixing machine used for an igniter wick composition. It was customary to insert a number of zinc alloy balls into the mixer so that mixing and the reduction of particle size took place simultaneously. On the day of the explosion some new balls had been used and these were found to be made from flint. Investigation showed that the composition was sensitive to friction between flint and brass.

Frictional ignition can also arise in circumstances outside the field of manufacturing processes. Spilled explosive can be subjected to friction during the course of transport or handling. Ignition can also occur in totally unexpected circumstances, as when a man playing tennis on a hard court suddenly found his leg enveloped in flames. Investigation showed that the court had been recently treated with sodium chlorate for weed killing purposes and that his rubber soled tennis shoe had provided not only the fuel to produce an explosive mixture with the chlorate but also the friction required to ignite it. Frictional ignition is also a common hazard to the makers of devices filled with home-made explosives. In one such instance (1972) two men were severely injured, one losing both hands and the second suffering the loss of one eye and damage to the other. The men had filled a steel tube with a home-made explosive mixture and this exploded when they were drilling a hole in it.

In assessing the probability of frictional ignition being the correct explanation for the initiation in a particular case, there is no necessity to know particular values for this property. It is sufficient to show that the explosive could be initiated by the friction present in the observed system. For this reason, published friction sensitivity results are often of little value to the investigator.

An early method of assessing friction sensitivity was to rub a small portion of explosive in a porcelain mortar with a porcelain pestle. A more modern version of this test uses a loaded porcelain pencil and a motor driven porcelain plate. While explosives can be placed in an order of sensitivity by these methods it is difficult to relate the figures to real situations in which porcelain surfaces are not involved. Many pieces of apparatus for measuring friction sensitivity have been designed around the principle of the pendulum. The mechanical action of such devices does not, however, reproduce that in the majority of real explosion situations and here again it is difficult to relate the figures to them. Results obtained from apparatus of the type known as Torpedo friction machines suffer from the same difficulty, though to a lesser extent since the action more nearly represents that occurring in accident situations.

For the explosion investigator the most satisfactory technique for assessing friction sensitivity is the traditional hand mallet and anvil test. Samples of the explosive to be tested are placed on a flat anvil and struck a glancing blow with a mallet. Assessment consists of judging whether or not the sample explodes. This test is simple and regarded by some as unscientific but it has the great merit of flexibility. It is quite easy to have a range of anvils and mallets of different materials. The tests can then be carried out with the materials involved in the explosion. The investigator is thus not involved in the difficulties of relating the results to the real situation and of convincing others of the validity of interpretations. Where necessary, actual materials and artefacts from the scene can by used as anvil and mallet.

HEAT

FLAME

In the initiation of an explosion by flame, two types of circumstance can be recognised: the flame may be brought to the explosive or the explosive may be brought to the flame.

Flame may reach an explosive in various ways. The most obvious is the case in which explosives or explosive devices are involved in a fire which has originated from some cause quite unconnected with the explosive. Matches have been a cause of initiation on countless occasions. Sometimes the presence of a match and its lighting are both accidental as in a factory accident (CXXVII) where a match was ignited by being trodden on in a 'clean' explosives workshop.

Investigation showed that it had probably been introduced into the workshop adhering to the bottom of a package of wrappers which were still in the parcel in which they had been delivered. Sometimes the presence of a match is deliberate but its lighting is accidental. There have been many incidents in which inveterate smokers broke safety regulations by taking smoking materials including matches, into 'no smoking' areas. From time to time the inevitable accidents have occurred. Sometimes the presence of a match and its lighting are both deliberate. After an explosion at Southport (1880) the investigator wrote: 'Two men had picked up an unexploded shell and had carried it into the premises of the Bald Arms Hotel, when, with a recklessness which is nearly akin to insanity, they applied a light to it, when it exploded, severely injuring one man, and doing considerable damage to the premises.' Finally, apart from the long history of human folly with matches, there is an equally long history of the use of matches as the basis for ignition devices in infernal machines.

Apart from matches, other sources of flame may be brought into contact with explosives and cause initiation. A man removed a petrol tank from a vehicle (1972) and put it in a safe place. However, a small amount of petrol spilled from the feed-pipe into the inspection pit. The man then used an oxy acetylene burner to weld the support for the petrol tank. He subsequently stepped into the pit to inspect his work with the burner still alight and an explosion occurred. In another case (1971) an oxyacetylene burner was used by thieves to cut away the concealed mortice locks of the door to a detonator store. In the process the flame reached the detonators and an explosion ensued. This blew open the door and scattered detonators over an area of 30 to 40 m^2. The thieves escaped undetected and there is, therefore, no information as to their injuries.

Most cases of initiation by flame in which the explosive moves to the flame, concern explosive gas/air or vapour/air mixtures. Thus, for example (1954), a motor cyclist had the fuel tank of his motor cycle filled to capacity at a petrol pump of a garage. He moved off the forecourt and then tipped the motor cycle in order to remove the excess petrol. Petrol vapour was ignited by a watchman's red danger light at an excavation nearby and there was a flash back to the fuel tank of the vehicle.

The distance the explosive mixture may move can be considerable. Thus (1959) petrol was being discharged into underground tanks on a hot, still day. The tank-vents were 3 m high and situated in an area confined on three sides by buildings. One of these was a house, the door of which was opened by a woman in order to shake a mop. An explosion occurred, her clothing was set on fire and materials in the house at ground floor level were set alight. It was established that the cause of initiation was the flame on a gas cooking stove which was situatcd 10 m from the vents. An even greater distance has been recorded in a case (1902) in which a woman was cooking at her stove when she was enveloped in flames. The source of the vapour/air mixture was traced to a boy who was washing out petrol cans over 90 m away.

Gas/air mixtures, being in general less dense than air, tend only to produce explosions when confined by some structure such as the interior of a building. Nevertheless, such mixtures can move over greater distances provided a suitable path is available. There are a number of instances of the partial or complete demolition of domestic dwelling houses by town gas/air mixtures where no gas supply was laid on to the house. The gas, originating in a nearby faulty gas main, reached the houses via fissures in the ground.

If the investigator can establish that a flame could have reached a condensed explosive then the possibility that this was the cause of initiation cannot be discounted. Whether this is to be regarded as a probable cause will depend on the nature and duration of the flame and the nature of the explosive. As a broad generalisation, primary explosives can be taken as being readily ignited and readily detonated, secondary explosives as being less readily ignited but liable to burn to detonation in relatively small quantities, and insensitive blasting agents as being difficult to ignite and only liable to burn to detonation in very large quantities, if at all. As in all classifications there are borderline cases. Propellent explosives tend to be readily ignited and produce a fierce fire with considerable heat radiation and, sometimes, detonation. Gunpowder is easily ignited and readily explodes. Thus, almost any flame will cause initiation of primary explosives, pro-pellents and gunpowder. Small and relatively transient flames how-ever may fail to initiate secondary and insensitive explosives. If there is any doubt on whether a particular flame could cause initiation of a particular explosive, the question can only be resolved by conducting appropriate experiments.

In the case of dispersed explosives the crucial parameter with flame initiation is not the flame but whether the composition of the mixture lies within the compositional explosion limits. It will probably not be possible for the investigator to prove that this was so but, provided both gas, vapour or dust and air were present, it will be equally impossible to prove that an explosive concentration never occurred. Indeed in these circumstances the presence of at least some explosive mixture is almost inevitable, whereas its absence is extremely improbable.

High Temperature

In the initiation of explosives by high temperatures two circumstances can be distinguished: the explosive may be subjected to slow heating until the ignition temperature is reached or it may be brought into contact with a very hot surface.

The gradual heating of an explosive can occur in many ways and three examples will illustrate this diversity. The first (1932) was a factory accident in which a fire broke out in a nitrocotton boiler. At the end of boiling, the steam was turned off and the water allowed to drain. After about twenty minutes a partial ignition occurred. It was found that, although the steam had been turned off, it was still leaking slightly into the vat and had impinged on to nitrocotton from which the water had already drained off. The second was an infernal machine. It consisted of a cartridge of gelignite and a detonator secured to the exhaust pipe of a motor vehicle in the vicinity of the petrol tank. It was detected before the vehicle was used but experiments showed that, after about twenty minutes running, the relevant part of the exhaust pipe would reach a temperature sufficient to cause the detonator to operate. The third (39) occurred in a melting pan in which TNT residues were melted for re-use. Various impurities tended to accumulate in the bottom of the pan which had a side-draining tap. In particular, potassium nitrate and cardboard were involved. It was found that self-heating set in at 242° C with pure TNT but that this could reduce to 140–150° C with these impurities and that ignition could occur. The latter temperatures were within the range of the steam heating system.

The effects of an initiation by gradual heating can be misleading. When a high explosive is ignited by a flame or a very hot point source the subsequent detonation is frequently only a partial one. When, however, gradual heating occurs there is a gradual increase in sensitivity so that when the ignition temperature is reached an efficient detonation occurs. Observation of the damage caused in the latter case can, therefore, lead to an overestimate of the amount of explosive involved unless this point is appreciated.

Initiation of explosives by contact with a very hot surface is an uncertain process since such contacts sometimes fail to cause initiation. This is illustrated by the contrast between the following two incidents. When repairs (1954) were being made to a nitroglycerine-soda solution gutter, molten solder was dropped and ignited solvent vapour from the nitroglycerine killer used to decontaminate the surrounding soil. The ignition caused detonation of a small quantity of unkilled nitroglycerine in the soil. On the other hand (1922) a fire occurred in a corrugated asbestos roofed store containing over 180 kg of picric acid in wooden barrels. Burning occurred but no explosion. Evidence was found which showed that the iron barrel hoops had melted but that the molten iron had run through the picric acid as globules without igniting it.

Other examples of the uncertainty of this type of initiation can be found in cases where lighted cigarettes are involved. A man (1926) who was cleaning gloves with petrol had the liquid in a bowl. He was smoking at the time and dropped his lighted cigarette near the bowl. It ignited the vapour and a portion of the building was practically burnt out by the ensuing fire. In many cases, however, lighted cigarettes have failed to ignite explosive vapour/air mixtures. A possible explanation is that the covering of ash which forms over the glowing surface provides protection from ignition in a manner similar to that provided by the gauze in the Davy safety lamp.

Finally, there is the case of the explosives scientist who fabricated an ash tray from cast TNT and kept it on his office desk for the use of visitors, only revealing its nature after they had extinguished a cigarette in it with no untoward results.

If the investigation of an explosion reveals a mechanism whereby the explosive could have been heated sufficiently to have reached ignition temperature, this can be accepted as causing initiation. Care should be taken, however, in deciding whether or not the temperature was an appropriate one for ignition to occur. The possibilities of reduced ignition temperatures due to impurities or other catalysts must not be overlooked. Another effect which could cause uncertainty is that described by Tulis and Erikson (40). Drops of nitroglycerine are placed on a heated metal plate. As the experiment is repeated at steadily increasing temperatures the nitroglycerine begins to detonate. A transition zone is then reached wherein the nitroglycerine flashes, followed by another in which the nitroglycerine vapourises without combustion of any kind. On a further increase in temperature the nitroglycerine detonates again. The transition zones vary with droplet size and the way in which the droplet is placed upon the hotplate, *e.g.* the height of fall.

Further investigation would be needed to determine whether heating was the only or primary cause. If there is a mechanism whereby the explosive could have come into contact with a very hot surface, the interpretation can only be that this may have been a cause of initiation. It may, however, be possible to establish it as being the primary cause by the elimination of all other possibilities.

ADIABATIC COMPRESSION

The behaviour on adiabatic change of an ideal gas is expressed by the well-known equation:

$$C_v \, dT + pdv = 0$$

where C is the heat capacity at constant volume, T the temperature, p the pressure, and v the volume. In an adiabatic compression dv is negative and hence dT must be positive so that a consequence of the adiabatic compression of a gas is that its temperature rises. If gaseous material is subjected to sudden compression, its behaviour will, for practical purposes, be adiabatic and its temperature will rise. If the temperature rise is sufficient, the ignition temperature of any explosive in contact with it will be reached. Initiation of explosives from this cause has been recorded from time to time.

During the hydraulic pressing of cordite (1951) an explosion occurred in a press cylinder which was, as a result, ruptured. Investigation showed that this was due to ignition by adiabatic heating of a solvent vapour/air mixture in the cylinder. On another occasion, when gelignite was subjected to a rapidly applied pressure in a cylinder, an explosion occurred. The apparent explanation was that initiation had occurred owing to the formation of a hot spot due to adiabatic compression of a pocket of air.

Heating owing to adiabatic compression can also contribute to initiation by impact. Liquid explosives are more readily initiated when they contain air bubbles than when they do not, since compression causes the bubbles to act as hot spot sources of initiation. In the case of solid explosives, it has been observed that interstitial air or other gases modify the sensitivity of granular explosives.

If the gas subjected to adiabatic compression is itself explosive, it can be initiated. In a case of this type (1968) a gas cylinder exploded in a private garage, killing a man who was the only occupant. Subsequent examination of the debris established that there had been a detonation of an oxygen/fuel gas mixture which had originated at the regulator valve. The exploded cylinder, and another found on the scene, were of the type used for medical gases. A third was a propane cylinder. The evidence indicated that propane had been transferred from the latter cylinder to the one which exploded and that this had subsequently been connected to the remaining cylinder which contained oxygen. It was presumed that the deceased was intending to produce a cylinder of oxygen/fuel gas mixture. The explosion was apparently due to the sudden release of high pressure oxygen into the regulator, thereby producing sufficient temperature rise by adiabatic compression to ignite the gas mixture.

In considering the possible role of adiabatic compressive heating in an explosion investigation, two aspects must be examined. Such heating could be the basic cause of the initiation of the explosive or it may have been a contributory factor by increasing the sensitivity of a condensed explosive. If it can be shown that the explosive could have been subjected to compressive forces, then initiation by adiabatic heating must be considered as possible.

SPARK

ELECTRICAL

Sparks deriving from electrical, as opposed to electrostatic, sources can arise from a number of mechanisms. Explosion initiation by such electric sparks can be classified as of two types: an intentionally produced spark causing the initiation of an explosive unintentionally present, and an unintentionally produced spark causing the initiation of an explosive intentionally or known to be present.

Various electrical mechanisms such as motor commutators and switches will produce sparks on operation. In places where explosives and inflammable gases are handled, the danger of ignition from this source is guarded against by the use of specially designed, flameproof electrical equipment. Such fittings are expensive and are not used other than in premises where special protection is needed. In consequence, explosive gas/air and vapour/air systems, accidentally produced, are liable to come into contact with ordinary, spark producing, electrical equipment. Many town gas/air explosions on domestic premises have been initiated by electric switches, particularly automatic ones in thermostatically controlled devices such as refrigerators.

Since special electrical equipment is, or should be, used in the presence of explosives, no electric spark initiations should occur where explosives are present. However, regulations are not always adhered to and even adequate equipment can be subject to accidental damage. In consequence, electric spark initiation has occurred in places known to be carrying an explosive risk. Thus (1929) an oil tanker was discharging petroleum spirit to a shore depôt. The ship's pump broke down and an engineer went to remedy the defect. After he had been in the pump room for about five minutes an explosion occurred and he was killed. The pump room contained a vapour/air mixture and it was concluded that this was ignited by a spark from a wandering lead, since there was evidence of sparking having taken place between one of the plungers in the lampholder and the lamp. An unusual explosion of this type occurred (1931) in a hospital operating theatre where a man was being given an anaesthetic of ether and oxygen and a pencil light was being used to see inside his throat. There was an explosion in the man's mouth and he died from his injuries. The light was defective and a spark from it initiated the explosive ether/oxygen mixture. Ignition owing to accidental damage to adequate electrical equipment is illustrated by a case (1972) in which rocket composition was ignited in a filling shop. A defect was found on a piece of mineral-insulated, copper-covered electric cable. This had either been installed originally with a curve of too small a radius or had been bent since installation. As a result, the mineral insulation had become damaged and a short circuit had occurred which had burned through the copper covering.

In considering whether an electric spark was the cause of initiation of a particular explosion the investigator must answer three questions:

1. Could a spark have occurred?
2. If so, did a spark occur?
3. If so, could it have produced initiation?

To answer the first question it is only necessary to examine the scene and determine whether or not any source of electricity was present. If there was none then no electric spark could have occurred.

If, however, any source of electricity was present, it is necessary to consider whether a spark could have been produced. Clearly the occurrence of a spark is a possibility if any mechanism involving a make and break is present and in use. In addition, all electrical appliances should be examined for defects which could have given rise to conditions requisite for spark production. Such faults include attacks on insulation by decay or vermin, loose connections and damage by impact. Care must be taken to distinguish between those faults where there is evidence that they existed before the explosion and those caused by the explosion.

If a possible source of sparks is located, it is then necessary to consider whether it could have caused initiation. Various pieces of apparatus have been devised for studying the initiation of explosives by sparks. All are based on the same principle, namely, subjecting samples to controlled sparks and determining the minimum energy dissipation required to bring about explosion. The minimum spark ignition energies for the initiation of some dust/air explosives are shown in Appendix K. These range from 11 to 440 mJ with a mean of 64 mJ or, if the somewhat untypical value for sodium carboxymethyl cellulose is omitted, from 11 to 128 mJ with a mean of 42 mJ. Minimum spark ignition energies for these systems can therefore be regarded as being of the order of tens of millijoules.

The minimum ignition energies for vapour/air systems varies both with the type of vapour and with the concentration. The values are, however, comparable with those for dust/air mixtures.

The minimum spark ignition energies for secondary explosives are higher; some representative values are shown in Table 6.3. As is to be expected, the minimum spark ignition energies for primary explosives are considerably lower; some typical values are shown in Table 6.4.

It will be seen that the minimum spark ignition energies of ex-

TABLE 6.3.

Explosive	Spark energy (J)	
	Ignition	No ignition
RDX	—	4·5
β HMX	4·5	0·45
PETN	4·5	0·45
Dynamite	4·5	0·45
Ammonium perchlorate/Al 50/50	0·45	0·045
Sulphurless mealed gunpowder	0·45	0·045

TABLE 6.4

Explosive	Minimum energy (μJ)
Lead azide	2
Dextrinated lead azide	20
Lead styphnate	11
Lead 2, 4-dinitroresorcinate	20

plosives of various types cover a considerable range. However, even the highest of these is several orders of magnitude below the energy dissipated in sparks either from typical make and break devices or from electrical faults. If, therefore, a source of electric spark can be identified at the scene of an explosion, then it must be presumed to have been a possible source of initiation.

ELECTROSTATIC

Static electricity is created by the relative movement of two materials and, in appropriate conditions, large charges can be built up by the movement of matter in all states (solid, liquid and gaseous). The discharge of such accumulations can produce spark energies high enough to cause the initiation of explosives. The diversity of the situations in which such initiation can arise and their continuance may be illustrated by a selection of cases.

An explosion occurred (1891) in a dry-cleaning plant in which wool and silk garments were cleansed in mineral spirit contained in an iron trough. Ignition occurred through the discharge of static electricity.

In 1922 (41) in New York, a device for the disposal of unwanted cats was wrecked by an explosion. The cats were dropped into an iron tank containing a lethal coal gas/air mixture. On one particular day a fourth batch of cats included a particularly fierce black male who clung to the basket in which he had been brought. This built up static electrical charge on his body so that, when he was eventually dislodged and fell through the opening to the tank, a spark ignited the explosive mixture remaining in it. There was an explosion and 'people from the office rushed in to find the place strewn with dead cats, the black Tom included, and the three executioners on the floor. Two were sent to hospital, one with a possibly fractured skull, and all were more or less burned and lacerated.'

A serious fire and explosion occurred (1951) when oil was being pumped from a tanker into a tank ashore. The rate of the flow of oil in the discharge pipe was such that it appeared probable that charges of static electricity were built up. At the time of the explosion a steel dip tape fitted with a heavy brass weight was being used. It was possible, therefore, for this tape to take up a charge of static electricity from the oil and for this to discharge with a spark against the edge of the hole in the top of the tank through which it was lowered.

Dipping and sampling operations were in progress (1965) on the top of a half-full 2,000 ton capacity tank used for storage of petroleum spirit. While work was proceeding, the weather conditions changed rapidly and a violent hailstorm occurred. While an operator was near one of the dip hatches there was a violent explosion under the roof of the tank which lifted and caused him to fall into the spirit where he was drowned. Subsequently it was found that the hailstorm which swept across the installation was no more than two to three hundred metres wide. Due to the particular atmospheric conditions, the hail stones were extremely highly charged electrically, sufficiently so as to burn through the paint where they struck the tank. The evidence indicated that there had been a major discharge of electricity to the tank roof immediately adjacent to the dip hatch by which the operator was standing. With the hatches open and a breeze blowing, explosive vapour/air mixtures would have developed both outside and inside the hatch.

A quantity of aviation fuel in a tank (1965) was treated with water to remove antifreeze with which it had become contaminated. The mixture was agitated with air under pressure and five minutes after the air flow was established the tank exploded. Agitation of petrol/water mixtures has long been known to produce intense charges of static electricity and, in this case, not only did the air serve to produce such charges but also an explosive vapour/air mixture.

The discharge of static electricity caused (1967) an ignition during the backflushing of a petroleum fuel filter. The filter, suspended by its polythene feed tube, was being lowered into a receiving tube at the time. Strong charging occurs when non polar liquids pass through filters.

Another source of static charges is found in those who handle explosives and other materials, since the human body can build up a considerable charge on itself. When domestic lighting by gas was more common than it is now, a spectacular parlour trick consisted in shuffling across a carpeted floor and then lighting a gas light from the spark generated between the fingertip and the earthed gasfitting. With the increased use of footwear with non-conducting soles and of clothing made from man-made fibres, the incidence of such charges is widespread. It is possible for an accidental spark from this source to dissipate 0·02 J, which is quite sufficient to initiate many dispersed phase explosives and the more sensitive condensed phase ones.

In considering whether there is evidence for an initiation by the discharge of static electricity, the investigator must decide first whether there was movement of materials such that electricity could have been generated. If the answer is positive he must then decide whether the conditions of electrical conductance were such that the electricity could have built up to a static charge. This could arise either from the intrinsic lack of a conducting path to earth or from the failure of an earthing system. Finally, if the answer to this is also positive, he must decide whether there is any evidence that there was a discharge at the explosion centre. There will normally be no direct evidence, though eyewitness testimony may sometimes be available. Indirect evidence based on the physical juxtaposition of objects will have to be used to show that the conditions for a discharge were present. If they were, the occurrence of a spark cannot be discounted.

If a spark is known to have occurred, or could have occurred, there still remains the question of whether it dissipated sufficient energy to cause initiation. In general, it may be assumed that if a spark occurred it would have been capable of producing initiation. If, however, the point is of crucial importance, or is in dispute, then deductive experiments must be carried out. These will involve replicating the conditions and determining by experiment whether or not the spark produced can initiate the explosive.

LIGHTNING

Lightning is an example of the phenomenon of the discharge of static electricity, but its scale is very much greater than that of the general types of electrostatic discharge already considered. In consequence, a number of phenomena peculiar to this type have been observed when lightning has caused the initiation of an explosion.

The initiation of any explosive, subject to a direct lightning strike, may be regarded as a certainty due to the vast energy input. It has, however, long been known that a strike away from a quantity of explosive is also capable of causing ignition. Thus, in a gunpowder mill explosion (1883) the ignition was caused by a lightning strike some way away. Investigation showed that the discharge had travelled along the ground and also along some iron railings.

In another case (1931) a storm broke over an explosives factory in Australia. There was much lightning accompanied by rain and hail. The lightning was reported to be very severe and several witnesses were able to testify to seeing a lightning strike in the vicinity of one of the final nitroglycerine washing houses. This caused an immediate explosion. The investigator pointed out in his report that final washing houses appear to have been destroyed more frequently by lightning than have other explosives factory buildings. He suggested that the reason for this susceptibility is probably the unavoidable film of nitroglycerine, capable of transmitting detonation, which occurs over the metal (lead) surfaces of these rooms.

A similar explosion also reported from Australia (1955) involved a nitroglycerine nitrating house. The building was protected by four lightning conductors on the corners of the mound surrounding the building. The height of the conductors was based on the assumption that the zone of protection is a cone with its apex at the top of the conductor and with a base radius equal to four times the height. Current recommendations advise that the base radius should be taken as equal to the height. The resistance to earth of the conductors was satisfactory and all metal in the house was efficiently bonded to earth. However, it is possible that a lightning strike outside the area of protection may have, as in the 1883 case, found a conducting path to the building and then discharged to earth via metal whose surface bore a film of nitroglycerine.

A curious case of initiation by lightning occurred (1917) at a factory. This contained a ton of nitrocellulose, wetted with alcohol and packed in hermetically sealed steel drums. Lightning struck the factory and the nitrocellulose exploded. The initiation in this case could not have been by the normal spark process since the explosive was protected in sealed metal drums. It is possible, however, that sufficient local heating occurred to raise the nitrocellulose above its ignition temperature.

These examples are sufficient to show that lightning can cause the initiation of explosives by mechanisms other than the direct impingement of an electrostatic discharge. If, therefore, the investigator has evidence of lightning at the time and in the vicinity of an explosion, he should not dismiss this as a possible cause of initiation merely because lightning conductors or other apparent protections were present.

CHEMICAL

The term spark is commonly used to describe two unrelated phenomena. The first, which has been discussed above, is that which occurs when an electric current is discharged through air or other dielectric. The second is that which occurs when small fragments of burning or glowing solid material are projected through air. For convenience the latter can be described as chemical sparks since the heat, which can be a source of initiation, is produced by chemical reactions.

As is the case with electrostatic sparks, chemical sparks can arise in many diverse situations. This may be illustrated by a selection of cases drawn from various periods.

A horse-drawn cart was used (1877) to transport gunpowder several times along the same road. There was a hole in the cart and some gunpowder spilled on the ground. On one journey this became ignited by a spark produced by one of the horse's shoes striking a stone. The report of this accident mentions a similar incident which occurred in 1810.

An explosion in 1893 (CIV) was found to have been initiated by sparks which flew from the chimney of a nearby boiler. A number of other instances of the same phenomenon are on record.

A man (1904) was showing some friends over a room in a bank in which were a number of unloaded flintlock guns. He demonstrated the action of one of these by snapping it and a spark fell into an open box of gunpowder. The ensuing explosion killed one of the party. The reason for the presence of these articles in the bank is not known but, presumably, they were originally intended for defence purposes. The report of the incident stated that the gunpowder had been there for about 100 years.

A shopkeeper brought (1945) his stock of fireworks from the basement and placed them on the sitting room table. He was sorting them out into their various grades and prices when he noticed a firework which he thought was a new type of sparkler. He lit it with a match and sparks from it ignited the bulk stock. In consequence, he was injured and his daughter, who was present, was killed.

An old steel fence was (1954) being cut down with an oxy-acetylene cutter. Sparks fell onto a disused steel tank in an adjacent chemical works. An explosion occurred which blew the ends off the tank and injured one man. One tank end was projected 320 m and the windows of 25 houses were broken. Scale from the tank was found to contain a high proportion of potassium dinitrophenate and the tank itself was identified as part of an old explosives plant.

A residual film of gunpowder/nitrocellulose dope ignited (1965) in a vessel under repair when a brass spanner was being used to remove a brass nut. The nut was difficult to turn and the fitter gave it a tap with the spanner. A spark was seen and the film of dope in the pot was ignited.

In considering whether a chemical spark could be the cause of a particular initiation, the investigator may be assisted by direct evidence of the presence of such a spark as in the last four cases cited. If, however, there is no direct evidence he must examine the circumstances to determine whether any materials and processes known to be capable of producing sparks were present. These would include flame cutting and welding operations, the burning of fires in general and pyrotechnic devices in particular, and pyrophoric materials or devices containing them such as cigarette lighters. If none of these were present but there was some material or process which the investigator considers might have given rise to a spark, then experiments must be carried out to determine whether the suspicion was justified.

In general, incandescent chemical sparks which come into contact with an explosive must be regarded as potential sources of ignition. Therefore, in considering whether chemical sparks are likely to have been a source of initiation in a particular instance, it is necessary to determine whether they could have reached the explosive at a sufficient temperature in relation to their size to transfer sufficient energy to cause initiation. To answer this question it will be necessary to conduct experiments with replicate conditions and determine whether or not initiation occurs.

CHEMICAL EFFECTS

Explosives are sometimes initiated by chemical initiators. These can conviently be divided into three types depending on the method of functioning: (1) chemical reactions producing heat; (2) chemical reactions producing flame; and (3) chemical reactions producing an immediate explosive effect when the reactants come into contact with each other. The last is to be distinguished from the chemical reactions of an explosive which only occurs after initiation by one of the means already discussed.

An early example (1896) of initiation by a chemical reaction producing heat involved an explosion in a shot hole which had been charged with gelatine dynamite. The shot hole had also had inserted into it some quicklime for drying purposes and it was concluded that the explosion was due to heat generated by a reaction between the quicklime and water. An attempt had been made a few years earlier (1892) to use the same reaction to produce an infernal machine. In that case a cartridge of dynamite was placed into a barrel of quicklime with the apparent intention that the moisture in the dynamite should react with the quicklime and so generate enough heat to initiate an explosion.

Initiation by chemical reactions producing heat has been used in recent times in devices such as the Cardox blasting charge for use in coal mines. This consists of a strong metal tube filled with liquid carbon dioxide and fitted with a bursting disc. An electrically ignited chemical heater causes the pressure to rise above the predetermined bursting pressure. The resultant mechanical explosion, occurring in a shot hole, breaks the coal without danger of igniting inflammable gases.

One of the chemical reactions producing flame, which has been used for many years, is that between concentrated sulphuric acid and a mixture of chlorate and sugar. It was used (1883) in an infernal machine in Glasgow during the Fenian outrages and appeared again in London in a series of bombings between 1968 and 1971. It has been used as the basis of ignition systems in both civil and military devices since the mid nineteenth century.

Chlorates have also been known to inflame in other circumstances as when (1895) a city stockbroker, leaving his inner private office hurriedly, bumped against the counter in an outer room. A hissing noise came from his pocket which then caught fire. It was found that he was carrying medicinal lozenges, which contained potassium chlorate, loose in his pocket and that these had been brought against the brassard of a safety match box.

Another well-known chemical reaction which produces flame is that between sodium and water. This has been used from time to time as the basis for fuzing infernal machines. It has also been responsible for initiation in accidents. The steamship *Hardy* (1912) was carrying a cargo of potassium chlorate and of tallow in the hold and two tons of metallic sodium in airtight and watertight packages on deck. A heavy sea caused the lashings on the sodium containers to part and they were hurled against a bulwark. They burst open and the sodium inflamed. The crew took to a boat and a violent explosion occurred, followed by a second one which cut the ship in two. It was presumed that the fire, started by the sodium/water reaction, had melted the tallow which then mixed with the potassium chlorate to form an explosive.

There are a number of chemical systems in which an explosion occurs immediately the reactants come together. For example (1893) an explosion occurred at a railway depôt and the investigation established that it was due to a mixture of sodium peroxide and a fuel, which exploded on contact with water. Another reported case (1934) concerned an explosion which occurred when samples of lead azide were being dried in a desiccator over sulphuric acid. A portion of about one gram of azide fell into the sulphuric acid and an explosion occurred immediately. Other examples of this behaviour include self-igniting liquid propellants and the reaction under appropriate conditions between silver nitrate, magnesium and water.

In the case of an accident, the identification of initiation by a chemical effect will depend on considering what materials were present. The investigator must consider not only those which were legitimately present but enquire into the possibilities of others which were there either by accident, by wilful disregard of safety regulations or by malicious intent. If any materials, such as those mentioned earlier or others which could cause an initiation when brought together, were present, then the possibility that they were mixed must be examined. If two substances are present in the same vicinity either simultaneously or consecutively, there is always the possibility that some mixing will occur due to spillage, the transfer of contamination from surface to surface or other mechanisms. This possibility can only be rejected if there is conclusive positive evidence that mixing could not have occurred.

In the case of the explosion of an infernal machine, the identification of an initiation mechanism based on chemical effects depends on the finding of parts of the device and the identification of appropriate chemicals. Where concentrated sulphuric acid is used it will almost inevitably be in a glass container. Release from the container may be by a slowly penetrated paper diaphragm, as occurred in the cases of 1883 and 1968–71 mentioned earlier, or by crushing, as in most manufactured devices incorporating this principle. Evidence for such containers may be found among debris from the scene.

In identifying chemicals, tests must be made for the presence of those produced by the chemical reaction being considered. Thus, if a sulphuric acid/potassium chlorate/sugar system is postulated, tests must be made for the identification of hydrogen (ion), potassium, sulphate, chlorate and sugar and, in addition, for the possible decomposition products chloride and perchlorate. The problem of control samples on which interpretations must be based is the same as that encountered in the identification of residues of the main explosive charge and this has been discussed in Chapter 5.

MISCELLANEOUS
Wave Mechanisms

A number of miscellaneous mechanisms whereby explosives may be initiated can conveniently be grouped together since all transmit energy to the explosive by a wave mechanism.

Liquid explosives can be initiated by ultrasonic waves. This mechanism is largely of academic interest and it seems most improbable that this form of initiation will be encountered by the explosion investigator.

Explosives may also be initiated by light. Some reactions, such as that between hydrogen and chlorine, are both explosive and photosensitive. Beams of coherent light produced by lasers can transmit sufficient energy to initiate condensed explosives. It has been found, for example, that pyrotechnic compositions can be ignited with a SO-W continuous CO_2 laser (42).

A mechanism which is far more likely to be of practical significance in explosion investigation is initiation by radio frequency radiation. No direct initiation of explosives can occur by this means, but it is possible for an electric firing circuit to be operated inadvertently.

The essential reason for a radio frequency hazard to electric initiators is that, when the lead wires and, where connected, the other circuit wires are laid out for use, they will act as a receiving aerial. This will absorb radio frequency transmissions and, in some circumstances, the electric current so produced can exceed the common 40 mW no fire level and so function the detonator. The parameters which determine whether this will happen are the strength of the field and the efficiency of pick up of energy. The latter is determined by the strength of the transmission, the distance from the transmitter and the configuration of the aerial. The former is determined by the type of transmission. The available evidence indicates that the hazard is eliminated when detonator wires are folded in the manner used by manufacturers when marketing their products, when detonators are packed in a metal box or when they are carried inside a vehicle of metal box construction or when a device containing an electrical initiation system is designed to be free from radio frequency hazards.

The most commonly occurring electrically operated explosive device is the electric detonator but, although this is produced and used in very large numbers, there have been few authenticated instances of electric detonators being operated accidentally by radio frequency radiation. It is, therefore, a very unlikely mechanism for the initiation of an explosion and the investigator can normally disregard it. Laymen, however, frequently are under the impression that it is not a remote hazard and so the investigator should be aware of the facts in order to justify his disregard. Detailed data on minimum distances recommended for the separation between transmitters of various types and detonator circuits are given in reference 43. If the investigator considers that there is a possibility that initiation by radio frequency radiation has occurred or if he wished to eliminate the possibility, he should carry out the following courses of action. He should recreate the conditions, using a detonator enclosed in a protective box in case it fires, and determine whether or not it fires. If it does, then clearly radio frequency radiation is a possible cause of the initiation. If it does not, he should call in an appropriate radio expert who can make field measurements on the explosion site and determine whether the field strength and aerial configuration are such that sufficient power could be induced into the circuit to fire the detonator.

If these show that the induced power could have approached that required to operate a detonator then the possibility that it did operate the actual one cannot be discounted. If the induced power was below this level, initiation by radio frequency radiation can be discounted.

The accidental functioning of military devices by radio frequency radiation can likewise be discounted since they are normally designed so as to safeguard them against this hazard.

OTHER MECHANISMS

While the various methods discussed above include virtually all the mechanisms for initiation ever likely to be encountered by an explosion investigator, he should nevertheless keep an open mind on the possibility of encountering the highly unusual. This may be illustrated by the case (1951) of an explosion which occurred when gas oil was being pumped ashore from a tanker. Part of the report was as follows:

> It is known that when tankers discharge different products they frequently clear the manifolds by pumping sea water through them to prevent contamination. Accordingly the Company had water bottoms in their gas oil storage tanks at Avonmouth. It was also stated that there was a good deal of corrosion of the tanks where the water bottom was situated. In view of this, and also of the fact that sewage might be discharged into the river Avon, it appeared that the water bottom of shore tank No. 13 might have contained sulphate-reducing bacteria, and these organisms may have produced some iron sulphide which might have ignited spontaneously when brought into contact with air. The contents of shore tank No. 13 were being disturbed by Hyett whilst dipping the tank.
>
> It was not possible to obtain a sample from the water bottom of shore tank No. 13 after the accident, but samples were obtained from shore tanks Nos. 18 and 30. Both these shore tanks were used for the storage of gas oil and the water bottoms in these two tanks would be comparable with that in shore tank No. 13. These samples were submitted to the Chemical Research Laboratory, Teddington, for examination, and sulphate-reducing bacteria were found to be present in the water bottom obtained from shore tank No. 30. It is possible that pyrophoric iron sulphide may have been present in shore tank No. 13 and glowing iron sulphide in this tank may have caused the ignition.

The possibilities of bacterially induced initiation can be further illustrated by another reaction. Some pyrotechnic compositions consist of barium chlorate and a suitable fuel bound with gum arabic. It has been repeatedly observed that, if a stale gum arabic solution is used, spontaneous ignition occurs (44). This has been found to be due to bacterial action in the gum arabic solution leading to the formation of acetic acid which acts as a trigger for chlorate/fuel reaction.

SPONTANEOUS EXPLOSION

When an explosion is caused deliberately some mechanism for initiation will have been provided. When an explosion occurs accidently a recognisable initiation mechanism will normally be found. In a very small proportion of cases, however, the explosion will have occurred without the application of any external stimulus. This phenomenon is known as spontaneous explosion.

Some explosives are well known to be liable to spontaneous explosion. Perhaps the best known of these is the mixture of a chlorate and sulphur. Many accidents due to the spontaneous explosion of compositions containing these ingredients occurred in the United Kingdom during the nineteenth century, ranging from the destruction of Mme Coton's firework factory in London in 1859 to one (1893) in which a man was travelling on the Manchester, Sheffield and Lincolnshire railway. He was conveying a quantity of such a composition in a leather bag. This was placed on the middle seat of a first class compartment and the contents exploded spontaneously. As a result of these, and many other incidents, Order in Council No. 15 was made by Queen Victoria on 30 April 1894 which effectively banned the use of these compositions. The restriction covered not only compositions containing the two ingredients but also manufactured devices in which compositions containing chlorate were in contact with compositions containing sulphur, since these also had been found to be liable to spontaneous explosion. Similar restrictions are in force in other countries.

The spontaneous explosion of chlorate sulphur mixtures is probably due to the following reactions (45). Air oxidation of the sulphur causes the formation of thionic acids which accumulate until a concentration is reached at which decomposition occurs:

$$H_2S_nO_6 \rightarrow H_2SO_4 + SO_2 + (n-2)S \tag{1}$$

The sulphur dioxide then reacts with the moist chlorate to produce chlorine dioxide:

$$SO_2 + 2KClO_3 \rightarrow 2ClO_2 + K_2SO_4 \tag{2}$$

The chlorine dioxide so produced reacts with sulphur to produce sulphur dioxide:

$$2ClO_2 + 4S \rightarrow 2SO_2 + S_2Cl_2 \tag{3}$$

Reaction (1) acts as a triggering reaction for reaction (2) and reactions (2) and (3) together constitute a chain reaction since less sulphur dioxide is consumed than is produced. The net energy and gas production leads to explosion. Carbon has been found to inhibit the reaction and sulphur dioxide to accelerate it.

Another well-known cause of spontaneous explosion is acidity, notably in explosives based on nitrocellulose and nitroglycerine. Acidity in these explosives causes instability resulting in exothermic decomposition. This can lead to sufficient self heating to bring the explosive to its explosion temperature. This phenomenon led to the realisation of the need for chemical stability tests and the consequent introduction of the Abel Heat Test and many others. The surveillance given to professionally manufactured explosives of these types nowadays ensures that the probability of spontaneous explosion because of chemical instability is negligible. Amateur experimenters and manufacturers, however, do not take the same care in purifying their products and, needless to say, do not subject them to stability tests. In consequence, the possibility of the spontaneous explosion of such explosives cannot be discounted.

Acid has also been responsible for spontaneous explosion in other cases. The explosion of lead azide when brought into contact with sulphuric acid has already been noted. Another example is the explosion (1900) of a percussion cap composition containing mercury fulminate, antimony sulphide and potassium chlorate. Acidity, due to sulphuric acid, was found in the antimony sulphide and the investigator having carried out a number of experiments concluded: '. . . it is highly probable that, if kept in bulk under conditions favourable to the retention of heat, it would ultimately explode spontaneously'.

Most chemical reactions increase in rate with increasing temperature. An explosive whose stability is such that the decomposition rate is normally negligible may develop a significant one if kept in conditions of high temperature. At the same time, a rate of heat loss which is normally sufficient to dissipate the heat liberated may be inadequate to dissipate the greatly increased heat output. In consequence self heating to explosion temperature may occur. Well-known examples of this phenomenon are explosions which occur as a consequence of explosives being subjected to a hot sun or being in contact with warm surfaces. A less usual instance occurred (1935) in a building on a fireworks factory. A fire started in the evening after the factory was closed. It was established that spontaneous ignition had occurred in the roof of the building. The building was very old and in the roof there was a collection of birds' nests impregnated with explosives dust. On the day previously there had been heavy rain followed by great heat. Such conditions are favourable for causing spontaneous heating and hence, where explosive is present, explosion.

There are a number of reported cases in which lead azide has apparently exploded spontaneously. Investigation has indicated that this phenomenon is associated with the formation of very large crystals. Such explosions are unlikely to occur nowadays in the course of professional manufacture or with the products of such processes since appropriate controls are applied. Amateur experimenters and manufacturers, however, produce a cruder product and the possibility of a large crystal spontaneous explosion cannot be discounted where lead azide from such sources is involved.

Aluminium is readily oxidised but the adherent oxide film acts as a protection against further oxidation. If, however, the oxide film is destroyed, for example in alkaline conditions, and the aluminium is in powdered form, the heat generated by further oxidation may be sufficient to cause ignition of a composition of which the aluminium is a component. Thus spontaneous ignition occurred (1932) in a wet mixture of barium nitrate, potassium nitrate, aluminium, dextrine and starch. Investigation showed that the tendency to spontaneous ignition could be prevented by the addition of a small proportion of boric acid to the composition. In a more recent occurrence (1968) of a similar nature, pressed stars of a composition including barium nitrate, potassium perchlorate and aluminium ignited spontaneously in an expense magazine during warm weather.

Apart from systems well known to possess the property of spontaneous explosion, this phenomenon is observed from time to time in others. For example (1954) an explosion in a Tetryl waste acid line shattered over 200 m of steel pipe causing the death of three men. There was extensive missile and blast damage to buildings. The pipeline concerned had not been used for several years and the investigators concluded that there may have been spontaneous decomposition of a layer deposit of Tetryl. This had possibly been contaminated with sensitive by-products associated with iron or its oxides. There was no evidence of any part of the line having been struck an initiatory blow or having been heated externally, nor had there been any recent introduction of waste acid. From measurements of the deposit inside undisintegrated sections of pipe it was estimated that over 100 kg explosive detonated.

While spontaneous explosions can and do occur, it must be emphasised that they are rare and such as are observed are mainly associated with one of the well-known systems discussed above. While, therefore, the investigator should not discount the possibility of spontaneous explosion, he should only adopt this as an explanation for the ignition after exhaustive consideration of other causes. He should guard against a too facile assumption of spontaneous explosion as an alternative to a detailed and, perhaps, time consuming investigation into the full range of potential initiation mechanisms.

When any particular initiation mechanism is postulated as that responsible for the explosion under investigation, the plausibility of the hypothesis can be strengthened if an experiment is conducted which demonstrates that the explosive involved can in fact be initiated by this means. The obtaining of such confirmatory evidence for spontaneous explosion is very difficult since, as is shown by the rarity of the phenomenon, the exact conditions required to produce it seldom occur and are hence difficult to determine and reproduce. Even with such a well-known example as compositions containing chlorate and sulphur the controlled production of spontaneous explosion can normally only be achieved at elevated temperatures. It is important, therefore, to appreciate that, if an investigator postulates the occurrence of spontaneous explosion, then it is not necessarily a valid criticism of his conclusion to produce evidence that neither he nor his critic have been able to demonstrate experimentally the spontaneous explosion of the composition concerned.

OPERATING MECHANISMS

In cases where an explosion has been deliberately caused, evidence as to the means of initiation may be obtained, as has already been indicated, by the recovery of identifiable fragments of detonators or igniters. In such cases, however, evidence of the means of initiation may also be obtained by the recovery of identifiable fragments of the mechanisms used to operate the detonator or igniter. These mechanisms can be broadly classified as of three types: *i.e.* (1) mechanical; (2) igniferous; and (3) electrical.

Mechanical operating mechanisms depend on the principle of a striker arranged to impinge on a detonator or percussion cap. The most usual arrangement is to use a spring loaded striker with a release mechanism based on the sear and bent principle, or on the withdrawal of a retaining pin, or on the fracture of a retaining wire.

Igniferous operating mechanisms depend on the principle of the production of a flame. This is usually achieved by the application of friction to a friction sensitive composition, *e.g.* a matchhead and brassard, or by a chemical device based on a reaction such as that between a chlorate and concentrated sulphuric acid. The flame so produced may be used to ignite the main composition directly, or to operate a plain detonator, or to ignite a fuse which then transmits the flame to the composition or detonator.

Electrical operating mechanisms depend on the principle of applying an electric current to an electric detonator or igniter. They, therefore, incorporate a battery, or other source of electricity, a switch or switches and appropriate wiring. The switch may be direct, operating by push, pull, disturbance, radio control or other stimulus or may be time controlled by a clockwork or other mechanism.

Within these broad classifications, a very large number of variants of detail are possible and do occur (11, 12, 13, 14, 15). It is essential, therefore, that the debris from the scene be searched thoroughly, preferably under laboratory conditions, and all fragments not clearly indigenous to the scene set aside for further consideration. These should then be examined by the investigator in the light of the references quoted and of experience. In examining each fragment the investigator must ask three questions:

1. Is it recognisable as part of a manufactured initiating device?
2. Is it recognisable as part of a home-made version of a manufactured initiating device?

If the answer to either of these questions is positive then the fragment should be regarded as providing significant evidence. If, however, the answer is negative to both questions a third must be asked:

3. Is it possible to envisage the fragment as being part of an initiating mechanism?

If the answer to this question is positive, the fragment should be regarded as being of potential significance. At the end of the examination it may be found that such fragments may be clearly associated with those of positive significance and help to create a complete reconstruction of the initiation mechanism. In some cases no fragments of positive significance will have been identified. Sometimes, however, in such cases a number of fragments of potential significance will have been found and these taken together may be seen clearly to constitute an initiation mechanism. If this is not so, the significance of such fragments must remain potential and the only conclusion which can be made is that they may have constituted part of the initiation mechanism.

If at the end of the examination no positive answers have been given to any of the questions for any fragments these should not be discarded. It is possible that other evidence from the scene, or from the premises, or from the person of a suspect may suggest a possible initiation mechanism. Re-examination of the fragments may then reveal a new significance in some of them. Thus, for example, if further evidence suggests the possibility that a spring clothes peg may have been used as the basis for a time delay switch, then small fragments of wood can assume a significance which they would not otherwise have. All such fragments would then be subjected to detailed examination to determine whether or not they could have been derived from such a device.

Chapter 7

EXPLOSIONS IN MOVING VEHICLES

SPECIAL PROBLEMS

Most explosions occur in some fixed location so that, although by its very nature an explosion scatters the available evidence, the area over which evidence may be found is relatively limited. Occasionally, however, an explosion occurs in a moving vehicle and this can present problems of investigation peculiar to this type of incident. One of these is that the evidence is liable to be scattered much more widely. Another is that much evidence may be lost through scattering into inaccessible places, as for example when an aircraft sinks into deep ocean water.

SPACECRAFT

Wherever man takes his technology he will also take the potentialities of explosion. It was inevitable, therefore, that this would be numbered among the hazards when space exploration began. Fortunately there has been so far only one such incident, the explosion in the Apollo 13 craft when on course for the Moon. This famous incident illustrates the problems likely to face future explosion investigators. In such circumstances direct examination of debris and damage is nearly impossible. This applies not only at the immediate time of the explosion but also later, since the return to Earth of the damaged vehicle is unlikely. This may be due to the fact that the explosion occurred, as in Apollo 13, in a part of the vehicle which is not returnable in any case, or to the fact that the explosion may damage a returnable part to the extent that its return becomes impossible. Investigation, therefore, must be carried out remotely from data supplied by the crew, if they are still in a position to supply it, or from monitoring of information received at the control base.

The identification of the cause of such an explosion becomes,

162

therefore, a process of formulating hypotheses and testing them for consistency with the available data. Such an investigation must be carried out with the utmost urgency since it will be the first stage in any attempts which may be possible for the rescue of the crew. Such urgency will not be so great in the case of unmanned craft but even here speedy investigation is necessary since the explosion may have left the monitoring broadcast system in a precarious state.

Naturally, investigation of this type of explosion will not be the province of the general explosion investigator. The speed with which answers will be required means that only people already fully conversant with the intricate systems of the craft can work on the problem. The general investigator may nevertheless have a part to play especially if the explosion is not a mechanical one, as in Apollo 13, but a malfunction of one of the explosive devices carried aboard such craft. It would be a wise precaution if the mission control for any space flight were to have an experienced explosion investigator either standing by or readily available in an emergency.

AIRCRAFT

The destruction of aircraft by explosives, apart from normal acts of war, is no new development. Apparently, the earliest recorded incident occurred in 1905. In that year an aeronaut made a balloon ascent at Grenville, Ohio. He took up with him eight cartridges of dynamite with the intention of showing how such explosive charges could be dropped in time of war. He was probably preparing a charge, when an explosion occurred and he was blown to pieces in mid-air.

This was clearly an accident but in recent decades there have been many explosions in passenger aircraft due to sabotage. So far as is known between the years 1946 and 1972, 35 aircraft were damaged or destroyed in flight by means of explosive devices. This figure can be regarded as conservative since it does not include unconfirmed cases or cases of aircraft missing in suspicious circumstances.

In these instances 543 passengers and crew lost their lives and 18 aircraft were totally destroyed. Some 19 different types of aircraft were involved and the incidents occurred in 21 different countries. There can be little doubt that the total would have been greater but for increased security measures at airports.

When, as the result of accident or sabotage, an aircraft is lost in flight a major problem which faces the investigator is that of locating the debris. If a plane breaks up in the air parts of the structure, baggage and passengers will be strewn approximately along the flight path. In cases where the breakup occurred at relatively low altitude the debris may be confined to a distance of a few kilometres. Where breakup occurs at normal cruising altitudes the spread may be much greater and a case is on record where debris was found over 160 km distance from the main wreckage. Apart from the normal problems of searching such a large area, recovery can be complicated by the hostility of the terrain or of its inhabitants. Thus one aircraft, whose loss was due to an explosive device, broke up and the debris was scattered in an area of jungle in which a war was being fought.

When an aircraft is lost over the sea further difficulties arise. Some of the wreckage will float but, by the time the scene is reached, this may have been carried considerable distances by the wind and by ocean currents. It is important, therefore, to study the local conditions at the time of the incident and from these estimate the optimum areas to be searched for floating debris. The bulk of the debris will sink. If the incident occurred over shallow seas this may be recoverable; if over the deeper ocean, probably it will not.

In investigating an aircraft accident it is important to recognise that damage very similar to that produced by explosive devices can occur from other causes. The mechanical failure and subsequent disintegration of a high-speed turbine disc can produce a noise which would be reported as an explosion. Pieces of metal could then penetrate the wing and fuselage structure producing effects not unlike those which would be caused by explosively projected fragments. Further damage to the structure will occur under the forces of disintegration in the air and on impact with the ground and this too can resemble some explosively produced damage. A lightning strike can also create local explosive type damage, particularly if the aircraft structural electrical bonding is faulty. Normally such lightning strikes will not cause extensive or catastrophic damage, but fire and explosion of fuel tanks is a possibility if low flash point fuel is in use and vented near the wing tips.

The flight data recorder can be a useful tool for the investigator. It will not show directly that a bomb has exploded in the aircraft but it will show the circumstances prevailing immediately prior to the disaster. This will normally allow a number of possibilities to be eliminated. If all the recorded parameters cease abruptly following an apparently smooth and normal flight with the 'g' record diverging suddenly off the plus and minus scales, this would indicate a violent and sudden disaster and would be consistent with an explosion. The cockpit voice recorder and the R/T tape may also provide useful information. Unfortunately these recorders, although designed to be crash-proof, may not always be recovered, particularly if the incident occurred over deep water.

In examining the available debris for evidence of an explosion the investigator should apply the normal principles of damage investigation discussed in Chapter 4. Although the determination of the explosion centre is an important aspect of investigation it will often be impossible in cases involving aircraft. If the explosion does not lead to total disaster, so that the plane can be landed, the normal techniques for determining the explosion centre can be applied. Where, however, substantial disintegration takes place, often with incomplete recovery of debris, such techniques cannot be used. In such cases the most informative approach is to study fragments.

The various diagnostic features which can be used to identify both primary and secondary fragments have been considered in detail in Chapter 4. Care should be taken to observe the warning that the characteristic features of secondary fragments become less pronounced the further away the charge was from the metal that was fragmented. This is particularly pertinent in aircraft crashes since considerable forces are involved and fragments similar to some types of secondary fragments from explosions can be generated by non-explosive forces. Thus a fragment with spike toothed edges has been observed to have been due to a control cable ripping through metal.

In some cases the direction of penetration of fragments may be observable on portions of the debris. If the original locations of these portions can be identified the site of the explosion centre can be found by projecting the directions backwards.

Diagnostic fragments which are derived from an initiating control mechanism are highly conclusive. Small, but identifiable, fragments of this kind may be found embedded in parts of the structure, in furnishings and in bodies, but, like all fragments in an air crash, only the most diligent and systematic search is likely to reveal them. Two aspects of such fragments are peculiar to aircraft cases. The main structure of aircraft is made almost entirely from non-ferrous metal and so the finding of ferrous metal fragments provides a strong indication that they are foreign to the scene.

Attacks on aircraft provide a further possibility to the initiation operating mechanisms discussed in Chapter 6. The decrease in pressure as the aircraft gains height can be used to operate a pressure switch which fires the charge; such devices have been recorded. The technique can also be adapted to come into operation by the pressure increase as the plane descends at its destination.

Chemical identification of traces of explosives is not generally successful in aircraft cases. Due to time lapse, weathering, fire, immersion in water, handling and other causes such traces as were present initially are frequently lost. Nevertheless, the taking of swabs from likely sites should not be neglected.

A further source of information in an air crash is the injuries to people. Pathological examination for blast effects on the eardrums and lungs, unusual or gross traumatic injuries not normally associated with an aircraft crash impact and examination of skin tissue for hot penetrations can all provide valuable diagnostic evidence. Every effort must be made to have the dead and, as far as possible, the injured X-rayed for the detection of buried particles. Any that are located should be recovered if possible. To this end the explosion investigator should maintain close collaboration with his medical counterparts. Owing to the differences throughout the world in the law relating to dead bodies considerable difficulties may be encountered in this part of the investigation and the full co-operation of the local legal and police authorities must be sought. It is essential that they be made aware of the reasons for any request and that the requests themselves should be confined to those clearly having a bearing on the investigation, otherwise they may meet with little sympathy.

RAIL AND ROAD VEHICLES

The problem of scatter of debris, which is acute in aircraft cases, is also encountered to a lesser extent in cases where explosions involve road and rail vehicles. The scatter is, however, less extreme and a more manageable area is involved. Even so, small but important fragments may be lost in such places as among the ballast on a railway track or in wet ditches beside tracks and roads. Small items may also be overlooked since the investigator is likely to be under pressure from the appropriate authorities anxious to restore communications along the rail or road.

A special situation in direction/damage determination arises when an attack is made on a moving surface vehicle. In this case, part of the scene remains stationary while another part moves away. This can lead to difficulties in deciding where the vehicle was relative to the explosive charge or the whereabouts of the explosive charge. An example of the former occurred when an attack was made on a train on the London underground during the Fenian outrages in 1883. After examination of the damage to the train and on the track, it was possible to establish the explosion centre for each and, by causing these to coincide, the position of the train at the time of the explosion was established. An example of the latter occurred when an explosion damaged a train on a London suburban line. The explosion broke glass in the windows of the train and this was found beside the track. Knowing the height of the windows above the track and the speed of the train, it was possible to calculate how far the train had travelled between the explosion and the point where the glass lay. By measuring backwards from the glass the explosion centre was found. This was beside a brick pier supporting a bridge. The correctness of the finding was confirmed by the observation that the edge of the pier formed a vertical screen for blast and fragments and that the fragments damage pattern on the train was characterised by a sharp vertical leading edge. A search of the railway bank in the vicinity led to the discovery of small fragments of the explosive device.

Explosions in vehicles give rise to problems of chemical identification. Many of the portions of debris will be covered with oil and dirt and these may underlie or overlie any residues which may be present. Swabbing or washing the surfaces will produce a sample for analysis which will contain a great many impurities. The problems engendered and possible techniques for overcoming them are discussed in Chapter 5.

SHIPS AND OTHER MARINE CRAFT

The special problems encountered when investigating explosions on ships and other marine craft are essentially the same as those for rail and road vehicles. Owing to the large size of a ship it is likely that significant debris will, to a greater extent, be retained within the structure. However, any fragments blown overboard are unlikely to be recoverable if the vessel is at sea. If the explosion occurs when the vessel is docked some fragments may be recoverable from the dockside.

Chapter 8

INJURY TO PERSONS

THE STUDY OF INJURIES

The study of injuries caused to persons by the effects of an explosion may be regarded as a special case of the observation and assessment of damage. The status of special case is justified not only by the difference between inanimate matter and living organisms but also by the fact that the resilience of the human body leads sometimes to unexpected resistance to damage. The latter point can be illustrated by four cases drawn from the last quarter of the nineteenth century.

A woman attempted to commit suicide (1876) by blowing herself up with gunpowder. The resultant explosion demolished the building in which the attempt was made but the woman herself was recovered alive from the debris.

A man had 700 g of dynamite (1881) together with detonators in his pocket. He placed a lighted pipe into the pocket and an explosion ensued. The man was severely injured but not killed and the investigator contrasted this with an accident with a similar quantity of dynamite in which four men were killed and six injured.

A quantity of a mixture of potassium chlorate and sulphur exploded (LXVII) in an iron closed mortar. A youth was blown up to the ceiling and his body made a hole in it. Though he subsequently died, he was still alive when found.

An explosion occurred in a gunpowder press house (1900) in which two men were working. One man was blown to pieces and only a few fragments of his body were recovered. The other was blown over some trees over 100 m away. Although dead, his body was unmutilated.

The types of injuries caused to persons by the effects of explosions can conveniently be considered as being of two types. The first consists of those injuries from which evidence about the particular explosion may be deduced. This includes deductions of blast pressures from injuries, deductions from the penetration of the human body by fragments and deductions from the positions of human remains. The second type consists of special injuries generally indicative of involvement in an explosion and which the investigator can expect to encounter in the course of his work. This includes injuries by toxic gaseous explosion products, the psychological effects of involvements in an explosion and the removal of clothing.

In addition, two other topics which are associated with injuries to persons merit consideration. Those are suicide and injuries caused indirectly by an explosion.

DEDUCTIONS OF BLAST PRESSURES FROM INJURIES

The human body contains cavities, notably the ears and lungs, which are separated from the outside by structural features which are effectively diaphragms. When a person is subjected to blast pressures these features act as pressure gauges and observation of the damage done can provide estimates of the pressures to which the body was subjected.

Three types of ear injury can be distinguished. At the lowest level of pressure there can be partial loss of hearing of high frequency sounds without rupture of the eardrum. The hearing loss is usually temporary and recovery is normally complete within a few days. At a higher level of pressure there is partial or total loss of hearing as a result of eardrum rupture. This hearing loss is also normally temporary, pending healing of the ruptured eardrum. At greater pressures permanent loss of hearing occurs owing to the dislocation or fracture of the bones of the middle ear or even from damage to the inner ear.

In order to cause lung injury it is necessary for the blast wave to strike the chest. Injury then occurs primarily as a result of the pressure exerted on the chest wall and not normally from the blast passing into the lungs via the mouth, nose, larynx and bronchi. When the blast wave strikes the chest wall this is displaced inwards and blood and other body fluids are driven into portions of the lungs which normally contain only air. As a result haemorrhage occurs. In addition, the movement of the chest wall both inwards and outwards leads to rupture of lung tissue and air is then forced into the portions of the lungs carrying fluid. Air bubbles can then be carried through the bloodstream and interfere with the working of vital organs such as the brain and heart and so cause death.

An individual's ability to withstand the effects of blast may vary with the pressure, its duration, the orientation and position of the person relative to the direction of travel of the blast and with their personal anatomical characteristics. As a result, divergent values have been quoted for the pressures required to produce various forms of injury. It is, therefore, only possible to give values which must be regarded as approximate in any given situation. Some useful figures applicable to blast pressures from condensed explosions are given in Table 8.1.

TABLE 8.1

Effect	Pressure kNm^{-2}
Slight chance of eardrum rupture	30
50% chance of eardrum rupture	100
Slight chance of lung damage	200–300
Severe chance of lung damage	500
Slight chance of death	700–800
50% chance of death	900–1200
Death almost certain	1400–1700

If the observed injury is eardrum rupture but no lung damage the pressure was probably 100–200 kNm^{-2} with the possibility of lower pressures down to about 30 kNm^{-2}. If the injury was severe, but not fatal, lung damage the pressure was probably of the order of 500 kNm^{-2}. If the injury was death with eardrum rupture and severe lung damage, the pressure was probably in excess of 1,000 kNm^{-2} with the possibility of lower pressures down to about 700 kNm^{-2}.

These values are applicable only to explosions due to condensed explosives. They involve the assumption that the duration of the pressure pulse is the same for all such explosives. Such an assumption is inaccurate but its adoption for this particular purpose will not lead to any great errors. Care should be taken, however, not to extend the assumption to other circumstances. Thus, with nuclear explosions where longer durations occur, the pressure required to produce a 50% chance of death is only about 350 kNm^{-2} (46).

It must be remembered that, in interpreting estimates of blast pressure from the observation of injuries to persons, due account must be taken of any enhancement or attenuation of pressure due to the immediate surroundings. The values obtained can, however, provide useful additional data for the pressure distribution diagram.

PENETRATION OF BODIES BY FRAGMENTS

Whenever an explosion produces fragment projection, people in the vicinity may be hit. Fragments penetrating the body are liable to injure vital organs and so can be a cause of death additional to the effects of blast. There are many such cases on record involving military munitions, improvised explosive devices, ill-considered experiments and at least one where the explosion was a mechanical one. This (1906) concerned a boy who dropped an empty ginger beer bottle on to a full one. The latter exploded and a piece of glass severed the boy's jugular vein.

In general, the occurrence of death by these means is not an observation which assists the investigator. Some other aspects of fragment penetration into bodies can, however, be useful on some occasions. Three such circumstances can be distinguished:

1. A body can act as a trap for fragments which can then be recovered for examination.

2. The direction of penetration of the fragments can indicate how the person was orientated in respect of the explosive charge. The value of this information will be discussed in the next section.

3. The existence of fragment penetration can provide evidence that an explosion had actually occurred. This may be illustrated by part of the investigation into the loss of the Comet B aircraft G-ARCO on 12 October 1967 (47). One male body was found to be peppered with minute dark specks on the upper part. The lesions in the skin showed puncture wounds with very definite evidence of burning. An X-ray photograph of the thorax was obtained and minute opaque fragments were observed. No more detailed examination was possible owing to the lack of refrigeration facilities. However, it was later found possible to recover one of the fragments from a pathology specimen and microscopic examination established that it had characteristics indicating that it originated from an explosion. This evidence agreed with other observations which also indicated that the loss of the aircraft was due to the detonation of an explosive device.

DEDUCTIONS FROM THE POSITION OF
HUMAN REMAINS

When a person is sufficienty near to the seat of an explosion his body, either whole or dismembered, will be projected by the blast wave. Observations of where the body is found in relation to the established explosion centre will enable the investigator to determine where the person was at the time of the explosion. Sometimes detailed study of the nature and location of damage to the body or of fragment penetration can help to determine the orientation of the person with respect to the explosion centre. Observations of this type can assist the investigator in establishing the sequence of events and highlight other significant evidence for determining possible causes of the explosion. This may be illustrated by the following three cases:

1. In an explosion in 1881 (XXXIV) which involved dynamite, bodies were found some way from the seat of the explosion. They were, however, but little dismembered and it was possible, therefore, to establish that the persons had run some way before the explosion occurred. It was clear, therefore, that the explosion was due to some foreseeable but unpreventable cause.

2. An explosion in 1887 (LXXVIII) involved about 3,450 kg of gunpowder in a glazing house. One man was blown to fragments, the largest piece not exceeding 100 g. All the fragments were found between 50 and 300 m to the north-east. Pieces of the machinery, however, were projected to the south-west, while the woodwork of the building went in all directions. This established his orientation in respect of the machinery and subsequent medical examination showed that the flesh on the back was torn and blackened. It was evident, therefore, that he was standing with his back to the machinery and not doing anything to it when the explosion occurred.

3. In 1940 an explosion occurred during the mixing of a TNT/ammonium nitrate/aluminium explosive which caused the death of a man who was in the mixing house at the time. The charge was being mixed in an edge runner mill and was due to be removed. It was concluded, however, that the deceased had not commenced this operation since the nature of his injuries and the position of the body indicated that, at the time of the explosion, he was between the machine and the door. It was evident that the explosion was initiated

by some defect in the machine and not by some action taken by the man. Other evidence supported this conclusion.

INJURIES BY TOXIC GASEOUS EXPLOSION COMPONENTS AND PRODUCTS

Injuries to people, sometimes fatal, can occur from effects other than blast and fragment projection. One, which the investigator must expect to encounter from time to time, is asphyxiation or narcosis, sometimes fatal, produced by exposure to explosion products or dispersed phase explosives.

The fatal inhalation of gaseous explosion products, in particular nitrogen dioxide, was formerly much commoner than at the present time. This is because of the attention paid by manufacturers to the production of explosives producing the minimum of harmful products. The testing of explosives for this property has been referred to in Chapter 2. The production of fumes by gunpowder and similar compositions used in fireworks cannot, however, be prevented. In consequence there is a long history of asphyxiation of persons involved in accidental fires involving gunpowder or fireworks when the fires have occurred indoors. Thus, for example (1970), a shopkeeper died from carbon monoxide poisoning whilst fighting a fire involving fireworks in his shop. The danger is not entirely absent outdoors as is illustrated by the Loch Fyne disaster of 1886, one of the classic cases in the history of explosions (LXXIV).

The Loch Fyne quarry was a deep one with the working face visible from the sea. It was decided to carry out a blast with a very large charge consisting of about 6,000 kg of gunpowder. Many people were given the chance to witness the spectacle from a boat which then landed them near the quarry mouth. After the smoke had cleared many entered the quarry to view the effects of the explosion. A number of people in the crowd started to collapse and all retreated, bearing the collapsed people with them. In all, seven people were found to be dead as the result of asphyxiation by carbon dioxide which had flowed out from the broken rock and had formed a layer on the quarry floor, somewhat in the manner of the Grotto des Chiens. The case is not unique.

The fatal ingestion of solid explosion products is also known.

After an accidental explosion at a mercury fulminate factory in Alderney (1903) the investigator wrote:

'In my opinion by far the most serious aspect of explosion is the consequent destruction of the cattle by mercurial poisoning, but I cannot hold Messrs Helcke Brothers to blame for not anticipating this damage in as much as I must admit that it is not one which I myself would have taken into account'.

When an explosion occurs in a building and a body is found among the wreckage the investigator must bear in mind that death may not have occurred as a result of the explosion. This is particularly the case where a gas explosion has occurred on domestic premises. At least three causes for death prior to an explosion can be recognised:

1. In cases of suicide by town gas the person may have died from carbon monoxide poisoning before accidental ignition of the gas/air mixture.

2. It has been known for a person to die from heart failure while attempting to light a gas appliance, for example with a view to making a hot drink because of feeling unwell. The escaping gas can then produce an explosive gas/air mixture which may subsequently accidently ignite with a resultant explosion.

3. It must never be forgotten that an attempt may be made to disguise murder as suicide by staging a gas explosion in the hope that this will be regarded as the cause of death.

In the first of these circumstances carbon monoxide in the form of carboxyhaemoglobin will be found in the blood. In the other two there are two situations to be considered. In neither will there be any carbon monoxide in the blood. If the gas supply contained carbon monoxide then it will be clear that death occurred prior to the gas escape. If the gas supply did not contain carbon monoxide then medical or toxicological evidence will be required to determine whether either possibility is the truth.

It is important to remember that carbon monoxide in the blood can be derived from a number of sources. It represents about 10-20% of town gas, as opposed to natural gas which contains none. It forms up to 6% of internal combustion engine exhaust gases and is produced in small quantities when any carbonaceous fuel is burned with an insufficient supply of air. This can occur when a heater burns in an enclosed space so that the oxygen supply becomes depleted or when a combustible solid smoulders.

The toxicity of air containing carbon monoxide is a function of several variables. It depends on the physiological make-up of the individual, the carbon monoxide concentration and the length of time it is breathed. Except for the extremes of very low and very high concentration, the relationship:

concentration × time of exposure = constant

holds good for any given degree of poisoning. If the time is expressed in hours and the concentration in parts per million then the lethal threshold is represented by a value of about 2,000 for the constant. Low concentrations are breathable almost indefinitely. If no more than 10% of the available haemoglobin is converted to carboxy-haemoglobin there will be little effect on a fit person and amounts such as this may be observed in heavy smokers. Conversion proportions above this will be progressively more dangerous, though healthy, young adults can survive values in excess of 50%.

Carbon monoxide is not the only gaseous substance associated with an explosion which may be detected in the body of a victim. Some gases, such as hydrogen sulphide, produce characteristic physiological effects. Others may be found by examination of the body cavities. If samples of blood, brain or lungs are stored in a closed vessel then ingested or inhaled gases can be detected by gas chromatography in the air above the sample.

In view of these possibilities it is essential that the explosion investigator should be furnished with the details of the post-mortem examination at the earliest possible moment.

PSYCHOLOGICAL EFFECTS OF INVOLVEMENT IN AN EXPLOSION

The best known psychological effect of involvement in an explosion is retroactive amnesia. In many cases, people who have been close to explosions but have survived them, have found that their memory of the event has been completely lost. This loss of memory can extend backwards in time to the events leading up to the explosion. Sometimes the memory returns after an interval but at other times the loss is permanent. This phenomenon is of particular hindrance to the investigator who may find that the one witness who could supply first-hand evidence is quite unable to do so. This phenomenon and various pseudo forms of it will be considered further in Chapter 10.

An unexpected psychological reaction to an exposion was noted in the explosion at Ronan Point (Chapter 4). No less than four tenants in the high-rise block reacted to the explosion, noises of collapse and rocking of the building by starting to make a cup of tea. For example, one witness stated that:

> 'Just before 6 a.m. I heard a terrific explosion. I looked out of the front door and then went out on the balcony on the north side of the block. I saw a white fog, or what looked like cement dust. I started to make a cup of tea and then a police sergeant came to the door and told me to get out.'

there appears to be no data at present available to determine whether this is a peculiarly English reaction to such a situation.

THE REMOVAL OF CLOTHING

It is well known that, in aircraft accidents, persons falling from a considerable height may often, but not invariably, be stripped of their clothing. A similar effect can occur to persons involved in explosions. Sometimes bodies are found which are completely naked and there is at least one instance on record (Stowmarket, 1871) in which a man was stripped of his clothing but was otherwise uninjured.

This makes deductions from the presence or absence of clothing of very uncertain value. Thus if, after a factory explosion, a man's body is found without protective clothes on, it is not correct to deduce automatically that the explosion may have arisen from some consequence of the man failing to wear his special clothing. It will be necessary for the investigator to consider whether there is any evidence, such as the presence or absence of scorch marks, to indicate whether or not the clothing was being worn at the time of the explosion.

SUICIDE

When an explosion results in a single fatality, the investigator must always be alert to the possibility that the case is one of successful suicide rather than accident or murder. A common method of committing suicide by the use of explosives is for the person to shoot themselves using a pistol, revolver, shotgun or even rifle. There is, however, a long history of suicide by the direct use of explosives. Cases have occurred where the means was the ignition of gunpowder or blasting explosive placed in the mouth, or the operation of a detonator placed in the ear. Suicidally minded persons have also used gunpowder, high explosive charges or military grenades held near to the body. The methods employed are as diverse as the imaginings of disordered minds can make them.

The possibility of suicide should not be overlooked in cases of multiple deaths. Some cases of aircraft sabotage may have been due to this cause, though the extension of proof from that of sabotage to suicide is generally not possible. There are on record, however, some instances in which such an intention was proved because the attempt failed. Thus, in 1958 a man planned his own death by putting a bomb in his luggage so that relatives could collect insurance money. The bomb exploded in a parked aircraft and killed a number of the airport employees. The man himself was arrested after a safe flight; safe because his luggage had accidentally been loaded into the wrong aircraft.

Multiple suicide by explosives for ethical reasons has also been known (1884):

> The King of Alaha being attacked by a Mohammedan force and, finding resistance impossible, assembled his family and principal officers and, after addressing them and intimating his determination never to accept Mohammedanism, and inviting those who did not agree with him to leave, he applied a light to a large quantity of gunpowder which had been collected for the purpose and blew the palace and all those who were in it to pieces.

INDIRECT INJURIES

Cases have been known in which explosions have caused fatalities due to effects other than the direct ones such as blast, fragments and asphyxiation. Such indirect injuries are not normally the concern of the explosion investigator as they do not contribute to the identification of the cause of the explosion. Since, however, they are a consequence of the explosion the investigator is always liable subsequently to be drawn in to any legal enquiry as to the cause of death. He should be aware of this possibility.

The following four cases, drawn from a long period, are illustrative examples of fatal, but indirect, consequences of explosions:

1. A woman was involved in an explosion at Clerkenwell, London, in 1867. She died in 1879 as the result of epileptic fits which were due to brain injuries received in the explosion.

2. A box of gunpowder was (1894) situated near the entrance to a menagerie at St. Giles les Brucelles, Belgium. The gunpowder exploded and set fire to the clothing of a woman acting as money taker. 'In the confusion a child fell close to a cage containing some bears, and was pulled in and torn to pieces.'

3. A bus conductor purchased (1950) some fireworks on 5 November. After some horseplay, he let one off in the driver's cab. The driver thereupon lost control of the bus which ran up a bank and overturned. A woman passenger was killed.

4. Two girls at a shop counter (1953) were making up fireworks into packets for sale. Bengal matches were then placed on the counter and an accidental ignition of these spread to the fireworks. Smoke rapidly filled the shop and its offices and, although the two packers scaped unhurt, six persons in the offices were injured. Five of these in fear of asphyxiation jumped about 6 m from windows to the street below. One of these died later from severe head and back injuries.

Chapter 9

THE EXAMINATION OF SUSPECTS

SOURCES OF CONTAMINATION

An important step forward in identifying the cause of a deliberate explosion is the apprehension by the police of a person suspected of being responsible. The police action will have been the result of normal criminal investigation procedure, but they will wish to ascertain if there is any supporting scientific evidence. The suspect may have been found to be in possession of a quantity of explosive, detonators or other material. In such cases the scientific evidence consists only of the identification of the materials as being explosives within the meaning of the definitions embodied in the appropriate law.

If the suspect has no obvious explosive in his possession, then an examination may be made to find out if detectable traces of explosive can be found on his person, clothing or possessions. The only part of the body likely to be subject to contamination by explosive is the hands. Such contamination can come about by various means which can be conveniently classified as criminal use, normal use and transfer. When explosives are used for criminal purposes it is a common practice for the explosive to be moulded or to be split up into small quantities, as in safebreaking. If this is done with the bare hands then there will be contamination on the skin and especially under the finger nails. These activities may have been carried out with the hands protected by gloves. In such a case there will, in general, be no contamination but some penetration to the skin may, nevertheless, occur.

When explosives are used for lawful purposes the preparation of the charge does not normally involve direct contact between the hands and the explosive. However, mechanisms for contamination of the hands do exist. A few explosives, such as guncotton slabs, are handled as bare charges. Industrial blasting explosives are commonly used in the form of waxed paper wrapped cartridges. These may

179

have slight traces of explosive on the outside arising from contamination in the manufacturer's filling machine and these may be transferred to the hands of the user. The priming of such a cartridge involves the undoing of the end folds of the wrapper, the making of a hole and the insertion of the detonator. Although these operations need not result in the transfer of explosive to the hands it is obvious that the potentiality of doing so exists, particularly with a clumsy operator. When safety or detonating fuse is used this will normally involve cutting it, with the consequent possibility of contact between the explosive core and the hands.

Contamination of the hands by explosive can also occur by transfer from a contaminated surface. Such contamination can come about in three ways. A surface may be in direct contact with explosives. Thus the transfer of explosives on to the hands can arise from handling bags in which explosive has been transported, or from handling paper or other sheeting in which explosive has been wrapped. The degree of contamination of the hands will depend on the degree of contamination of the box, bag, paper, etc. This will in turn depend, in the case of the box or bag, on the nature and condition of the explosive. Thus, a cast pentolite charge will transfer little material on to a box or wrapper whereas a deteriorated gelignite will transfer much.

The second form of contaminated surface from which transfer of explosive on to hands can occur is debris and other surfaces at the scene of an explosion. The efficacy of this process has been only too apparent to a number of investigators who have suffered from nitroglycerine induced headaches when examining debris from the scenes of explosions. Since the distribution of unconsumed explosive on debris and other surfaces may be essentially even or may be irregular in discrete particles, the resultant transfer on to a hand may produce a faint trace or an appreciable quantity respectively.

The third form of surface from which transfer of explosive on to hands can occur is the contaminated hands of another person. This may be a process of direct transfer such as by shaking hands. It may also be a process of indirect transfer in which the originally contaminated person handles a surface which is subsequently handled by another. The transfer from hand to object has been demonstrated on a number of occasions when detectable traces of nitroglycerine have been found on steering wheels and other controls of motor vehicles used by criminals. The double transfer has been demonstrated experimentally, when it was found that a hand contaminated with nitroglycerine could leave detectable traces on a drinking glass and that the glass so contaminated could transfer detectable amounts of nitroglycerine on to a clean hand. Where the suspect is female and traces of explosive are found on her skin, it is advisable to enquire if she has a husband or other intimate male associate and then, if possible, to test his hands also.

The contamination of clothing by explosive can arise in a number of ways. There can be transfer by direct contact with explosive. This can arise if explosive is carried in the pocket or if it comes into contact with the clothing during manipulation. It is also possible for unconsumed explosive at the scene of an explosion to contaminate the clothing of a person present at the time or subsequently. In the case of a relatively efficient explosion the probability of acquiring detectable traces of explosive by this process is slight. In other cases it may be much greater. Thus a home-made bomb consisting of a length of steel pipe, filled with a mixture of sodium chlorate and sugar, found its way into a quantity of scrap metal. When this was placed under a guillotine cutter an explosion occurred and the operator was killed. Subsequent examination of his clothing revealed readily detectable sodium chlorate and sugar.

Explosives can also contaminate the possessions of a user. The possibilities for the contamination of bags, boxes and other containers have already been indicated. There may also be contamination of a portion of a floor, shelf or other place where explosive has been placed. Detectable traces will only be left if the explosive was unwrapped or if, through deterioration or some other cause, the outside of the package is contaminated. Motor vehicles can become contaminated either from the hands of the driver and/or other occupant, or from contact with explosive carried in the vehicle, or by reasons of small fragments of explosives dropped in the vehicle by an occupant.

DETECTION TECHNIQUES

The first step in the detection of explosives on hands is to take swabs from them. For this purpose it is most desirable for the investigator, police officer or other person charged with the task of taking the swabs, to be equipped with a set of equipment known to be free from explosive. A set of proven usefulness consists of a sealed box containing the following:

A pair of plastic gloves.
A pair of disposable tweezers.
Packets of surgical cotton wool swabs.
Small wooden sticks.
A bottle of diethyl ether.
Sealed ampoules of distilled water.
A sheet of glazed paper.
New plastic bags of the self-seal pattern.

In assembling the contents of the box, the gloves, tweezers, sticks, paper and bags should all be taken direct from new packets and should never be reused. The packets of cotton wool and ampoules of distilled water should likewise be from new stock and should retain their original sealing intact. The ether bottle should be a new one, filled from stock bottle of ether which has been tested and is analytically free from explosives. If sealed ampoules of ether can be obtained these should be used instead. The sets of equipment should be assembled under conditions known to be free from explosives.

The method of using the equipment is as follows. The operator should first wash his own hands thoroughly. He should then unseal the box, put on the gloves and spread the sheet of paper on the table at which the swabbing is to be done. He should then take a series of swabs in the following order:

1. Left hand, dry swab.
2. Right hand, dry swab.
3. Left hand, swab wetted with ether.
4. Right hand, swab wetted with ether.
5. Left hand, swab wetted with distilled water.
6. Right hand, swab wetted with distilled water.

After each swabbing the swab should be placed in a plastic bag, sealed and marked. A third party can conveniently do the marking. The ether and the distilled water should be poured over the swab which should not be allowed to touch the bottle or ampoule respectively. After the swabbing, the wooden sticks should be used to take scrapings from under the finger nails of the left and right hands respectively. This operation can be done directly over a plastic bag which is then sealed and labelled. At the end of the operation all unused material together with the gloves, tweezers and paper should be replaced in the box which should then go for laboratory examination together with the swabs and nail scrapings. This ensures that used material is not reused and also that, in any case of doubt, control tests can be carried out on the remaining materials, though if adequate precautions are taken in the assembly of the equipment this is unlikely to be necessary.

Since any explosive present is likely to be in trace quantities only, it is desirable to use analytical techniques likely to give unequivocal results. This is important since subsequent further testing either by the investigator or by a representative of the suspect may not be possible owing to exhaustion of the sample.

A method, which uses a negligible amount of any explosive which may be present, is to test the atmosphere in each bag with an explosives vapour detector. This may be used as a preliminary check before applying other analytical methods. If the detector is of the type which gives a print-out chromatogram, an identification is obtained in a form which can be physically produced as evidence.

A powerful and useful technique for examining swabs and nail-scrapings is thin layer chromatography. However, when applied in this way thin layer chromatography has an important limitation. Thin layer chromatography is normally used in closed situations, that is in systems in which there are strictly limited possibilities. Thus, the applications described in Chapter 5 relate either to the identification of the components of a sample known to be an explosive or to samples taken from the scene of an explosion. The role of the thin layer chromatography is, therefore, to identify which explosive or explosives are present in a system known to involve explosives.

With hand swabs, however, the role of the thin layer chromatography is different, namely to ascertain whether an explosive is present or not. In such circumstances no limitation can be placed on the possibilities of substances which might occur in the sample. Clearly there will be some limitation, in that positive results can only be produced by compounds capable of giving the correct response with the visualising reagent. Even so, the situation remains an open one since it is never possible to know what is the full range of such compounds which may be derived from manufactured chemicals, by-products and naturally occurring substances.

In these circumstances it is not sufficient for positive identification that the questioned substance exhibits the same visualisation and Rf as a control of an explosive with a single eluent. Thus, for example, if the method described in Appendix J is used, it is possible to obtain a result indistinguishable from that for RDX from an ether swab of a hand subjected to tobacco smoke. It is necessary, therefore, to carry out at least one confirmatory test if thin layer chromatography is used in these circumstances. This can take the form of a second and, perhaps, a third thin layer chromatogram using different eluents and visualising reagents. Another possibility is to use a second, independent method of analysis such as infrared spectroscopy or gas chromatography with or without linking to mass spectroscopy. A third possibility is that consideration of all the data as discussed in Chapter 13 may reveal other confirmatory evidence.

A third approach to the analysis is to use directly one or more of the techniques suggested for the confirmation of thin layer chromatography.

Whatever approach is selected it is vital in such an open-ended situation that adequate confirmatory tests should underlie any assertion of positive identification.

A useful first step in examining clothing is to test the atmosphere inside the bag containing the exhibit with an explosives vapour detector. Here again the type giving a print-out chromatogram can provide conclusive evidence. The next step, or the first if a vapour detector is not available, is to examine the garment visually for the presence of any material which might be explosive. Examination under ultraviolet light can be useful. If anything suspected of being explosive is located it should be scraped off, removed with a swab or extracted with solvent as appropriate according to the amount there and the nature of the surface. The sample can then be examined by appropriate techniques.

If the visual search reveals no suspected explosive then swabs can be taken or solvent extracts made of those parts of the garment most likely to have come into contact with explosive. These can then be examined as before.

The examination of other possessions of a suspect follows the same general lines as the examination of clothing, namely:

1. Explosives vapour detector (if appropriate).
2. Visual examination, followed by removal and testing of any suspected explosives.

3. Swabs taken from any sites which might have been in contact with explosive, followed by their testing for explosives.

In the case of motor vehicles, swabs should be taken from any points which might have been touched by a contaminated hand. These include controls, door handles, window winders, seat belt fasteners and seat surfaces. The possibility of transfer from contaminated shoes to a foot control pedal or a floor mat should not be overlooked. After the swabs have been taken, the vehicle should be thoroughly swept out and the sweepings examined visually for evidence of explosives. The vehicle should, of course, be examined for concealed explosive or explosive devices.

THE CONCLUSIONS

It is pointed out in the discussion on negative evidence in Chapter 12 that the failure to detect explosive on the person of a suspect is not necessarily evidence of innocence. Care must be taken to ensure that police officers, lawyers, judges and juries are made aware of the conclusions which can legitimately be drawn.

When the results of a hand test give strong, positive results for all or most of the swabs and nail scrapings, it is probable that the suspect has handled explosive. When the results indicate only traces, particularly if these are only on some or even only on one of the swabs or scrapings, several conclusions become possible. One is that the suspect has handled explosive at some time, perhaps as much as 24 hours, before the swabs were taken. In the intervening period, normal washing and contact with various objects will have removed the bulk of the original contamination. Another explanation is that the suspect has had more recent but only partial contact with explosive. A further explanation is that the suspect has been contaminated by contact with another person or by contact with a contaminated surface. It should be noted that the presence of explosive under the finger nails should not necessarily be regarded as evidence of direct contact with or manipulation of explosive. Even small traces on the palm are readily transferred to under the finger nails on clenching the hand. When the explosive detected is nitroglycerine in trace quantities the results obtained from dry and ether swabs can be informative. If nitroglycerine is found on the dry swab only, this indicates recent contact, since there has been insufficient time for absorption into the subcutaneous tissue. If nitroglycerine is found on both the dry and ether swabs, this is consistent with less recent contact but not with a heavier contamination reduced by time and washing which would remove the surface material. If nitroglycerine is found on the ether swab only, this is consistent with reasonably less recent contact or more recent contact where the contamination has been recuced by time and washing. All three of these circumstances can arise when the original contamination is by direct manipulation of explosive or by partial contact with explosive or by contact with a contaminated surface.

All these various interpretations of the findings of trace quantities of explosive on a suspect's hands are feasible ones. Attempts or temptations to select only one that is consistent with the guilt or the innocence of the suspect should be firmly resisted. Any valid distinction between them must depend on the existence of other evidence.

When explosive is found on clothing as definite pieces, it is probable that the suspect has been involved in the manipulation of explosive. When, however, only traces are found, other conclusions are also valid. One is that the suspect could have become contaminated by being present where explosives were being used. It should be noted, however, that this implies contact with a particle of explosive. This could occur either before or after the explosion. Other possible conclusions include contamination by contact with a contaminated hand or surface, or contamination of the garment while being used by somebody other than the owner.

Similar considerations apply to the interpretation of the finding of explosives and explosives traces on or in motor vehicles and other possessions. With motor vehicles in particular the possibilities of contamination by persons other than the suspect must be considered. The vehicle will most probably have carried persons other than the owner and may have been used by somebody else with or without his consent or even without his knowledge.

When traces are found by swabbing contaminated surfaces, great care must be taken in drawing any conclusions as to the length of time which may have elapsed since the contamination took place. If the explosive is one which, under normal conditions, is a solid, for example RDX or TNT, then virtually no conclusion at all can be reached. The contamination may be very recent or may have occurred at any time, the limit being determined by the age of the surface or the year of the adoption of the material as an explosive, whichever is the earlier. If the explosive is a liquid, such as nitroglycerine, then an upper limit on the length of time may be calculated from the amount originally present, the history of the ambient temperature, the degree of ventilation and the vapour pressure. Since, however, any information on the first two quantities is extremely unlikely to be available, the possibility of carrying out such a calculation can be discounted. Because of the low volatility of nitroglycerine, materials contaminated by it can remain contaminated for long periods. This is a familiar situation in explosives factories where it is considered that the only safe thing to do with disused buildings and equipment contaminated with nitroglycerine is to burn them. An example of gross contamination persisting for 25 years was given in Chapter 1. The examination of metallic fragments from safebreaking exhibits showed that, when these had been kept in plastic bags pervious to nitroglycerine vapour, then nitroglycerine from the explosion could be detected after a year (26). Trace quantities of nitroglycerine on cloth samples have, likewise, been observed to persist over long periods. When, therefore, a surface is found to be contaminated by nitroglycerine, any assessment of the date of contamination is virtually impossible. It could have occurred at any date within the previous year and dates more remote than this are by no means improbable.

In all cases where contact is postulated, it is necessary to consider how such contact could have come about. If the person has been in a place where explosive is known to have been present, then contact is a possibility, though not inevitable. Contact is likewise a possibility if the person has been in a place where an explosion has occurred. If the person has associated with those who are known to have had explosives or are known to have been contaminated with explosives, then contact could have occurred. If, however, none of these circumstances exists then contamination by contact becomes an unlikely hypothesis. If, nevertheless, there is chemical evidence for explosive on the person then this should be scrutinised carefully and consideration given to the possibility that the substance present was other than that originally postulated.

Chapter 10

ANALYSIS OF WITNESSES' STATEMENTS

THE VALUE OF WITNESSES' STATEMENTS

The bulk of the evidence which the explosion investigator gathers and from which he draws his conclusions is direct evidence of the type discussed in Chapters 4 to 9. The investigator should not, however, overlook another potentially valuable source of data, namely indirect evidence obtained from witnesses. This can often be a source of information not otherwise available, such as, for example, an account of a sequence of events by the only person present in a room in which an explosion occurred.

In evaluating such evidence, the investigator must take account of the limitations of human testimony. He should, therefore, assess the pressures on and various personal aspects of the witness and take these into account when considering what significance to attach to any given statement.

The investigator must also appreciate another limitation of statements made by witnesses. From the point of view of evidence in a court of law, statements made by other people are, in respect of the investigator's testimony, hearsay. It will not, therefore, normally be possible for the investigator to use this information unless it has already been proved before the court by the direct testimony of the witness concerned. Therein lies the danger that, under pressure of cross examination, a weak or overawed witness may change his evidence. Unless on re-examination this can be rectified, the point which the investigator wished to make will be lost, and he should remember that this will be so whether or not the original testimony was accurate.

PRESSURES ON WITNESSES

Witnesses in explosion cases are liable to various pressures which can affect, consciously or unconsciously, the accuracy of their testimony. Eight such influences can be readily recognised.

1. *Psychological effects of the explosion*

Reference was made in Chapter 8 to the phenomenon of retroactive amnesia whereby a person closely involved in an explosion may lose all memory of the event itself and, sometimes, of the circumstances preceding it. Even when this extreme effect is not present the suddenness of the event and the shock induced by it is apt to cause confusion in the minds of witnesses. In consequence, their recollections may be vague and uncertain.

2. *Fear of consequences*

Some witnesses are reluctant to say anything since they fear that blame will be attached to them. This is particularly so if they suspect that they have done something unsafe or if they know that they have deliberately ignored safety regulations. They are then liable to fall back on deliberate lies or a feigned lack of recollection. This pseudo-amnesia can develop between the time of informal conversation with the investigator and the appearance as a witness in a court of law or judicial enquiry.

3. *Threats*

It is not unknown for a witness to falsify his evidence under duress. In a report on an explosion which occurred in 1887 (LXXVII) reference is made to a witness who was in a position of being able to give evidence showing carelessness and disregard for the law by the owner of the store in which the explosion occurred. The man had been injured and the investigator interviewed him in hospital. In his report he said: 'There is good reason to believe that he had previously been tampered with and coaxed or coerced into telling lies'. Forthright comments of this sort will not normally be found in print in more recent times but there is no reason to suppose that human nature and consequent behaviour has changed in the meantime.

4. *Covering up*

When an accidental explosion occurs, there is a temptation for the witnesses to falsify evidence in order to attempt to avert blame from a fellow worker who has deliberately or accidentally done something wrong. This can be illustrated by an extract from the report on another explosion which occurred some time ago, namely in 1900 (CXXXVII):

> The evidence given to me during the course of my enquiry and at the inquest, although agreeing in the main outlines of the accident, as given above, differed a good deal in detail and, as has been pointed out before, the prospects of an action in connection with the Employer's Liability Act appears to cause the recollection of what occurred to assume a different form in the minds of the workpeople to that which remains in the minds of those in authority over them.

In order to counter this temptation, it is important that a witness should be made to realise that, while the result of the investigation may be to place blame on somebody, its most important result is to ensure the future safety of himself and his fellow workers. Anybody capable of wilful disregard of safety procedures should not be working with explosives and the action of covering up for such a person is placing the witness at permanent risk in the future.

5. *Desire to please*

Sometimes a witness will give an untrue answer to a question, not from any desire to mislead his questioner but because he wishes to give the answer which he thinks the questioner would like to hear. Such behaviour usually becomes apparent as the questioning continues since the witness will make contradictory statements.

6. *Discussion with others*

When witnesses have had the opportunity to talk about the incident with other people then their subsequent account of events is liable to be a mixture of their own observations and ideas from others. This is particularly the case where two witnesses are husband and wife. Their individual evidence is generally best regarded as embodying combined observations.

7. *Expectant attention*

Many people, if asked what they saw, will describe not what was actually observable but what they know was there or what they think ought to have been there. This failing is well illustrated by the behaviour of people endeavouring to learn to draw the human figure. In their initial attempts they will include features which they know to be present in the human body but which are in fact not visible in the pose being studied. On progressing to painting the same subject they will initially represent the whole of the skin as pink, brown or other colour according to the ethnic origin of the sitter, though observation reveals that human skin is multi-coloured.

8. 'News'

Explosions are liable to be spectacular occurrences and hence receive extensive cover by the various news media. In consequence the fresh impressions of witnesses are liable to be distorted by information derived from the press, radio and television.

The problems of gaining reliable evidence when any of these factors is operative can be considerable. Genuine amnesia produces an insoluble problem, though some return of memory may occur with time. The witness motivated solely by a desire to please the questioner likewise poses a well-nigh insoluble problem and the only likely result of questioning such a witness will be to furnish a test of the patience of the questioner.

The problems arising from threats to witnesses, discussion with others and exposure to news media can be largely overcome by early questioning, followed by a sceptical attitude to any subsequent changes in the witness's story.

The problems arising from fear of consequences and covering up for others can usually be overcome by appropriate reassurance of the witness.

THE PERSONALITY OF A WITNESS

There is a number of personal aspects of a witness which must be taken into account when considering the reliability of his account of the incident. Three such aspects can be readily recognised:

1. Is the witness a trained observer?

Most people are not trained observers and, therefore, tend not to notice details of objects around them or of occurrences in their vicinity. Some people, however, have been trained or have trained themselves to observe details. Training in observation is an integral part of the studies undergone by such people as policemen, scientists, doctors and professional artists. Similar standards in observation are acquired by many amateur artists, botanists, ornithologists and others. In assessing the reliability of a witness as an observer, it is important to pay attention to the nature of their occupation and other interests.

2. What is the medical condition of the witness?

It is important to establish whether witnesses are in full possession of their faculties. Obvious defects which can affect observation are impaired eyesight, including colour blindness, and deafness. Temporary disabilities include such things as the effects of alcohol and drugs and of other substances such as carbon monoxide.

3. Was the witness awake?

Most witnesses to explosions will have been awake at the time of the explosion. On occasions, however, a witness will have been awakened by an explosion. This may affect their recollection since many people tend to be mentally confused on first awakening.

ASSESSMENT OF REPORTS OF SOUND

The sound of an explosion is often its most obvious immediate effect. It is also the effect observable at the greatest distance from the seat of the explosion. The extreme case is the mechanical explosion which disintegrated Krakatoa in 1883 and which was heard at distances extending to nearly 5,000 km. Another well-known instance is the audibility in England of battles on the Western Front during the 1914-18 War and the author can personally testify to hearing in London the explosions involved in the raid on Dieppe on 19 August 1942. In the latter case the distance involved was 200 km. There have been many instances in which explosions involving quantities of the order of 1,000 kg have been heard at distances up to 50 km.

The distance at which an explosion is heard is not likely to be a matter of significance to the explosion investigator. However, an aspect of the sound of an explosion which can be of considerable significance is the tendency of witnesses to report the sound of two explosions. Such a report may be due to the fact that there were two explosions. Frequently, however, there will only have been one and the effect experienced by the witness will have been due to other causes. Three such causes can be recognised.

ATMOSPHERIC EFFECTS

The main parameters which govern the velocity of sound in air are temperature, wind velocity and direction. If an explosion occurs in a region where there is no wind and the temperature of the air decreases regularly with altitude, the behaviour of the sound waves is simple. In practice, however, such conditions are very unlikely to obtain and the mode of propagation of the sound waves will be affected by such phenomena as temperature inversions, cloud layers and multi-directional winds. In such a complex system, reflections and refractions can lead to sound waves reaching a given point by more than one path. If they arrive with only a slight difference in phase, there can be an increase in intensity up to a hundredfold. Such an effect can give rise to reports that some witnesses heard the sound at distances greater than those at which others heard nothing. If sound waves reach a given point by sufficiently different paths, then the time difference between them will give rise to a report of hearing two explosions.

Possibly the most striking incident illustrating two sound paths was that observed by Captain W. E. Parry in the course of experiments on the propagation of sound carried out in the Arctic (48). In experiments on 9 February 1822 a base-line of 5,645 feet (1,720 m) was marked out over flat ice. At one end was a six-pounder gun which was pointed along the line with an elevation of about 10°. Observers were stationed at the other. The temperature was −25° F (−32° C). Fifteen rounds were fired and the velocity of sound determined by measuring the time interval between seeing the flash and hearing the sound of the gun. It was observed that: '... the officer's word of command 'Fire' was several times distinctly heard ... after the report of the gun'. This effect was not observed on any other occasions when similar experiments were conducted.

The effect often reported by witnesses is well illustrated in the following extract from the evidence given by a police officer during the enquiry into the explosion at Ronan Point on 16 May 1968 (49):

Q. When you were in that place did you hear something?
A. Yes, I heard the sound of a double explosion.
Q. Definitely two explosions?
A. It sounded like two to me, yes, Sir.
Q. Would you describe them?
A. I thought they were the product of a sonic boom from aircraft.

Q. Did the second explosion follow shortly after the first? What sort of interval was there?

A. There was barely an interval; they were almost simultaneous.

The complexities of the structure of the atmosphere are such that reports of two explosions in quick succession from witnesses is totally inadequate evidence for the actual occurrence of two explosions. Any attempt to use it as such should be firmly resisted. The same considerations clearly do not apply to reports of two explosions separated by an interval of time too great to be accounted for by alternative acoustic paths.

ECHO EFFECTS

At smaller distances, atmospheric effects will not produce sufficient time differences to creat the illusion of two explosions. It can, however, arise from echoes off adjacent buildings. The possibility of this will depend on the environment of the particular explosion, but echo paths giving rise to delays of the order of a second between the original sound and the echo can readily occur. These should be looked for by the investigator when assessing evidence of two explosions given by witnesses.

OTHER SOUNDS

Apart from echo and other alternative acoustic paths, other sources of sound can occur which may give rise to reports of a second explosion. These are general structural collapse of a building, the impingement of fragments on surrounding structures and similar phenomena. It is possible, therefore, that there will be witnesses who, though reporting two explosions, in fact are describing the noise of one explosion followed by noise generated by one of the other mechanisms. It is normally possible to distinguish evidence of this sort by considering the words used by the witness to describe the quality of the sounds. There will be a tendency to use different words to describe the sound of the actual explosion and the sound of the subsequent event.

This may be illustrated by an analysis of the evidence given in the Ronan Point Investigation (49). After the elimination of witnesses who had apparently heard effects due to atmospheric conditions and to echo effects, there remained thirteen who reported two noises. The

TABLE 10.1

Witness	First Sound	Second Sound
1	High-pitched bang	Sort of boom
2	Explosion	Bang, not an explosion
3	Loud, sharp bang	Quiet boom
4	Explosion	Bang
5	Explosion, bang	Explosion, bang, crashing
6	Explosion	Crash, not an explosion
7	Loud crack	Bang
8	Explosion	Bang
9	Explosion	Bang
10	Loud crash	Crash, rumbling/rending sound
11	Explosion	Bang
12	Crack	Small bang
13	Explosion, crack	Explosion, crack

expressions used were as shown in Table 10.1. It will be seen that eight of the witnesses use the term explosion to describe the first sound, whereas only two use it to describe the second. Moreover, two specifically say that the second sound was not an explosion. The general impression, gained from the descriptions used for the first sound, leaves little doubt that the witnesses are attempting to describe the sound of an explosion. The general impression gained from the descriptions used to describe the second sound is different, the tendency being to use words such as bang (eight times), crash (thrice), and boom (twice). There is little doubt that the witnesses are attempting to describe the sound produced by a different phenomenon from that which produced the first sound. The second sound was, in fact, readily accounted for as the effect of the collapsing building in general and the fall of the initially displaced structural panel in particular.

ASSESSMENT OF REPORTS OF SMOKE

The potential interest of a smoke cloud associated with an explosion is twofold. If smoke producing pyrotechnics were involved, the colour of the smoke can provide evidence or confirmatory evidence of their nature. In other cases the smoke cloud will contain light debris and explosion decomposition products. Observations of the colour of the smoke cloud may, therefore, give an indication of the nature of the explosive. Thus, a white smoke cloud may indicate the involvement of gunpowder and a black cloud the presence of an oxygen deficient carbonaceous system.

In order to obtain a reliable estimate of the colour of an object, various conditions must be fulfilled. The explosion investigator will not usually be concerned with all of these since some have only a minor effect on the impression made on the observer. Three are, however, of major importance and must be taken into account when assessing witnesses' descriptions of the colour of smoke clouds.

THE COLOUR OF THE INCIDENT LIGHT

When an object is seen in daylight it is normal to regard it as being viewed by white light. In fact, there are continual variations in daylight but the eye adapts to these. In consequence, these variations are not often noticed, nor are their effects on coloured objects, and the light is considered as white, except perhaps during some highly-coloured sunset. It has been said (50) that: 'People talk about white light as though it were some definite thing . . . white light is what you see most of'. Colours seen by daylight are, in general, reliably reported, but assessment of the reliability must take account of the possibility of the light being far removed from white.

The reporting of colours seen by artificial light can be very unreliable due to the limited range of wavelengths emitted by most lighting sources. The colour distortion induced by sodium vapour streetlamps is well known and is so gross as to be obvious to most people. Less pronounced distortions occur with other sources but must nevertheless be taken into account by the investigator.

THE BRIGHTNESS OF THE BACKGROUND

The brightness of the background against which an object is seen can have a profound effect on the impression gained by an observer. Where the brightness of the background is comparable with or less than that of the object being viewed, the colour of the object is readily perceived and may by accurately reported. If, however, the background is much brighter than the object, then the latter will appear dark and, in extreme cases, black. This effect can be simply demonstrated by holding a small coloured object, such as a pen, against a background of bright sky. Whatever the colour of the object, it will appear very dark or black. If a sheet of white paper is now placed behind the object so that the background brightness is reduced to that of the light transmitted through the paper, the colour of the object is revealed.

It is important, therefore, in assessing the description of the colour of smoke given by a witness, that attention be given to the relative position of the observer and the smoke. If the smoke was seen against a bright background, notably the sky, then allowance must be made for the fact that such circumstances will cause the colour to be reported as being darker than would have been the case if it had been seen against other backgrounds. In particular, a misleading report of black smoke can occur from this cause when, in fact, the smoke contained no black components such as carbon.

Reflected or Transmitted Light

Smoke clouds are, in general, translucent. It is important, therefore, to consider whether the witness is reporting the colour of the smoke as seen essentially by reflected light, or as seen by a combination of the two. The profound differences which can occur can readily be seen by observing clouds on a sunny day. Those seen in the direction of the sun will appear grey, sometimes dark grey, whereas those seen in the opposite direction will appear white. If the wind is in the same direction as the sun changes in colour of a single cloud can be observed. An even more striking example occurs when an airplane takes off on an overcast day. The cloud bank seen from below by transmitted light is grey and seen from above by reflected light is white.

In assessing the significance of a report of the colour of a smoke cloud, it is important, therefore, to consider the colour of the incident light and the position of the witness relative to the smoke and its background.

ASSESSMENT OF REPORTS OF FLASH AND FLAME

Reports of the colour of flash and flame given by witnesses are easier to assess than reports of the colour of smoke. Since these phenomena are self-luminous, their appearance is not affected by the nature of the incident light. Since, moreover, they constitute the brightest thing visible at the time, no distortions of colour arise from the relative brightness of the background. The reports given by witnesses are, therefore, usually accurate and can be accepted with few, if any, reservations.

The flash seen when an explosion occurs is a result of a combinaion of the initial chemical reactions involving the initial reaction products and, if present, slower reacting components of the explosive. As the hot gases expand, finely divided material from the scene becomes entrained in them and this can contribute to the colour effects observed.

Many explosives contain an excess of carbon. Carbon is also commonly entrained into the gases from the scene and there is a tendency, therefore, for the flash from an explosive to assume the yellowish colour of incandescent carbon. The presence of entrained dust causes the absorption of shorter wavelength light and, in consequence, where appreciable dust is present there is a tendency for the flash to appear orange or even red.

In some circumstances, however, different colours may be seen and can have diagnostic value. When organic vapours or gases are mixed with air, either as the stoichiometric mixture or as a composition within the explosion limits containing excess air, the colour of the flash of the explosion is usually described as blue or bluish-white or in some equivalent terms (*e.g.* like a photographic flash). When, however, such a mixture having a composition within the explosion limits is deficient in air, the colour of the flash is usually described as yellow, golden or orange. Observations of the colour of the flash in the case of these systems can, therefore, give a guide to the proportios of constituents. It should be noted that gas/air and vapour/air mixtures often occupy a considerable volume and that the composition is unlikely to be constant throughout. Witnesses may, therefore, report different colours of flash from the same event because they have seen the flash from different parts of the explosive. It is important, therefore, when witnesses describe the colour of flash, to record their exact location in respect of the explosion and to ascertain exactly whereabouts they saw the flash. It will normally be found that reports of different colours are not in conflict and, moreover, that they contribute to a greater understanding of the conditions obtaining at the time of the explosion.

When an explosion involves pyrotechnic compositions, the initial flash may be followed by a more or less prolonged period of burning with the production of flame. In any such explosion the colour of the flash and flame can be of considerable diagnostic value in identifying the nature of the explosive. Many pyrotechnic compositions contain components intended to produce coloured light effects (Chapter 5) and these will be observable in accidental explosions involving these compositions or in deliberate explosions involving their misuse.

ASSESSMENT OF REPORTS OF ODOUR

Reports of odours observed by witnesses can sometimes provide useful information for the investigator. In such cases where vapour/air and gas/air mixtures are involved, witnesses may be able to report an odour which was observable before the explosion and so give an indication of the nature of the explosive.

Most of the substances listed in Appendix L have appreciable odours. They will, however, be unfamiliar to most people, the only one likely to be recognised by the casual observer being petrol. It is probable, however, that explosions involving the vapours of these substances will occur as accidents at places where they are used. The available witnesses are likely, therefore, to be familiar with their odour and will be able to identify them.

Similar considerations apply to the gases listed in Appendix M, though the odours of ammonia, hydrogen sulphide and the stenching agent in coal gas may be recognised by lay witnesses.

In assessing the value of reports of odour made by witnesses, it is important to consider whether the witness has any special experience which would enhance his ability to recognise and describe an odour. Clearly a description given by a professional chemist could be of considerable value. So also could be one given by a perfumier. Informative descriptions and reliable identifications can also be obtained for particular substances by those accustomed to work with them.

When considering reports on odours, careful consideration must be given before accepting negative evidence. People exposed to an odoriferous vapour soon suffer from olfactory fatigue and lose their ability to detect it. This phenomenon appears to be independent of concentration. A person exposed to a low concentration can become fatigued and then be unable to detect a higher concentration, although to an unfatigued person both concentrations are detectable and the difference between them is obvious. It is possible, therefore, for a witness to become fatigued by a small unimportant escape of vapour or gas and so fail to detect a subsequent major release. Another possibility is for the witness to suffer olfactory fatigue by exposure to a low concentration at a distance from the source of vapour or gas and then fail to observe any odour on moving into a region of higher concentration. The latter phenomenon is illustrated by a case (49) in which a town gas leak developed during the night. The leak was in the kitchen of a flat and the gas slowly spread. The occupant was subjected to a non-lethal concentration while asleep. On getting up, she went into the kitchen, and, on attempting to light the gas stove, initiated an explosion. She failed to observe the odour of the gas stenching agent and it was concluded that this was due to olfactory fatigue which developed while she was asleep.

Accounts given by witnesses of odours after an explosion can sometimes be of value. Unconsumed vapours or gases may be detected. A particular case where this is likely is that of an explosion consequent upon attempted arson, since in these circumstances portions of the unevaporated accelerant frequently remain on the scene. Reports of the odour of gaseous explosion products are not likely to be informative unless given by a witness familiar with the odours produced by explosions. The probability of such a witness being available is slight, though there is a case on record (LIX) in which the explosion was due to an infernal machine which exploded in a public place. One of the passers-by at the time was an army officer who was able to give an informed account of the odours of the explosion products.

EVIDENCE FROM PERSONS NOT PRESENT AT THE SCENE OF THE EXPLOSION

In considering witnesses who may be able to give useful information, the investigator should not overlook the possibility that persons who were not present at the time of the explosion may, nevertheless, be able to contribute important data. These persons may conveniently be considered as being of two categories, namely those who can provide information relevant to the particular occurrence and those who can provide information about similar occurrences.

Information about the particular occurrence can be of three types. The first is information about the explosive present at the scene. In the case of a factory accident, a witness may be able to describe the materials he took to the building in which the explosion occurred. He may also be able to give an account of what materials he had seen there. Less directly, witnesses may be able to testify to such matters as quantities withdrawn from stores, types and quantities of materials made up for dispatch and other information from which deductions can be made as to the probable identity and quantity of explosive involved in the explosion. In the case of an infernal machine, witnesses may be found who saw the device at some period before the explosion and who can give a description of its appearance.

The second type of information in this category is information about the procedures which would normally have been going on at the scene of the explosion. Witnesses may be able to describe the standard procedures for a manufacturing process or a blasting operation. These can be analysed for possible causes of initiation and can be examined for consistency with observations from the scene. Any inconsistencies may indicate the possibility of potentially hazardous departures from safe practices and hence a possible cause of the explosion.

The third type of information in this category is information about people killed in the explosion. Friends and workmates may be able to testify that the deceased was a careful and systematic worker, making it unlikely that he or she would have done anything foolish. They may also be able to testify to the contrary, though it may be difficult to persuade them to disclose this. Information may also be available concerning the deceased's actions and personal circumstances prior to their death. This may show that they were suffering from tiredness or stress which could have been conducive to the making of hazardous errors. In extreme cases of stress the possibility of suicide cannot be discounted. An example of this type of evidence is found in the case (1970) of a man who was killed when an explosion occurred in a nitroglycerine eductor annexe. Investigation suggested that the explosion occurred when he was sampling incoming emulsion. It is possible, therefore, that he dropped the sampling vessel containing separated nitroglycerine when working in a confined space, thereby causing the explosion of the contents of two separators. At the inquest, evidence was given to the effect that the man was blind in one eye and was not in the best of health. These physical deficiences could well have resulted in some clumsiness and hence have an important bearing on understanding the cause of the explosion.

Information about possibly similar occurrences can come from two sources. The first is professional investigators and explosives scientists. The information may be obtained in some instances direct from such a person known to the investigator. Otherwise the investigator must rely on written accounts published in the various appropriate journals. The second source is private citizens who have experience to recount. There is a tendency for solicited and unsolicited information of this sort to emanate from cranks and, therefore, to be regarded as being of no value. A number of the comments received will be,simply, baseless assertions or flights of fancy. A proportion, however, will come from thoughtful people with worthwhile contributions to offer. All should, therefore, be considered carefully.

Chapter 11

UNLIKELY OCCURRENCES

THE SIGNIFICANCE OF THE UNUSUAL

Sherlock Holmes observed (*A Case of Identity*) that: '. . . life is infinitely stranger than anything which the mind of man could invent. We would not dare to conceive the things which are really mere commonplaces of existence'. The explosion investigator will find that for the most part his observations will be consistent with his normal expectations from explosives technology. Likewise, his observations of the behaviour or persons involved with the explosion will be consistent with his expectation of human behaviour. From time to time, however, he will come across a physical observation or a human action which is so far removed from the normal that he will be tempted to discount it as being a false observation. He should be on his guard against too facile a rejection of this kind. He must test his evidence but should never reject it as false merely on the grounds that is seems incredible that it could be true. The history of explosion investigation records some unlikely occurrences and the investigator should bear these in mind when confronted with something he regards as improbable. The selection of cases which follow are drawn from the Annual Reports of H.M. Inspectors of Explosives for the years concerned or the author's experience and are illustrative examples of some of the more bizarre episodes on record.

FOOLISH BEHAVIOUR

A number of explosions have occurred owing to foolish behaviour, as distinct from carelessness or lack of appreciation of the possible consequences. The investigator of an accident in 1902 observed that it was 'due to the unfortunately not uncommon practice of exploding a gelignite cartridge at a wedding as a sign of rejoicing'.

In 1913 a schooner went aground off the Nore in heavy weather.

The captain thereupon ordered the mate to fire signal rockets. The mate entered the cabin and, apparently, tried to light a rocket there. He failed and so the captain went to try and subsequently fired the rocket. The rocket then ignited other rockets and flares in the cabin and these set the ship on fire.

A Mills hand grenade was retained as a souvenir of the 1914–18 War and was used as an ornament. It contained no detonator but evidently retained its high explosive filling. One day in 1923 it was placed in an oven and some time later, when this was used, the bomb exploded, killing a child and wounding two other persons.

In 1953 a boy was filling a small metal tube with a potassium chlorate/sulphur mixture when it exploded, resulting in lacerations to his left hand. Arrangements were made for the police to caution him while a parent was present. Unfortunately he paid little attention to the warning and, some months later, assisted another boy to tamp a piece of metal pipe with a mixture of potassium chlorate, sulphur and phosphorus. A piece of metal was being used to fill the tube when the mixture exploded. The boy was so seriously injured that he died some time later.

A man brought two aircraft cannon shells home as souvenirs of the 1939–45 War. In 1955 he used one of them as a hammer. The shell exploded, blowing off his right hand. His face and chest were severely injured and he died.

In 1956 a boy aged 12 prepared a flash mixture with magnesium powder and potassium permanganate. He placed some of the mixture in a carton which he had made by pasting together pieces of paper and lit it with a match. An explosion occurred which caused him severe injuries. The instructions for making the mixture were obtained from a book presented to the boy for regular attendance at Sunday School.

Also, in the same year, a child aged 3 was given a lighted sparkler to play with in a shop which sold fireworks. The child immediately ran round the back of the shop and plunged the burning sparkler into a box of fireworks in a cupboard.

In 1961 a youth aged 18 was killed by an explosion in his bedroom. Examination of the debris suggested that he was tampering with a tin of gunpowder at the time. The room was found to contain considerable quantities of explosives of various kinds including about 20 kg of blasting gelatine, signal rockets and several hundred detonators.

In 1969 an ignition of petroleum vapour occurred, fortunately without explosion. The occurrence took place in the inspection pit of a garage where two men were working on the petrol tank of a car. As the tank was not fitted with a drain plug the pipe connection was loosened and attempts were made to catch the petrol in a drum. Much, however, spilt on the floor of the pit. The oil fired boiler of the heating system, however, was in the inspection pit and this ignited the petrol vapour/air mixture.

UNUSUAL MOTIVATION

In most cases in which people cause explosions they either do so by accident or by a deliberate intent motivated by perverted political consideration or by readily discernible personal problems. Occasionally, however, people set out to cause explosions for very ususual reasons. A multiple suicide for religious reasons has already been noted in Chapter 8. Another example of a religious motivation occurred in 1902. On 25 October, Rev. George Martin, a priest in the Church of England, was arrested in London and found to have a tin of gunpowder in his pocket. His intention was to blow up a public viewing stand at St. George's Church as a protest against its erection on consecrated ground. In more recent times many explosions have been caused in Ireland by people bearing religious designations, but it seems doubtful whether the motives can correctly be described as religious.

In 1904 a man found some detonators and was seriously injured by an explosion which occurred when he tried to force them open. His motive in so doing was that he thought they might contain hidden treasure. This case is paralleled by one in 1967 in which a group of tinkers encamped near an explosives store. They broke into this, took some detonators and placed them on a bonfire. In the ensuing explosion an 8-year-old boy was severely injured and lost the sight of one eye. The reason for placing the detonators on the fire was thought to have been an attempt to recover scrap metal.

INCOMPREHENSIBLE BEHAVIOUR

From time to time, persons concerned in explosions behave in a manner which is so far beyond foolishness or recklessness as to be incomprehensible to normal people. On 14 April 1904 a fisherman picked up a keg of gunpowder off the North Foreland at the mouth of the Thames. Two days later the temporary skipper of the fishing smack was seen to be tampering with the gunpowder and was warned not to interfere with it. He asked for a flare and, on this being refused, he put the keg into a small boat and, saying that he had a match, moved away a short distance. Soon there was a loud explosion and both he and the boat sank.

In 1956 a boy aged 14 was making a bomb with potassium chlorate and sulphur. It exploded and caused such severe injuries to his hand that this had to be amputated. The police removed the chemicals he had been using. The boy's father, however, requested their return so as to enable his son to continue his experiments when he came out of hospital.

UNEXPECTED CONSEQUENCES OF EXPLOSIONS

Explosions sometimes produce what seem to be freak effects. The investigator will usually find, however, that due consideration to such matters as blast wave enhancement or attenuation due to topographical features can furnish an explanation of the observed phenomenon. Sometimes, however, the effect observed, while explicable, is of such a nature as to be regarded as a very rare event. In 1897 an explosion involving about 7 kg dynamite occurred in a private house. Two women in it were blown to pieces and the house was demolished. Nevertheless, a hen which was sitting on eggs in the room where the explosion occurred was rescued from the ruins completely uninjured.

In 1910 an employee at an explosives factory in the United States was lighting a cigar when an explosion occurred. The explosion stripped his index finger and thumb of flesh. This was apparently due to the presence of nitroglycerine under the nails of the finger and thumb.

In 1960 a contractor was engaged to remove some tree stumps by blasting. He used electrically fired detonators and was electrocuted when the force of an explosion blew the wire connecting the battery to the detonator on to overhead high-tension electric cables.

OLD EXPLOSIVES

It is a common misconception among laymen that explosives will cease to be active if they are old. This belief has been proved false on many occasions as the following examples show. In 1894 an explosion occurred in Lyons. This was caused by someone dropping a burning match into an artillery shell which had been kept as a souvenir of the Franco-Prussian War of 1870. Similar accidents with old war souvenirs have occurred more or less regularly ever since. For example in 1940 an old sea-mine was being broken up for scrap by an oxy-acetylene cutter when it exploded. The worker was killed. The mine had been lying on a beach from 1916 to 1930, when it had been towed up river to a boat yard and used as an ornament.

In 1956 a boy broke into an explosives store which had been disused since 1923. The axe he was using struck a detonator which exploded, causing minor injuries. A number of other detonators were found after the accident. They were all identified as being of 1923, or earlier, manufacture and as being quite serviceable.

In 1970 some gunpowder filled friction igniters were found behind some panelling in Woolwich Arsenal. The electrician who found them, not knowing what they were, pulled the operating wire of one of them and received burns to his hand when it functioned. They were identified as having been made about 1850.

UNEXPECTED PRESENCE OF EXPLOSIVES

Explosives have been found from time to time in most unexpected places, with consequent danger to the finder.

In 1905 a woman found a lump of coal in her garden and alleged that it had been thrown there by her neighbour. On investigation it was found to have been split, hollowed out, filled with mercury fulminate and glued together again.

In 1907 on 3 September, while a seven year old boy of Cheboygan, Michigan, was being punished by his mother with the assistance of a strap, a detonator in his pocket exploded, killing the boy and injuring his mother'.

In 1922 a barge, containing dynamite, other blasting explosives and detonators, was attempting to pass under a bridge when an accident occurred. The barge was stove in and beached. The presence of the explosive was, of course, known but, on examination, it was found that nitroglycerine displaced by the water had reached a depth of 10 cm in the bottom.

In 1945 an explosion occurred in a detonating fuse packing house and the building was completely destroyed. The building had contained disused plant for the stabilisation of PETN and a still for the recovery of acetone liquor. This had last been used in 1942. A similar still at another factory was found to contain 113 kg of explosive.

In 1947 a man received injuries to his hands while cutting up timber. This was found to be due to a 20 mm aircraft cannon shell which had become lodged in the trunk of the tree during the 1939–45 War. A similar accident took place in 1965 when an explosion occurred while a concrete pile was being shortened with a pneumatic drill. The drill operator was hit by a flying fragment. The explosion was found to have been due to a railway fog signal in the concrete and later another was recovered from the debris of a second pile. The source of the fog signals, which must have been in the ready-mixed concrete, was not established.

These instances relate to cases in which manufactured explosive has been found in unexpected places. Records also exist of the unexpected formation of explosives. In 1972 two explosions occurred in the drains of hospital laboratories. In both cases waste saline solution had been poured down the sinks. The saline solution, however, contained sodium azide as a bacteriocide and, although the concentration was only 0·1%, there was sufficient reaction with the copper pipe to produce a significant deposit of copper azide.

In 1970 an explosion occurred in a rubbish fire on a demolition site. Subsequent investigation showed that an acetylene cylinder had been inadvertently buried beneath the rubbish. In a similar occurrence in 1965 a large amount of damage was done to surrounding property and thirteen people were injured.

Chapter 12

NEGATIVE EVIDENCE

THE SIGNIFICANCE OF NEGATIVE EVIDENCE

Possibly the most famous passage in the Sherlock Holmes stories occurs in *Silver Blaze*. It is a conversation between a police inspector and Sherlock Holmes:

'You consider that to be important?' he asked.
'Exceedingly so.'
'Is there any other point to which you would wish to draw my attention?'
'To the curious incident of the dog in the night-time.'
'The dog did nothing in the night-time.'
'That was the curious incident', remarked Sherlock Holmes.

This passage embodies a very important investigational principle, namely that positive information may sometimes be derived from negative observations. In this example the observation led to the conclusion that an intruder in the night must have been somebody well known to the dog, which consequently did not bark. Evidence of this kind not infrequently occurs in explosion investigation and the investigator should be alert to its possibilities. Both he, persons concerned in judicial enquiries and courts of law should, however, realise that deduction based on negative evidence can unwittingly be false and they should be on their guard against this pitfall.

Negative evidence can lead to three types of conclusion, namely positive, neutral and negative. The latter is sufficiently obvious as to need no elaboration. The first two, however, merit further consideration and some examples are discussed below.

NEGATIVE EVIDENCE LEADING TO POSITIVE CONCLUSIONS

Positive conclusions about explosions can be derived from negative evidence in a number of ways.

THE PROCESS OF ELIMINATION

The clearest example of the process of elimination in explosion investigation occurs in the determination of the cause of initiation. As was shown in Chapter 6, there are many possible mechanisms for initiation and all must be considered. Sometimes there will be clear evidence at the outset that a particular mechanism was involved and all others can, therefore, be readily dismissed. Thus, in attacks on safes or other security containers, identifiable fragments of fired detonators can usually be found and these clearly represent the means of initiation. Often, however, no such clear evidence is apparent. Then the various possibilities have to be explored and, if possible, all but one eliminated. Some of the eliminations will be of the type where negative evidence leads to positive elimination. Thus, if the initiation of the explosion has occurred in a room to which there is no supply of electricity, then clearly the cause of initiation cannot have been an electric spark from an electricity system.

Sometimes such eliminations from negative evidence can only be qualified positive ones. Thus, in the example given above, the deduction that the cause of initiation cannot have been an electric spark from an electricity system is an absolute one. If, however, it is desired to extend this to the general statement that the cause cannot have been an electric spark, regarding for this purpose sparks deriving from electrostatic charges as being a separate phenomenon, then it will be necessary to establish that no portable source of electricity was present. Search of the debris may reveal no evidence of an electric battery, but the conclusion from this observation that no battery was present, while probably true, or most probably true, cannot be regarded as absolute. This is because the possibility that the remains were either too small to be recognised or were projected to a distance and not observed, cannot be entirely discounted. Further investigation may fail to reveal any evidence that an electric battery was removed from the scene by somebody after the explosion. It must be remembered, however, that such factors as fear of consequences may cause a witness to remove what they believe to be incriminating evidence and then conceal the fact that they have done so. Therefore, only a qualified, positive conclusion can be drawn, namely that, since a careful investigation has failed to reveal any evidence of an electric battery, it is most probable that no such battery was present and, therefore, that the cause of initiation was most probably not an electric spark.

Another example of the process of elimination where negative evidence leads to positive conclusions is the use of control samples in chemical analysis. The difficulties of obtaining meaningful control samples from the scene of an explosion have been discussed in Chapter 5. When such controls are subjected to chemical tests in parallel with the case samples and give negative reactions it may be concluded that any positive reactions given by the case samples are significant. Owing, however, to the difficulties already mentioned, the positive conclusion must be associated with some degree of reservation. Care should be taken, however, not to push the reservation beyond the bounds of common sense or else the investigator will place unrealistic obstacles in the way of his investigation. Similar extreme reservations should likewise be avoided by an interested party since such arguments will only serve to weaken their position.

An argument concerning negative evidence in chemical identification which has been put to the author in a court of law related to thin layer chromatography. It was suggested that the reported positive finding of explosive in the case sample was really due to an error; that the control sample of explosive and the case sample had been inadvertently interchanged. The apparent positive result for the case sample was, therefore, due to the control sample. Such an argument is not, however, tenable. If the two samples had been interchanged there would have been a positive result for the apparent case sample and a negative one for the apparent control. This negative result would have immediately led to the positive conclusion that something was wrong and the test would have been repeated. Only if both control and case samples give positive results on a thin layer chromatography plate is the identification reported as being positive.

The Absence of a Particular Explosive Effect

The various types of damage produced by explosions and their diagnostic implications have been discussed in Chapter 4. In some instances the absence of one or more of these effects can be used to make positive deductions, as the following examples show.

When an explosion has been due to a condensed explosive, the site of the charge can be derived from a determination of the point of maximum damage. Further examination of this area will reveal whether or not primary fragments have been generated. Such fragments produce holes, pits and gouges in the nearby surfaces and the fragments themselves can usually be found embedded in various places. If, however, careful examination fails to produce any evidence of these characteristic features of the explosion of a cased charge, it may be deduced that the charge was of bare explosive or was confined in some insignificant material such as paper or plastic sheeting.

Another characteristic feature which may be found at the site of the explosion of a charge of condensed explosive, is a crater. Where, however, the evidence from the damage clearly indicates a condensed explosive, but no crater is found, the absence of the crater leads to two alternative positive conclusions. If other evidence indicates that the charge was situated on the surface, then the explosive must have been a low brisance one. If, however, the evidence indicates that the explosive was of high brisance, then the charge must have been located sufficiently far above the surface that no cratering occurred.

The absence of other types of explosive effect can sometimes lead to positive conclusions. Thus, if the explosion clearly involved a considerable quantity of explosive and witnesses to the event are available, then the absence of white smoke shows that no significant quantity of gunpowder could have been involved.

The Absence of Particular Residual Materials

Sometimes the investigator will be called on to investigate a series of essentially similar explosions. A notable example of this type is attacks on safes or other security containers. After considering a number of such explosions, the investigator will become familiar with various features which can be repeatedly observed. These will include residual materials. In some cases it will be found that one or more of these materials is absent and certain positive conclusions can be drawn from this negative evidence.

In safebreaking cases it is almost always possible to determine whether a plain or electric detonator has been used. If it is the latter, then the detonator lead wires can normally be expected to be found on the scene. Sometimes, however, there are none. There are two possible reasons. One is that the attacker cut the lead wires off close to the detonator and used a length of electric flex to make the connection to his source of electricity. This technique has the advantage to the attacker that, if he is apprehended before the attack, the detonator is more easily concealed or disposed of and normal electric flex is not likely to arouse suspicion. The other possible reason is that the attacker, realising the diagnostic value of the detonator lead wires, removed them from the scene after the explosion. In either case the original negative observation gives useful positive information about the method of operation of the criminal. It also indicates that he is likely to be an experienced operator. The further use of this type of information is discussed in Chapter 13.

Similar observations can be made on other features of attacks on safes with explosives. Some criminals use tamping material over the explosive charge, whereas others do not. Some attempt to muffle the sound of the explosion, whereas others do not. Observations after the explosion can provide positive evidence for the uses of tamping or muffling. They can, likewise, provide negative evidence from which the positive conclusion can be drawn that these techniques were not used. In either case, valuable evidence of methods of operation can be obtained.

NEGATIVE EVIDENCE LEADING TO NEUTRAL CONCLUSIONS

There are a number of circumstances in which negative evidence leads to neutral conclusions. It is most important that the investigator should realise this and should also be on his guard against attempts by other people to draw either positive or negative conclusions from such data. There are several familiar circumstances in explosion investigation where this pitfall occurs.

TRACES OF EXPLOSIVE ON A SUSPECT

Sometimes a person is detained by the police on suspicion that they have been concerned with the unlawful use of explosives. In such cases, it is common practice to take swabs from their hands and submit these, together with items of their clothing, for laboratory examination. The examination is directed to tests for explosives in general and to ones involved with the explosion or explosions under investigation in particular. Sometimes positive identifictions are made and sometimes the results of the laboratory tests are negative. In the latter circumstances there is a temptation, particularly for the legal adviser of the suspect, to seek to draw the conclusion that the suspect had not been in contact with explosives and hence could not have been concerned in the explosion. This is a perfectly valid conclusion, but there is another equally valid positive conclusion that can be drawn. By the use of gloves and care a person can handle explosives without getting any detectable traces on his person or clothing. Negative results from the laboratory tests are, therefore, also to be expected in the case of a person who has handled explosives in this manner. Any attempt, therefore, to draw only the former conclusion must be countered by pointing out that the correct conclusion to be drawn from the negative evidence in these circumstances is neutral. A positive result to the tests shows that the suspect has been in contact with explosives. A negative result is inconclusive.

Similar considerations apply to a suspect's car, house or other possessions. Positive results to laboratory tests show that the object in question has been in contact with explosives. Negative results neither establish that it has nor has not been in such contact.

REPLICA EXPERIMENTS

In considering possible causes of initiation, it is common practice to set up a replica experiment and observe whether or not initiation occurs. If the experiment is to give a complete and meaningful answer it is necessary to proceed as follows. A series of levels of the postulated stimulus must be chosen. These may be a series of electric sparks dissipating different energies, a series of graded mechanical impacts, a series of temperatures or other stimuli. A number of tests are then carried out at each level so as to determine the proportion of initiations at each. When sufficient data has been obtained it is then used to determine the input level at which there is a 50% probability of initiation, and, if the distribution is normal, to calculate the standard deviation. This information can then be used to calculate by normal methods of statistical analysis the probability of initiation at any given level of input stimulus. It will then be possible to make the assessment of the probability that the postulated initiation mechanism was in fact responsible. In practice if the postulated stimulus is less than that required to achieve a probability of initiation of 0·50 it is normally sufficient to compare the value of the postulated energy input in terms of the coefficient of standard deviation with the values in Table 12.1. It will be seen that, if the coefficient of the standard deviation is greater than 3, the postulated mechanism of initiation is unlikely to be the correct one. If the coefficient is 4 or more, the probability is so small that the postulated mechanism can provisionally be discounted.

TABLE 12.1

Coefficient of standard deviation	Probability
1	0·159
2	0·023
3	0·0013
4	0·00003

The experiment must then be repeated with every other plausible initiation mechanism. The probabilities of initiation can then be ranked in order. Normally that with the greatest probability can be accepted as the most plausible. If, however, two or more have reasonably high levels of probability, none of these can be discounted unless other evidence can be found as a basis for selection. If the mechanism with the highest level of probability nevertheless has a very low value, this should be taken as an indication that none of the postulated mechanisms is the correct one and that further consideration should be given to the matter.

This procedure has the disadvantage that it is very time consuming and costly. It may also be difficult in some cases to overcome the practical problems of setting up the replica experiments so as to ensure their validity. This will, especially, be the case for explosions in which only packaged products were involved. There is a tendency, therefore, to carry out a limited number of tests at a single level of input stimulus. If such a test results in a positive result, namely that the test specimen is initiated, this result can be accepted as indicating that the postulated mechanism is a plausible one. If, however, after a few tests only negative results are obtained, the investigator must be careful not to draw a false conclusion. He must also be on his guard against false conclusions drawn by other people from experiments giving this result whether they were conducted by himself or others.

The temptation is to conclude that the postulated mechanism could not have been responsible for the initiation. It must be realised, however, that there is no knowledge of the level at which the stimulus will produce a probability of initiation of 0·50, nor of the standard deviation. There is, therefore, no knowledge of the probability of initiation at the particular level used in the limited number of experiments. It may be quite high or it may be remote. Two or three negative results are just as consistent with a level of probability of initiation which makes the postulated mechanism a likely one, as with a level of probability of initiation which makes it so unlikely as to be completely discountable. It is important, therefore, to emphasise that negative evidence of this kind can only lead to a neutral conclusion, namely that the postulated mechanism may or may not have been capable of causing the initiation. In a case which illustrates this pitfall (1907) a man dropped a can containing a solution of nitroglycerine in acetone in the proportions 80:20. An explosion occurred and the man was killed. The report on the case observes that:

> This accident is a demonstration of the unreliability of negative evidence in connection with explosives in as much as experiments had previously indicated that nitroglycerine mixed with only 10 per cent by weight of acetone could not be exploded even by a 15 grain detonator.

There is another question relating to negative evidence that can arise in replica experiments. Explosive substances, whether recognised explosives or not, must, if they are to cause an explosion, receive a sufficient stimulus to produce initiation. It does not follow, however, that in any particular set of circumstances the deflagration or detonation will be sustained throughout the mass. There is a number of parameters which have critical values in relation to the ability of explosives to sustain the explosive reactions. The most important ones are charge diameter, to which can be related the size of the charge and its confinement, and the density of the explosive.

Detonation waves propagate through charges of limited diameter at less than the maximum velocity. Two main approaches have been used for hypotheses to explain this effect. One is based on the experimentally observed curvature of the wave front due to lateral expansion of the product gases. The equation of Eyring, Powell, Duffey and Parlin is of this type:

$$D/D_0 = 1 - z/d \quad \text{(for } z/d < 0·25)$$

where D is the detonation velocity for a charge of diameter d, D_0 is the detonation velocity in a charge of infinite diameter, and z is the reaction zone thickness.

The other approach is to explain the drop in velocity as a result of incomplete chemical reactions in the detonation wave. Cook has propounded an equation of this type:

$$(D/D_0)^2 = 1 - \left(1 - \frac{4ad^1}{3td}\right)^3$$

where D, D_0 and d are all as defined as above, a is a constant, d^1 is $d - 0.6$ cm, and t is the reaction time.

With either explanation it will be seen that decreasing diameter results in a diminution of detonation velocity and this is increasingly marked at small diameters. In practice the lower velocities represented by either of the above equations are not observable since the detonation wave fails to sustain propagation at the diameters concerned. A charge below the critical diameter may, however, have its ability to sustain the propagation of a detonation wave restored by confining it in a heavy casing.

The effect of confinement is also an important parameter in the behaviour of deflagrating explosives. In general, these burn with little or no explosive effect if ignited when the charge is unconfined. A charge of the same explosive ignited in a strong metal container will produce a powerful explosion.

For a given explosive, the detonation velocity for large diameter charges is known to be a linear function of loading density. The value observed for this rate of change varies from one explosive to another. In general, the nearer the oxygen balance to zero the greater the rate of change and it has been found (51) that detonation velocity can be expressed as a function of oxygen balance and density.

The existence of these relationships has important repercussions on the design of replica experiments. If an experiment involves a full-scale replica of the original situation, including the correct conditions of the various parameters discussed above, and an effective explosion occurs, it may be concluded that similar behaviour would have occurred in the original. If, however, no explosion, or a partial explosion, occurs it does not follow that this represents the behaviour of the original. As with experiments on initiation, there is no knowledge of the values of the parameters required to produce a 0.50 probability of sustaining an explosion, nor of the standard deviation. It is important to realise, therefore that a negative result can only lead to a neutral conclusion, namely that the observed conditions may or may not have been capable of sustaining a complete explosion.

If, for convenience, as sometimes must be the case, a model experiment is conducted, it becomes very difficult to draw any conclusions at all. If a complete explosion is obtained, it cannot be assumed that this would necessarily have been the case in a full scale experiment. The initiating stimulus cannot be scaled and, therefore, represents what could possibly be a crucial change in conditions. A reduction in the charge size can be compensated by increased confinement but the equivalence to the original would be a matter of speculation. Attempts to compensate for size by increasing the density of the explosive have sometimes been tried in these circumstances, but an increase in density can lead from a charge which is capable of sustaining a detonation to one which cannot. It follows, therefore, that the interpretation of a positive result in a model scale experiment is a matter of great difficulty and can lead to controversy, genuine or not. The interpretation of a negative result is equally difficult and can only justify a neutral conclusion.

A classic case which illustrates the uncertainties of drawing conclusions from negative results in model experiments is one in which the great pioneer in explosives research, Sir Frederick Abel, was injured (1884). A report on the incident says:

> At the same time the explosion affords another useful illustration of the impossibility of arriving at satisfactory results based on experiments with small quantities of explosive. As above stated, when a smaller experiment was made with only 10 tins (about 25 lbs) of gun cotton no explosion occurred, when the quantity was increased to 896 tins (1 ton) the result was an explosion of very great violence a few seconds after the application of the fire.

THE NEGATIVE HYPOTHESIS

The comparison of two things is a common requirement in forensic science. Such comparisons often take the form of that between a sample and a control or other reference in order to determine whether or not they are identical. Problems of this type arise in explosion investigations in such matters as the identification of samples of explosives, or of small arms cartridges, or of detonators.

The method of making such a comparative examination is to start by comparing the sample and the control in respect of some particular property. The result will be a decision that the two are, in respect of this property, either different or the same. If they are different, the investigation is complete. If they are the same, then it is legitimate to draw the conclusion that the sample and the control may be identical. Clearly, however, a greater degree of certainty than 'may be' is desirable. The next step is, therefore, to make a similar comparison between the sample and the control in respect of a second, independent, property. Once again, the result will be a decision that the two are, in respect of the second property, either different or the same. As before, if they are different the investigation is at an end. If they are the same then the conclusion still is that the control and sample may be identical. The obvious point, which is of crucial importance in the field of evidence, is how far must this process be taken in order to establish that the sample is identical with the control. In other words, what constitutes certainty?

In a limited population it would be possible to take the process to certainty by taking a sufficient number of properties to ensure a unique combination for each member. Such a situation occurs, for practical purposes, in the case of small arms cartridges. Catalogues exist which are sufficiently comprehensive as to be acceptable as exhaustive and a sufficient number of characteristics are recorded (dimensions, materials, markings, etc.) for a unique combination to be specifiable for each. A sample cartridge may, therefore, be identified with certainty. A similar situation obtains with industrial blasting explosives provided that the consideration is limited to the products of one country.

Unlimited populations can be of two kinds. The first is one in which the number of members is theoretically ascertainable but is so large as to make a complete compilation impossible in practice. Alternatively, the compilation may be impossible owing to virtually insurmountable difficulties in acquiring the information. An example of this type of unlimited population is that of industrial blasting explosives without a territorial limit. The number is obviously limited but the likelihood of identifying all manufacturers and then of ascertaining the composition of all their products is slight. The likelihood of compiling the corresponding list of military explosives is even more remote.

The second form of unlimited population is that where the number of members is not ascertainable at all. An example of this type is that of some given class of organic chemical such as amino acids or organic nitrates.

In an unlimited population certainty of identification can never be achieved. This is due to the fact that what is to be proved is that the sample matches the control in all properties studied and that such a match occurs with no other substance or article. Thus, what is required to be proved is a negative hypothesis and it is held in the methodology of science that a negative hypothesis can never be proved conclusively true.

Various methods are used to attempt to circumvent this predicament. One is to make the comparison in respect of as many properties as possible. Clearly the greater the number used then the greater the probability that the sample and control are identical. With an unlimited population, however, it is not possible to quantify this probability. Since the probability of a match with each property is not ascertainable, neither is the product. However, the proposition holds true that in general the greater the number of properties compared the greater is the probability that the match is unique. Even so the investigator is strictly not entitled to claim more than that he knows of no other match with this number of points of correspondence.

An alternative is to use a small number of properties and then to attempt to show that no other member of the population shares them. This is an unsatisfactory approach. Even if the probabilities cannot be quantified it is clear that, in general, a match based on the product of a large number of probabilities will be more conclusive than one based on a small number. Furthermore, the conclusiveness of the small number cannot be enhanced, as is sometimes supposed, by a series of comparisons which show that the sample does not match a number of controls. The probability that the sample will match the next control to be examined remains the same no matter how many comparisons have already been made.

Chapter 13

DRAWING THE CONCLUSIONS

ARRIVING AT FALSE CONCLUSIONS

As the previous chapters demonstrate, an explosion is a complex phenomenon and it follows, therefore, that the total body of data collected by an investigator can be considerable. It is necessary from this to draw the correct conclusions as to the cause of the explosion. When endeavouring to do this there are two particular reasons for arriving at false conclusions which should be guarded against. These are unconscious bias and the taking of individual items of evidence out of their context. Many people have misled themselves in these two ways in the past and there is no reason to suppose that similar errors will not be made in future. Investigators should, therefore, be alert to these possibilities.

Sherlock Holmes observed (*A Scandal in Bohemia*) that: 'It is a capital mistake to theorise before one has data. Insensibly one begins to twist facts to suit theories, instead of theories to suit facts.' This is an error against which any scientist will, by his training, be on his guard. There are occasions, however, in explosion cases when unconscious bias must be particularly guarded against. This is especially so when a person is suspected of causing an explosion or is actually on trial. It is only too easy in these circumstances to take for granted that he is guilty through the assumption that the police have charged he right person. Experienced investigators will know that this is often true and this fact makes this form of unconscious bias particularly hard to resist. Other reasons for the development of unconscious bias include the knowledge that the suspect has previous convictions for similar offences, indeed his name may figure more than once before in the laboratory case records or the investigator's experience, or the fact that the explosion concerned has had particularly distasteful consequences, such as the death of an innocent passer-by or of a child.

Unconscious bias towards innocence can also occur. Thus, a

221

scientist consulted by the defence must give of his professional expertise to the full, but should not allow himself to be influenced in this by the assumption that his client must necessarily be innocent. When conclusions are drawn, whether by others or by the investigator himself, they should be carefully examined for unconscious bias. It is a frequent requirement in forensic science to direct an examination to the answering of the question of whether two samples derive from a common source. In explosion investigation this includes such questions as: 'Was the explosive involved the same as that stolen from X?'; 'Was the explosive involved the same as that detected on the suspect's hands?'; and 'Was the fragment of metal found at the scene from a detonator type Y?'. The possible conclusions which can be drawn from the results of appropriate tests on the two samples or a sample and a control can be arranged in tabular form thus:

1. They are definitely not the same.
2. They are unlikely to be the same.
3. They are possibly the same.
4. They are probably the same.
5. They are definitely the same.

Unconscious bias towards guilt will produce a tendency to select a conclusion too far down the table. Unconscious bias towards innocence will produce a tendency to select a conclusion too far up the table. When a conclusion has been drawn, therefore, it is important to examine it critically and to consider whether the one above or the one below it does not more correctly interpret the results obtained.

There are many occasions in explosion investigation in which a selection must be made from a number of possible answers. This arises when there is no unequivocal evidence to select one from several uneliminated possible forms of initiation. Another instance is that in which chemical identification of an explosive is wholly or partially lacking and conclusions as to its identity must be drawn from other observations. In all such cases there will be at least several possibilities from which to choose. The possible conclusions can range from a high probability that one particular possibility is the correct one, to a complete inability to regard any one possibility as being more probably correct than the others. Unconscious bias towards guilt will produce a tendency to select a specific conclusion consistent with this view and an unconscious bias towards innocence will produce the opposite tendency. When such a conclusion has been drawn it should be critically examined to consider whether the conclusion correctly justified by the results should be more specific or less specific than that selected.

The guideline for drawing conclusions as free as possible from unconscious bias was given by Sherlock Holmes (*The Reigate Squires*): 'Now, I make a point of never having any prejudices and of following docilely wherever fact may lead me. . . .'. If following the facts leads to a definite conclusion, well and good. If, however, it leads to only several possibilities, then this is the conclusion which should be drawn and this should be made plain. Sometimes observations may be obtained which are inconclusive. In such a case the only valid conclusion is that the observations are inconclusive and, in the absence of fresh relevant data, attempts to regard the observations as being more conclusive than they are should be resisted.

Explosion investigation is a multi-disciplinary science involving various branches of chemistry, physics, mathematics and, to a lesser extent, other branches of science. When evidence in an explosion case is examined by a scientist who is not an explosives specialist he will tend to isolate those parts of the data which relate to his own discipline. The commonest tendency of this type is to isolate the chemical data. This can lead, and has led, to false conclusions.

One error made is to fail to take account of the extreme physical conditions of temperature, pressure and time in which the chemical reactions in an explosion take place. The kinetics of reactions may, therefore, be very different from those obtaining when the same or similar substances react under normal laboratory conditions. Sudden condensations of explosion products on to surfaces can, therefore, sometimes produce unexpected chemical species. Thus nitrite has been detected on surfaces after the explosion of amatol type explosives.

It is very important that any conclusions drawn from chemical tests should be consistent with the physical and other data. As an example, the identification of the chemical species ammonium, sodium, nitrate and chloride on debris might be interpreted as decomposition products of an explosive containing the reversed ion mixture ammonium chloride and sodium nitrate. These mixtures are, however, confined to a very limited number of coal mining explosives. If, therefore, the damage observations indicate a high brisance, this interpretation is not a valid one. A possible alternative is that the explosive contained ammonium nitrate and that the sodium chloride was derived from a sodium chlorate igniter system. This is not inconsistent with the observations of high brisance.

When drawing conclusions about an explosion, it is important to remember not to take groups of observations in isolation. Any hypothesis formed must be consistent with all the data.

EVIDENCE FOR CONNECTIONS

Accidental explosions are normally single events. Deliberate explosions may be single events or may be part of a series. Thus, an attack on a safe may be part of the work of a regular safebreaker and a bomb attack may be part of a sustained campaign. The investigator is, therefore, liable to be asked if there is evidence to indicate that a given explosion is connected with others, or whether it can be shown that a series of explosions are associated.

In considering evidence for association, two circumstances can be identified. One is that the available data relate to the explosions studied and to no others. The second is that the available data relate to the explosions studied and to others as well.

In the analysis of the first type of situation a table should be constructed which lists for each explosion the details of as many significant features as possible. Thus, for safebreaking the features might include the explosive, the type of detonator, details of ancillary equipment, details of the method of attack, the night of the week, the nature of the premises and its geographical location. For bombing attacks the features might include the explosive, the type of initiation, details of the operating mechanism, the nature of the target and its geographical location and the nature of the outer container for the bomb.

The table can then be examined and comparisons made between explosions for each feature. A number of conclusions can be drawn. If several of the features are alike in all the cases, then this observation is consistent with the hypothesis that all the cases are associated. Sometimes it is not possible to identify a particular feature in every case. Gaps in the data do not destroy the validity of the conclusion that the observations are consistent with the hypothesis that all the cases are connected. While this view is logically defensible it should not be pushed to extremes. A table with only a few gaps can be convincing but one containing more gaps than data, though strictly being consistent with the hypothesis, is unlikely to convince a jury.

If some of the features are alike and others differ, the nature of the differences should be considered. When an associated series of explosions occurs there can be changes in the materials used. For example, the initial supply of explosive and detonators may have consisted of five detonators and sufficient explosive for ten explosions. After the fifth explosion, therefore, a fresh supply of detonators would be necessary and these might not be of the same type as the originals. This is especially likely to be the case when the detonators are obtained illegally. The consequence is that the table of explosion features would show the same explosive in all cases, associated with one type of detonator in the first five, followed by association with a second type in the latter five. Thus, although the type of detonator is not constant throughout, there is a well-defined sequence. Similar sequences can occur with other features. Thus, in bombing attacks there may be a change of target or a change of initiating mechanism. It is important, however, not to designate a change in a feature as representing a sequence unless it is clearly defined and there are other features which are common to all cases. Such circumstances can also be regarded as being consistent with the hypothesis that all the cases are associated.

If the table presents no defined pattern, no particular conclusions can be drawn. This result may be due to the fact that there is no connection between the cases. Another possibility is that the same perpetrator is responsible for all of them but that he is having to rely on chance sources of supply of materials and has no consistent technique. Yet another possibility is that the same perpetrator is responsible but that he is a criminal with sufficient experience or intelligence to keep changing his materials and techniques in an attempt to avoid detection.

It must be emphasised that, where the available data relate to the explosions to be studied and to no others, the most that can be said is that the evidence is or is not consistent with the hypothesis that the explosions are associated. No assessment of the probability that the hypothesis is correct can be made. It is not possible either to make any statement as to the nature of the association. Associations in cases of this sort include a common perpetrator or different perpetrators who are themselves associated in a more or less well-defined organisation, or who have a common source of supply, or a common source of training, written instructions or other method of gaining expertise.

If the data available are more extensive it may be possible to make estimates of the probability that a number of explosions are associated. The basic collection of data can be from all the bombings in a given area in a given period, or from all the attacks on property or persons. Another possibility is all the attacks on safes in a given area in a given period. From the main body of data a set of cases is selected to be tested for evidence of association. The basis for selection is that the set should have a common feature. The set must consist of all the cases having this feature, so that the feature is found in all the cases in the set and in none of the remainder. Thus the set to be tested may be all the cases in which a given explosive or detonator has been identified or in which a given type of target has been attacked.

The procedure for testing for association is then as follows. The total body of data must be formed into a table showing the identity of as many features as possible. A convenient format is to have a series of columns in which the first column lists each case in chronological order, the second one lists, in the corresponding line, the identity of the explosive in each case, the third one lists, in the corresponding line, the identity of the detonator in each case and each subsequent column lists the identity of each of the other features for which data are available. The set of cases to be studied can then be identified by some appropriate marking.

A subsidiary table must then be formed for each feature other than the one which forms the reason for selecting the set of cases to be tested for association. Thus, for example, if bomb attacks are under consideration and if the set to be tested is selected on the basis of being the bomb attacks against military installations, then the first subsidiary table could relate to the explosive. The quantities to be listed would then be:

a = the number of cases in which the attacks were NOT against military installations in which the explosive was identified as X.

b = the number of cases in which the attacks were NOT against military installations in which the explosive was identified as being other than X.

$c =$ the number of cases in which the attacks were against military installations in which the explosive was identified as X.

$d =$ the number of cases in which the attacks were against military installations in which the explosive was identified as being other than X.

These data can then be stated in the form of a 2×2 table as follows:

	Cases in which explosive X was identified	Cases in which an explosive other than X was identified	Totals
Attacks not against military installations	a	b	$a+b$
Attacks against military installations	c	d	$c+d$
Totals	$a+c$	$b+d$	$a+b+c+d$

The probability that this set of entries should have occurred by chance is:

$$\frac{(a+b)! \ (c+d)! \ (a+c)! \ (b+d)!}{(a+b+c+d)!} \times \frac{1}{a! \ b! \ c! \ d!}$$

to which must be added the corresponding probabilities for any more extreme sets of frequencies which might have occurred.

A calculation using actual numerial values would be as follows:

Let $\quad a = 2$
$b = 15$
$c = 10$
$d = 3$

Then the 2×2 table is:

	Cases in which explosive X was identified	Cases in which an explosive other than X was identified	Totals
Attacks not against military installations	2	15	17
Attacks against military installations	10	3	13
Totals	12	18	30

The probability that this set of entries should have occurred by chance is then:

$$\frac{18!\ 12!\ 17!\ 13!}{30} \left(\frac{1}{2!\ 3!\ 10!\ 15!} + \frac{1}{1!\ 2!\ 11!\ 16!} + \frac{1}{0!\ 1!\ 12!\ 17!} \right)$$

which evaluates to:

$$\frac{619}{1330665}$$

or 1 in nearly 2,150. This shows that, if the hypothesis of proportionality is true for the data studied, then values of the kind suggested above would be highly exceptional.

A convenient way to make this argument intelligible to non-mathematicians is to express it in terms of percentages. It will be seen that the explosive X was used in 12 of the total number of 30 attacks, that is in 40%. If the attacks on military installations are a random selection from the total, it would be expected that about 40% of these would have involved the explosive X, *i.e.* about 5 of the 13 cases concerned. In fact, the observed number is 10, or about 77%. The probability that this proportion should occur if the attacks are a random selection is about 1 in 2,150. It is, therefore, highly improbable that the attacks on military installations are a random selection from the whole.

The more remote the probability found by analysis of the 2×2 table the less likely it is that the values have resulted from chance. The borderline for the probability to be regarded as significant is a matter of arbitrary selection but the figure commonly used is 5% or 1 in 20. In explosives cases much more remote probabilities are often found and values of 1 in a million or even more are not uncommon. Such figures indicate that the values observed are unlikely to have occurred by chance beyond not only reasonable but even the most unreasonable doubt.

The mathematical analysis goes no further than to indicate the probability that the observed figures have occurred by chance. It is possible, however, to consider the implications of this finding. It is a simple logical deduction that, if chance is improbable, then the only possible alternative, namely causation, is probable. Furthermore, the greater the improbability of chance the greater the probability that the observed values have arisen from some cause. There are several possibilities.

One possibility is that there is an association between the feature used as the basis for selecting the set for analysis and the second feature of the 2×2 table, *i.e.* that the variables are not independent. In other words, the second feature is a necessary, or nearly necessary, consequence of the first. Similar considerations apply when the second feature, although independent of the first, is commonly associated with it. Two circumstances can be distinguished. The first is that the association between the two features is a general one, such as that between electric detonators and detonator closing plugs, or between high explosive and detonators, or between attacks on safes and the technique of the insertion of the explosive through the keyhole. In such circumstances the proportion of cases exhibiting the second feature will be much the same in the set selected for analysis and in the remainder. Analysis of the 2×2 table would, therefore, have indicated a high probability that the observed values had occurred by chance and, therefore, no grounds for further consideration would have arisen. The second circumstance is that the association between the two features may be one peculiar to the set selected for analysis. Thus, in the specific example considered above, the presence of a night watchman could be a selected feature. This is, however, a feature commonly associated with military installations but much less commonly associated with other places. Analysis of the 2×2 table would be likely, therefore, to show that the observed values were unlikely to have arisen by chance. Since, however, the two variables are not independent, and can be seen to be such, then this is the only deduction to be made.

If, however, there is no necessary or normal association, then the finding that the observed values were unlikely to have arisen by chance leads to the conclusion that there is, in fact, an association between them, and that the set selected for analysis is an associated set. If other features of the set are likewise analysed and it is found that these values also are unlikely to have arisen by chance, the conclusion that the selected set is an associated one is strengthened, often to the point of being beyond argument.

Although a mathematical and deductive analysis of the type discussed above can lead to the conclusion that a given set of incidents is an associated set, it provides no information as to the nature of the association. As has already been said, such association can arise in a number of ways. These include a common perpetrator, or different perpetrators who are themselves associated in a more or less well-defined organisation, or who have a common source of supply, or a common source of training, written instructions or other methods of gaining expertise. The mathematical analysis can show that it is probable, highly probable or beyond even unreasonable doubt that there is an association, but the nature of the association must be established, if it is possible to do so at all, from other evidence.

Mention has already been made of the possibility of a feature in an associated set exhibiting the phenomenon of a sequence. An apparent sequence may occur in a set of data which is capable of mathematical analysis. If the set being analysed contains several other features which establish it beyond doubt as being an associated set, then the assumption that the apparent sequence is a real one is similarly confirmed.

Sometimes the set which it is desired to analyse is too small to give statistically significant results. The strict view then is that the data are not significant. If, however, several features can be considered then the probabilities can be multiplied together, provided that it is quite clear that the features constitute independent variables. It may then be found that the level of probability is significant. Considerable caution should, however, always be exercised when drawing conclusions from small bodies of data. It is best to err in the direction of refraining from drawing a conclusion, but it should also be remembered that to allow mathematical caution to override commonsense can result in unconvincing evidence. Each set of data and the results of its analysis must be considered carefully, both in the light of mathematical principles and of the whole body of data available.

Appendix A

DISTANCE-WEIGHT-PRESSURE VALUES
DERIVED FROM COOK'S EQUATION

100kN ≈ 14·5 psi
7kN ≈ 1 p.s.i

TABLE A.1

*Blast pressures generated at given distances
by given weights of explosive*

Distance (cm)	Weight (g)	Pressure (kNm^{-2})
100	100	207
100	200	391
100	500	945
100	1,000	1,872
100	2,000	3,737
100	5,000	9,376
100	10,000	18,832
200	100	40
200	200	66
200	500	137
200	1,000	253
200	2,000	484
200	5,000	1,176
200	10,000	2,337
500	100	10
500	200	14
500	500	21
500	1,000	31
500	2,000	48
500	5,000	95
500	10,000	170
1,000	100	5·1
1,000	200	6·4
1,000	500	8·9
1,000	1,000	11
1,000	2,000	15
1,000	5,000	23
1,000	10,000	35

231

2,000	100	2·5
2,000	200	3·2
2,000	500	4·4
2,000	1,000	5·5
2,000	2,000	6·9
2,000	5,000	9·6
2,000	10,000	12
5,000	100	1·0
5,000	200	1·3
5,000	500	1·8
5,000	1,000	2·2
5,000	2,000	2·8
5,000	5,000	3·8
5,000	10,000	4·8
10,000	100	0·52
10,000	200	0·66
10,000	500	0·90
10,000	1,000	1·1
10,000	2,000	1·4
10,000	5,000	1·9
10,000	10,000	2·4

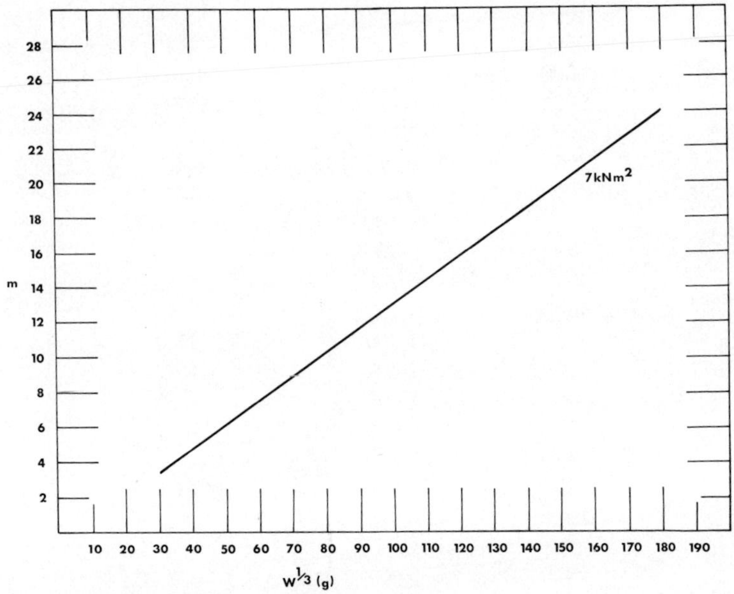

Fig. A.1   Distance v weight of explosive for blast pressure of $7\mathrm{kNm}^{-2}$ from cylindrical charges of TNT

Appendix B

THE IDENTIFICATION OF INDUSTRIAL BLASTING EXPLOSIVES BY SPOT TESTS

PRELIMINARY EXAMINATION

A preliminary examination is made of the whole sample for odour, colour, consistency and any visually observable ingredients. Ingredients with characteristic odours, such as mononitrotoluene, may often be detected at this stage. The colour and consistency can give a guide to the general type and sometimes to the particular explosive. Some ingredients, such as blown aluminium, can be readily identified by their characteristic appearance. Visible contaminants can also be observed at this stage.

MAIN EXAMINATION

Each test is carried out on a fresh portion of the unmodified explosive on a white spot plate unless otherwise stated. For the major ingredients about 2 mg of sample is sufficient but for minor ingredients a somewhat larger sample may be needed. For relatively coarse grained components, such as woodmeal, the sample must be large enough to contain at least one identifiable piece. All tests may be observed with the naked eye but for many it will be found advantageous to observe with low power ($\times 10$) magnification. Except where indicated, none of the components usually present in industrial blasting explosives interferes with the tests.

Group 1. *Nitroglycerine and ammonium nitrate*

1. Add one drop of a 0·1% solution of diphenylamine in nitrogen-free concentrated sulphuric acid. An intense deep blue colour denotes NITRATE, but is also given by most other oxidants.

2. Add one drop of 1% sulphanilic acid in 33% acetic acid and two drops of α-naphthylamine in acetic acid. A red colour denotes NITRITE. If the sample contains metallic particles a red colour may develop in the absence of nitrite if nitrate is present. If no colour change occurs add a few milligrams of powdered Devada'a alloy. A red colour denotes NITRATE. The α-naphthylamine reagent is prepared by boiling 0·2 g α-naphthylamine with 70 ml water, decanting the solution and adding 30 ml glacial acetic acid. Store in an amber bottle.

233

3. Add one drop of A.R. absolute alcohol and one drop of Nessler's reagent. A yellow or orange-brown colour denotes AMMONIUM. If this changes to black, NITROGLYCERINE is also present. An immediate black colour is given by nitroglycerine in the absence of ammonium. A deep red colour denotes TNT and this may mask the other two colours. If TNT is present the test should be repeated on a water extract. A black colour is also given by aldehydes, thio compounds and alkali sulphides and a grey by some other compounds, but none of these are normal constituents of industrial blasting explosives and should cause no confusion.

Group 2. *Organic nitrobodies and nitramines*

1. Add one drop of 1/1 acetone/ethanol and one drop of 20% aqueous tetramethyl ammonium hydroxide. NITROGLYCERINE gives a faint yellow colour. DNT (and some other dinitro aromatics) gives a blue colour which becomes dark green when nitroglycerine is also present. Red denotes TNT (and some other trinitro aromatics). If DNT, TNT and nitroglycerine are all present a transient green, changing to red, may be observed.

2. Add one drop of 1/1 acetone/ethanol and one drop of piperidine. A red colour denotes TNT (and some other trinitro aromatics). This test gives no colour with DNT.

3. Add a few milligrams of powdered thymol, five drops of nitrogen-free concentrated sulphuric acid and one drop of distilled water. A red colour is produced by RDX and HMX. Sugar also gives a red colour. Pink is produced by some compounds not normally present in explosives. Nitrates give a green colour. A deep pink colour is produced if the sulphuric acid is not nitrogen-free and it is essential, therefore, to carry out a blank test. The presence of RDX may be confirmed by taking a few mg of the sample in a test tube and adding 200 mg thymol and 0·3 ml (6 drops) of concentrated sulphuric acid. Warm the tube for 5 minutes at 100° C and then add 5 to 10 ml ethanol. A rich blue solution is produced by RDX but not by sugars, aldehydes or HMX.

Group 3. *Inorganic cations*

1. Add one drop of 1/1 acetone/ethanol and two drops of a saturated aqueous solution of zinc uranyl acetate. A slowly developing yellow-green fluorescence, visible under ultraviolet light, denotes SODIUM.

2. A flame test is carried out on a sample moistened with concentrated A.R. hydrochloric acid. If sodium is present, this must be burned off. After dipping the wire in concentrated A.R. hydrochloric acid, the flame should be observed for the characteristic colours of CALCIUM and BARIUM. If further confirmation of sodium, calcium or barium is considered necessary this may be conveniently done spectroscopically.

3. If the sample is black or brown in colour add one drop of 1/1

acetone/ethanol and one drop of benzidine reagent. A blue colour denotes MANGANESE as manganese dioxide. The benzidine reagent is prepared by dissolving $0 \cdot 5$ g benzidine in 10 ml glacial acetic acid and diluting with 100 ml water. Manganese dioxide may be confirmed by boiling a sample of the explosive with 1–2 g sodium bismuthate or red lead in dilute nitric acid. The appearance of a pink colour denotes manganese dioxide.

Group 4. *Inorganic anions*

1. Add one drop of 5% silver nitrate in dilute nitric acid. A white cloud changing to violet denotes CHLORIDE. If the cloud emerges from the sample at a few positions only, then a low chloride content is probable. High chloride contents give an immediate cloud which envelops the sample.

2. Add one drop of standard bench reagent ammonium molybdate in dilute nitric acid, one drop of benzidine reagent (as in Group 3, Test 3) and three drops of a saturated aqueous solution of A.R. ammonium acetate. A rich blue colour denotes PHOSPHATE. A slight blue can develop from silicates and from phosphates in other ingredients but this is readily distinguishable from the colour produced by phosphate as a component.

3. In tests where acid reagents are used, gas evolution will occur if CARBONATES are present and may occur with metals.

Group 5. *Carbonaceous materials*

1. Add one drop of 1/1 acetone/ethanol, break up the mass, and allow to evaporate. Add one drop of phloroglucinol reagent and observe after one and five minutes. Bright red particles of characteristic shape denote WOODMEAL. Oblong pale yellow shapes with red edges denote HUSK MEAL. The phloroglucinol reagent is prepared by dissolving 1 g phloroglucinol in 2 ml ethanol and diluting with 50 ml 1/1 hydrochloric acid.

2. To the above add two drops of N/50 iodine. A cloud of blue-black spots denotes STARCH. Husk meal produces a few blue-black spots in this test.

Group 6. *Elementary substances*

1. Mix a few mg of the sample with about ten times its weight of benzoin in a small ignition tube and warm to about 160° C with a basic lead acetate paper over the mouth of the tube. A black stain denotes SULPHUR.

2. ALUMINIUM observed in the visual examination may be confirmed as follows. Add three drops of 1/1 acetone/ethanol to 50 mg of the explosive in a test tube and shake. Add 3 ml dilute hydrochloric acid and warm. When all metallic particles have dissolved, add 1 ml of $0 \cdot 1\%$ aqueous aluminon reagent and excess dilute 1/1 ammonium hydroxide/ammonium carbonate. A flocculent red precipitate denotes aluminium.

IDENTIFICATION OF SAMPLE

By means of these tests it is possible to deduce the presence of nitro-glycerine, mononitrotoluene, dinitrotoluene, TNT, RDX, ammonium, sodium, calcium, barium, sulphur, aluminium, manganese dioxide, nitrate, nitrite, phosphate, carbonate, woodmeal, husk meal and starch. The absence of these ingredients may also be deduced but with less certainty, and negative results should be used with care.

Some deductions can be made in respect of the combinations of inorganic anions and cations.

1. The presence of ammonium and phosphate can normally be interpreted as ammonium phosphate since this is the only phosphate likely to be present in an industrial blasting explosive.

2. The presence of ammonium and nitrate can normally be interpreted as ammonium nitrate since this is a very common constituent of industrial blasting explosives.

3. The presence of sodium and chloride can normally be interpreted as sodium chloride since this is a common major ingredient of coal mining explosives.

4. If ammonium, nitrate, sodium and chloride are all present this may mean ammonium nitrate and sodium chloride or, alternatively, the reversed ion mixture ammonium chloride and sodium nitrate. The former is far more likely since reversed ion mixtures are very uncommon. The point may be resolved, however, by extracting a portion of explosive with ether and acetone and examining the residue microscopically for the characteristically cubic crystals of sodium chloride.

5. The presence of barium normally denotes barytes since this is the only barium salt normally used as a constituent of industrial blasting explosives.

By close observation and attention to detail, experienced operators can make other deductions with varying degrees of certainty.

After taking into account any known or suspected contaminants, the observations are then compared with the specified compositions of explosives by manufacturers whose products are normally used in the country in which the investigation is taking place or of some other country, if this appears relevant. This may be quickly and conveniently done if the components of the various explosives are recorded on punched cards. It will often be found that only one explosive has the particular combination of ingredients. Where there are two or more the observations of colour and consistency will often resolve the question, but, if this is not so, then a quantitative determination must be made. It is often not necessary, however, to determine all the ingredients since normally there will be one ingredient that is present in markedly different proportions in the possible explosives.

Appendix C

QUANTITATIVE ANALYSIS OF INDUSTRIAL BLASTING EXPLOSIVES

This scheme of analysis is applicable to explosives based on TNT and ammonium nitrate (*Type A*) and to explosives based on gelatinised nitroglycerine (*Type B*).

EXTRACTIONS

1. Volatile matter

Type A. Weigh accurately about 2·5 g of the explosive into a tared sintered glass crucible (porosity 3) and dry in vacuo over concentrated sulphuric acid for 24 hours. Weigh.

Type B. Friable explosives. Weigh accurately about 2·5 g of the explosive into a V.M. cone and dish apparatus and heat on a boiling water hot plate for two hours. Cool and weigh.

Type B. Gelatinous explosives. Weigh accurately about 2·5 g of the explosive and place on about 3 g dried French chalk in a mortar. Cover with a little more chalk and press gently with the pestle until it forms a thin layer. Grind *gently, avoiding hard impact*, until a friable mass is obtained. Proceed as for friable explosives.

In all cases the loss in weight is taken as the total volatile matter.

2. Solvent extraction.

Type A. Use the crucible with the residue from the volatile matter determination or weigh a fresh portion of explosive (2·5 g) into a tared SG 3 crucible. Attach the crucible to a filter flask, half fill the crucible with dry benzene, stir up the contents with a small glass rod and break up the mass to a fine powder. Cover the crucible with a watch glass and allow to stand for 10 minutes. Remove the benzene by suction, but do not suck air through, and repeat the extraction four more times. Dry the crucible for one hour at 100° C, cool and weigh. The loss in weight is taken as the benzene soluble material (aliphatic and aromatic nitrocompounds, wax).

Type B. Proceed as for the benzene extraction for Type A, substituting ether for benzene and giving 10 extractions. Dry the crucible for half an hour at 60° C, cool and weigh. The loss in weight is taken as the ether-soluble material (aliphatic and aromatic nitrocompounds, nitroglycerine, nitroglycol and resin).

237

238   EXPLOSION INVESTIGATION

3. Water extraction

Types A and B. Attach the crucible containing the residue after solvent extraction to a filter flask. Fill the crucible two thirds full of water and stir the contents with a small glass rod. Allow to stand for a few minutes and remove the water by suction. Repeat the extraction ten times. Dry the crucible for 2 hours at 100° C, cool and weigh. The loss in weight is taken as the water-soluble material (ammonium nitrate, sodium chloride, sodium nitrate, ammonium chloride, ammonium phosphate and any other water-soluble inorganic salts).

4. Acid extraction

Type A. Remove the residue from the crucible after the water extraction and transfer it to a 250 ml beaker. Place the crucible also in the beaker and digest with concentrated hydrochloric acid on a hot plate until all gas evolution ceases. Remove the crucible, wash it into the beaker and dry and filter the contents of the beaker through the crucible. Dry the crucible for two hours at 100° C, cool and weigh. The loss in weight is taken as the acid-soluble material (aluminium, Fe_2O_3).

Type B. Remove the residue from the crucible after the water extraction and transfer it to a 150 ml beaker. Place the crucible also in the beaker, add 50 ml N/100 hydrochloric acid and digest for one hour on a boiling water bath. Remove the crucible, wash it into the beaker, dry and filter the contents of the beaker through the crucible. Dry the crucible for two hours at 100° C, cool and weigh. The loss in weight is taken as the acid-soluble material (calcium carbonate, starch and wheatflour). Some forms of starch are not dissolved by this treatment and may need more vigorous hydrolysis with 1/1 v/v hydrochloric acid.

5. Acetone extraction

Type B. Attach the crucible containing the residue after acid extraction to a filter flask. Fill the crucible two thirds full of warm acetone and stir the contents with a small glass rod. Allow to stand for a few minutes and remove the acetone by suction. Repeat the extraction four more times. Dry the crucible for one hour at 100° C, cool and weigh. The loss in weight is taken as the acetone-soluble material (nitrocellulose). The filtration may be very slow if starch or a high china clay content is present, in which case it is best to proceed with ignition and to determine the nitrocellulose separately on a fresh portion of the explosive.

6. Ignition

Types A and B. Heat the residue after acid and acetone extraction in the crucible at 500–600° C for two hours, allowing free access of air. Cool and weigh. The loss in weight is taken as the combustible material remaining after the extractions (nitrocellulose if not already extracted, woodmeal and carbon).

7. Residue

The remaining weight after the previous operations is taken as the residue (china clay, kaolin, kieselguhr, talc, barytes and grit).

EXAMINATION OF EXTRACTS

1. Ether extract

Transfer the extract to a 150 ml flask. Distil off the solvent until only a few ml remain and remove these in a current of cold air. Add 25 ml of freshly prepared methyl alcohol/sulphuric acid mixture (40 ml concentrated acid gradually added to 60 ml methyl alcohol with cooling and swirling). Cover with a watch glass and heat for 45 minutes at 60° C. Cool for 30 minutes at room temperature.

Dilute the solution with 50 ml water and transfer to a separating funnel. Wash out the flask with 30 ml ether into the funnel. Shake to extract nitrobodies from solution and repeat the extraction with 30 ml ether three times in all. Combine the extracts in another separating funnel and wash with water until free from acid. Transfer the ether extract to a tared flask, distil off the ether until about 2 ml remains and remove this with a current of cold air. Dry in vacuo over concentrated sulphuric acid and weigh. The extract is taken as combined nitrocompounds. The difference between the total ether extract and the sum of the volatile matter and nitrobodies is taken as the nitroglycerine.

2. Water extract

(a) *Ammonium.* Place an aliquot in a 250 ml conical flask and add 100 ml standard N/10 aqueous sodium hydroxide. In another flask place another portion of sodium hydroxide to act as a blank. Place small funnels in the necks of the flasks to prevent mechanical loss and boil until a paper moistened with mercurous nitrate solution placed in the vapour no longer turns black. Cool. Add methyl red indicator and back titrate the excess sodium hydroxide with N/10 acid. The difference between the blank and the sample corresponds to the amount of ammonium present.

(b) *Alkali metals.* Take an aliquot of the extract containing about 0·25 g extracted material. If phosphate is present, boil the solution and for each 3 mg extracted material present add 0·3 ml bench reagent ferric chloride solution. Add, gradually, a slight excess of dilute ammonium hydroxide solution and boil for 2 minutes. Allow to settle, filter, wash residue and use filtrate in the determination.

Evaporate the solution in a beaker with 1 ml concentrated sulphuric acid almost to dryness and transfer with the least quantity of water to a tared platinum or silica crucible. Carefully evaporate to dryness and ignite at dull red heat. Cool, add 2 ml water and 0·05 g powdered ammonium carbonate and evaporate again to dryness. Ignite at dull red heat, cool and weigh. The weight is taken as sodium or potassium sulphate. The cation can be identified by flame test.

(c) *Nitrate.* Take an aliquot of extract containing about 0·1 g nitrate, transfer to a 150 ml beaker and make up to 100 ml with water. Add ten drops of dilute sulphuric acid, heat to boiling and add 12 ml nitron acetate solution. Cool in ice for two hours and filter through a tared SG3 crucible. Wash with 10 ml ice cold water and dry to constant weight at 105–110° C. Cool and weigh as nitron nitrate. Perchlorates, chromates, picrates and iodides interfere with this reaction.

(d) *Chloride.* Place 50 ml of extract into a 250 ml flask. Add five drops dichlorofluorescein indicator and a small amount of dextrine. Titrate with N/10 aqueous silver nitrate.

Appendix D

THE IDENTIFICATION OF MILITARY HIGH EXPLOSIVES BY THIN LAYER CHROMATOGRAPHY

Substance	Solvent	Eluent	Visualiser	Colour	Rf
Mononitrotoluene	1	1	1	Faint yellow	0·48
Dinitrotoluene	1	1	1	Yellow	0·40
Trinitrotoluene	1	1	1	Brown	0·44
Nitroglycerine	1	1	2	Yellow/red	0·38
Ammonium nitrate	2	2	3	Red on pink	0·58
Ammonium nitrate	2	2	4	Mauve on pink	0·58
Nitroguanidine	3	2	2	Red	0·53
Nitrocellulose	4	2	2	Red	0·00
RDX	4	3	4	Mauve on pink	0·47
HMX	4	3	2	Red	0·40
PETN	4	3	2	Red	0·69
Tetryl	4	3	2	Red	0·66

Plate coating: Silica gel + UV indicator, 0·25 mm.

Sample aliquot: 1 μl.

Solvents:
1. diethyl ether.
2. water.
3. hot water.
4. acetone.

Eluents:
1. benzene.
2. ethanol.
3. chloroform/acetone 1/1.

Elution distance: 19·25 cm.

Visualisation reagents:
1. The plate is sprayed with a 15% solution of titanous chloride in hydrochloric acid and allowed to dry in air. It is then sprayed with a solution consisting of 1 g *p*-dimethylaminobenzaldehyde dissolved in a mixture of 30 ml ethanol, 3 ml hydrochloric acid (1/19) and 180 ml *n*-butanol.

2. The plate is lightly sprayed with N sodium hydroxide, dried in an oven at 100° C for 10 minutes, cooled and sprayed with Griess reagent (Appendix B, group 1 test 2 solutions mixed).

3. The plate is sprinkled with powdered Devada's alloy and then sprayed with Griess reagent.

4. 1·5 g thymol and 10 ml nitrogen-free concentrated sulphuric acid are mixed and warmed to form a viscous yellow solution. This is sprayed lightly on to the plate which is then placed in an oven at 100° C for about 10 minutes.

Appendix E

THE IDENTIFICATION OF MINOR COMPONENTS OF PROPELLENTS BY THIN LAYER CHROMATOGRAPHY

(T. H. McIntyre and A. N. Beaton, *ICI Nobel Division Report No. R132*)

1. *Stabilisers*

Rf values with various eluents

Substance	1	2	3	4	Colour
Resorcinol	0·00	0·32	0·00	0·16	Brown
2-nitrodiphenylamine	0·71	0·86	0·41	0·66	Red
Methyl centralite	0·01	0·69	0·00	0·20	Red
Ethyl centralite	0·02	0·75	0·01	0·33	Red
p-nitro-N-methylaniline	0·25	0·58	0·05	0·37	No change
N-nitrosodiphenylamine	0·58	0·82	0·24	0·69	Blue
4-nitrodiphenylamine	0·39	0·66	0·08	0·55	Violet
2, 4-dinitrodiphenylamine	0·37	0·78	0·08	0·57	No change
2, 4-dinitro-N-methylaniline	0·27	0·67	0·05	0·38	No change
Diphenylamine	0·74	0·78	0·48	0·69	Blue

Plate coating: Silica gel, 0·25 mm.

Sample aliquot: 5 μl.

Eluents:
  1. benzene.
  2. benzene/petroleum ether (40/60)/methanol 27/9/4.
  3. benzene/petroleum ether (40/60) 1/1.
  4. benzene/ethyl acetate 85/15.

Elution distance: 16 cm.

Visualising reagent: Maraour's reagent:
  Potassium dichromate, 5 g.
  Glacial acetic acid, 100 ml.
  Concentrated sulphuric acid, 50 ml.
  Water, 100 ml.

243

2. *Phthalates*:

Rf values with various eluents

Substance	1	2
Dimethyl phthalate	0·38	0·47
Diethyl phthalate	0·44	0·54
Dibutyl phthalate	0·50	0·65
Amyl phthalate	0·59	0·68
Dicyclohexyl phthalate	0·53	0·66

Plate coating: Silica gel, 0·25 mm.

Sample aliquot: 50 μl.

Eluents:
1. Dichloromethane.
2. Benzene/ethyl acetate 85/15.

Visualising reagent:
1% resorcinol in concentrated sulphuric acid. After elution the plate is air-dried and sprayed. After heating at 140–150° C for 15–20 minutes a yellow-green colour is produced.

APPENDIX F

THE IDENTIFICATION OF CHLORIDE, CHLORITE, CHLORATE AND PERCHLORATE BY PAPER CHROMATOGRAPHY

(B. L. Harrison and D. H. Rosenblatt, *J. Chromat.* 13 1964 p. 271).

Paper:

Whatman No 1 filter paper 5 × 43 cm, spotted 4 cm from end.

Elution:

For 16 hours with 2-propanol/water/pyridine/concentrated ammonium hydroxide 15/2/2/2.

Visualisation:

The paper is dried at room temperature and then treated in strips measured from the starting line, the remainder being shielded from the visualising reagent.

0-11 cm. Spray with 0·2N aqueous silver nitrate and dry. Expose to UV lamp for 2 minutes. Chloride produces a dark purple spot at Rf 0·25 ± 0·02.

11-24 cm. Spray with freshly prepared 3M aqueous hydrochloric acid/acetone 1/1 and 5% ethanolic diphenylamine. Chlorite produces a blue spot at Rf 0·36 ± 0·02 and chlorate, after drying 2–3 minutes, a green spot at Rf 0·54 ± 0·02.

24-43 cm. Spray with saturated aqueous sodium acetate, dry and overspray with 0·2% aqueous methylene blue. Perchlorate produces a violet spot on a blue background at Rf 0·71 ± 0·02.

Appendix G

TESTS FOR SOME COMMON COMPONENTS OF FIREWORK COMPOSITIONS

Aluminium	Appendix B, group 6 test 2.
Antimony	A crystal of pyrogallol is stirred into one drop of a test solution, which must be slightly acid. A microcrystalline precipitate of characteristic shape indicates antimony.
Ammonium	Appendix B, group 1 test 3.
Barium	One drop of test solution is placed on absorbent paper and spotted with a drop of a freshly prepared 0·1% aqueous solution of rhodizonic acid. A reddish-brown spot is produced which becomes brilliant red on the addition of a drop of dilute hydrochloric acid.
Copper	A paper impregnated with a 2% alcoholic solution of α benzoinoxime is dried and spotted with a drop of the test solution. It is then exposed to ammonia and dried. A green colouration denotes copper.
Iron	One drop of test solution is mixed with one drop of 1% aqueous solution of acridine hydrochloride and one drop of a 1% aqueous solution of ammonium thiocyanate. The formation of red crystals, observable under the miscroscope, denotes iron.
Magnesium	Add to the test solution one drop of magneson reagent (0·5% solution of p-nitrobenzene-azo-resorcinol in sodium hydroxide) and sufficient sodium hydroxide solution to produce a strongly alkaline condition. A blue colour denotes magnesium.
Potassium	Appendix I.
Sodium	Appendix B, group 3 test 1.
Strontium	As for barium but the brown spot is decolourised by the addition of hydrochloric acid.
Titanium	A drop of the test solution containing sulphuric acid is mixed on a spot plate with 5 drops of the reagent solution. A violet

246

colour indicates titanium. Reagent: 0·02 g chromotropic acid dissolved with warming in 20 ml concentrated sulphuric acid.

Carbonate	Appendix B, group 4 test 3.
Chlorate	Appendices F and I.
Nitrate	Appendix B, group 1 tests 1 and 2.
Perchlorate	Appendix F.
Gunpowder	Chapter 5, propellents.

Appendix H

THE IDENTIFICATION OF SOME PRIMARY EXPLOSIVES AND INITIATORY COMPOSITIONS

1. *Primary explosives by thin layer chromatography* (O. Bohm, Explosivstoffe)

Substance	Rf with various eluents			Colour with various visualisers		
	1	2	3	1	2	3
Mercury II	—	—	0·14	Orange	—	Grey-brown
Lead II	0·37	0·36	0·00	Yellow	—	Brown-grey
Styphnate	0·73	0·71	0·89	Yellow without visualisation		
Fulminate	0·64	0·63	0·95	—	—	Brown-grey over 100° C
Azide	—	0·49	0·62	—	Red	—

Plate coating: MN silica gel N, 0·25 mm.

Solvent: 20% aqueous ammonium acetate/ethanolamine 4/2/3.

Sample aliquot: 2 μl.

Eluents:
1. Methanol/2N hydrochloric acid 80/20.
2. Methanol/2N hydrochloric acid/acetone 65/15/10.
3. Acetone/concentrated ammonium hydroxide 75/25.

Visualisation reagents:
1. 2% aqueous potassium iodide.
2. 2% aqueous ferric chloride.
3. 2% aqueous acidified sodium sulphide.

248

2. *Identification of components of an initiatory composition*

Sample
↓
Benzene extraction → extract = organic high explosives, DDNP
↓ (Appendices D & J, Chapter 5)
Residue
↓
Acetone extraction → extract = nitrocellulose
↓ (Appendix D)
Residue
↓
Cold water extraction → extract = potassium chlorate, barium
↓ nitrate
Residue. (Appendix G)
↓
Ammonium acetate extraction → extract = lead azide
↓ (50% aq.) (Appendix H)
Residue
↓
Hot water extraction → extract = tetracene
↓ (Chapter 5)
Residue
↓
Dil. acetic acid extraction → extract = magnesium, carbonate
↓ (Appendix G)
Residue
↓
Hydrochloric acid extraction → extract = antimony sulphide, calcium
↓ silicide
Residue (Appendices G & H)
glass, carborundum

Antimony sulphide:
If this is present the odour of hydrogen sulphide will be noticed as it dissolves. An orange precipitate will form in the extract which will redissolve as more hydrochloric acid comes through the filter.

Calcium silicide:
If this is present it will react with the hydrochloric acid forming rings and leaving a greenish residue.

Appendix I

THE IDENTIFICATION OF THE COMPONENTS OF SOME COMMON IMPROVISED EXPLOSIVE MIXTURES

Preliminary examination:

A preliminary examination is made under low power ($\times 10$) magnification. Coloured components (*e.g.* permanganate, sulphur and aluminium) can be recognised and it will often be possible to distinguish the number of substances present. If the components are not finely ground, it may be found possible to separate fragments of individual ones for separate analysis. If this is not possible, components may still be distinguished by carrying out spot tests under magnification with samples spread out so that the reactions of individual particles can be observed.

Identification of common oxidants:—

Chlorate	Spot test: the addition of a solution of aniline hydrochloride in concentrated hydrochloric acid produces a blue colour with chlorates. TLC: Appendix F.
Nitrate	Spot test: Appendix B, group 1 test 2. TLC: Appendix D.
Permanganate	The characteristic purple coloured aqueous solution is rendered green by alkaline reduction and decolourised by acid.
Ammonium	Appendix B, group 1 test 3.
Potassium	Yellow precipitates are produced in aqueous solution by the addition of aqueous sodium cobaltinitrite or sodium picrate. These reactions are also given by ammonium salts which, if present, must be removed before this test is carried out. The flame test may also be used.
Sodium	Appendix B, group 3 test 1.

Identification of common fuels:—

Aluminium	Appendix B, group 6 test 2.
Sugar	1. Fehling's test. 2. Hydrolyse the sample by boiling with dilute hydrochloric acid, cool and neutralise with sodium hydroxide. To the

neutral solution add a few drops of a freshly-prepared 0·5% solution of 2, 3, 5-triphenyltetrazolium chloride and make slightly alkaline with N/10 sodium hydroxide. Sugar produces a red colour. Excess of alkali also produces a red colour and a blank test should always be run.

Sulphur	Appendix B, group 6 test 1.
Starch	Appendix B, group 5 test 2.

Appendix J

THE IDENTIFICATION OF EXPLOSIVES TRACES BY THIN LAYER CHROMATOGRAPHY

Substance	Rf	Colour on visualisation
TNT	0·70	Brown before visualisation
PETN	0·60	Pink
Nitroglycerine	0·60	Pink
Tetryl	0·40	Yellow before visualisation, yellow-brown after
RDX	0·05	Pink
Nitrocellulose	0·00	Pink

Plate coating: Silica gel with UV indicator, 0·25 mm.

Solvent: Diethyl ether.

Sample aliquot: 2 μl.

Eluent: Toluene.

Visualisation reagent:
The plate is lightly sprayed with N sodium hydroxide, dried in an oven at 100° C for 10 minutes, cooled and sprayed with Griess reagent (Appendix B, group 1 test 2 solutions mixed).

Appendix K

EXPLOSION PARAMETERS OF SOME DUSTS

(*Fire Research Technical Report No. 21*)

Substance	Minimum ignition temp. °C	Minimum explosible conc. gl⁻¹	Minimum ignition energy mJ	Maximum explosion pressure kNm⁻²
		gl^{-1}		kNm^{-2}
Acetyl salicylic acid	550	0·015	16	599
Aluminium, 6 micron	—	0·03	13	634
Benzoic acid	600	0·011	12	655
Caprolactam	430	0·07	60	544
Carbon, 13% volatile	590	—	45	296
Cellulose acetate	340	—	—	765
Coal, pulverised 100 BSS	550	—	—	537
Cork	400	—	—	599
Cyclohexanone peroxide	—	—	21	579
Diphenylol propane	—	0·012	11	558
Epoxy resin	490	0·03	32	427
Flour, wheat	390	—	—	655
Grain, distillers dried solubles	420	0·06	128	544
Lauryl peroxide	—	—	12	620
Maize husk	430	—	—	517
Melamine formaldehyde resin	410	0·12	68	599
Nitrocellulose	—	—	30	1,765
Nitrofurfural semicarbazone	240	—	—	985
Phenol formaldehyde resin	450	0·015	—	737
Polythene	390	0·02	38	599
Polypropylene	380	—	43	310
Potato, dried, 80 BSS	450	—	—	668
Rubber, crumb	440	—	—	579
Sawdust	430	—	—	668
Senna	440	0·01	105	337
Sodium acetate	560	0·15	—	137
Sodium carboxymethylcellulose	320	1·10	440	357
Sodium propionate	470	—	—	482
Sugar	330	0·045	48	641
Tea	500	—	—	641
Tobacco, dried	320	—	—	585
Urea formaldehyde resin	430	0·02	34	758

Appendix L

EXPLOSION COMPOSITIONAL LIMITS FOR MIXTURES OF FLAMMABLE VAPOURS WITH AIR

(*International Maritime Dangerous Goods Code*)

Substance	Explosion limits % min.	max.	Flash point °C
Low flashpoint group			
Acetal	1·6	10·4	21
Acetaldehyde	4·0	57·0	−27 cc*
Acetone	2·0	12·8	−20
Acrolein	2·8	31·0	−18
Acrylonitrile	3·0	17·0	0 cc
Allyl chloride	3·3	11·1	−29
Iso-butyraldehyde	1·0	12·0	−24 cc
Carbon disulphide	1·0	50·0	−30 cc
Diethylamine	1·8	10·1	−39
Diethyl ether	1·7	48·0	−40 cc
Dimethyl sulphide	2·2	19·7	−37
Di-isopropyl ether	1·5	21·0	−36
Divinyl ether	1·7	27·0	−30 cc
Ethyl formate	3·5	16·5	−34
Iron carbonyl	3·7	12·5	−15
Methyl formate	5·0	22·7	−32
Monopropylamine	2·0	10·4	−37
Petroleum, flashpoint below −18 °C	1·1	8·7	−18
Propyl chloride	2·6	10·5	−18
Propylene oxide	2·0	22·0	−29 cc
Tetrahydrofuran	1·0	56·0	−18
Vinyl ethyl ether	1·7	28·0	−46
Vinylidine chloride	5·6	11·4	−10
Intermediate flashpoint group			
Allyl alcohol	2·5	18·0	21–32

* cc denotes flashpoint determined in a closed cup.

254

	Explosion limits %		
	---	---	---
Substance	min.	max.	Flash point °C
Allyl bromide	4·4	7·3	−1
Amyl alcohols	1·2	7·6	21–57 cc
Amylamine	2·2	22·0	0 cc
Amyl chloride	1·4	8·6	1 cc
Benzene	1·4	8·0	−11 cc
Tertiary butanol	2·4	8·0	11 cc
Isobutyl acetate	2·4	10·5	18 cc
N-butyl acetate	1·3	15·0	22
Iso-butylamine	3·4	9·0	−9 cc
N-butylamine	1·7	10·0	−12 cc
N-butyl chloride	1·8	10·1	−9 cc
N-butyl formate	1·6	8·3	18 cc
Butyraldehyde	1·4	12·5	−7 cc
Coal tar naphtha	1·3	8·0	16–25
Crotonaldehyde	2·95	15·5	13
Dichloroethylene	5·6	16·0	6
Dimethylamine, 20% aqueous soln.	2·8	14·4	0
Dimethyldichlorosilane	1·4	9·5	−9 cc
Dioxane	2·0	22·0	12 cc
Ethanol	3·3	19·0	13
Ethyl acetate	2·18	11·5	−4 cc
2-ethylbutyraldehyde	1·2	7·7	21 cc
Ethylene dichloride	6·2	15·9	13 cc
Ethyleneimine	3·6	46·0	−11 cc
Ethyl methyl ketone	1·8	11·5	−1 cc
Ethyl propionate	1·8	11·0	12 cc
Methanol	6·0	36·5	12 cc
Methyl acetate	4·1	13·9	−10 cc
Methyl acrylate	1·2	25·0	−3 cc
Methyl isobutyl ketone	1·4	7·5	24 cc
Methyl hydrazine	2·5	98·0	23 cc
Methyl methacrylate	1·5	11·6	8 cc
Methyl propionate	2·4	13·0	−2 cc
Methyl propyl ketone	1·5	8·1	7 cc
Naptha, solvent	1·3	8·0	16–25
Propanol	2·0	12·0	15 cc
Isopropanol	2·0	12·0	22 cc
Isopropyl acetate	1·8	7·8	2 cc
N-propyl acetate	1·8	8·0	14 cc
Propylene dichloride	3·4	14·5	15 cc

Substance	Explosion limits %		Flash point °C
	min.	max.	
Propyl formates	2·4	7·8	−3 cc
N-propyl nitrate	2·0	5·1	24
Pyridine	1·8	12·4	20 cc
Toluene	1·27	7·0	7 cc
Triethylamine	1·2	8·0	−7 cc
Vinyl acetate	2·6	14·0	−8 cc
Xylenes	1·1	7·0	35 cc
High flashpoint group			
Acetic acid (80% acid)	4·0	17·0	43
Amyl alcohols	1·2	7·6	21–57 cc
Butanol	1·4	11·2	29 cc
N-butyl bromide	5·2	5·6	24 cc
Chlorobenzene	1·3	15·9	60 cc
2-chloroethanol	4·9	15·9	60 cc
p-cymene	0·7	5·6	47 cc
Diacetone alcohol	1·8	6·9	61 cc
Dibutyl ethers	1·5	7·6	38 cc
Dichloropropene	5·0	14·0	29 cc
Ethyl lactate	1·5	11·4	46 cc
Formaldehyde, aqueous solution	7·0	73·0	32–61 cc
Methylisobutyl carbinol	1·0	5·5	55 cc
Styrene	1·1	6·0	32 cc
Tetraethyl silicate	1·3	23·0	37 cc

Appendix M

EXPLOSION COMPOSITIONAL LIMITS FOR MIXTURES OF FLAMMABLE GASES WITH AIR

(*International Maritime Dangerous Goods Code*)

Gas	Explosion limits % min.	Explosion limits % max.	Density air = 1·0
Acetylene	2·1	80	0·907
Ammonia	15·0	30	0·6
Butadiene	2·0	44	1·84
Carbon monoxide	12·0	75	0·97
Coal gas	4·5	40	0·4–0·6
Cyanogen	6·6	43	1·9
Deuterium	5·0	80	0·14
Diborane	0·9	98	0·95
1,1-difluoroethane	5·0	17	2·3
1,1-difluoroethylene	2·3	25	2·2
Difluoromonochloroethane	8·5	14	3·5
Dimethylamine	2·8	14	1·6
Dimethyl ether	2·0	50	1·6
Ethane	3·0	16	1·05
Ethylamine	3·5	14	1·6
Ethyl chloride	3·5	15	2·2
Ethylene	3·0	34	0·98
Ethylene oxide	3·0	100	1·5
Ethyl methyl ether	2·0	10	2·1
Hydrogen	4·0	75	0·07
Hydrogen cyanide	5·6	40	0·93
Hydrogen sulphide	4·0		1·2
Methane	5·0	16	0·55
Methylamine	4·3	21	1·09
Methyl chloride	8·0	20	1·8
Methylmercaptan	4·0	22	1·7
Oil gas	5·0	33	—
Trifluorochloroethylene	24·0	40	4·0

Gas	Explosion limits %		Density air $= 1.0$
	min.	max.	
Trifluoroethane	9.5	19	2.9
Trimethylamine	2.0	12	2.1
Vinyl chloride	4.0	31	2.2
Vinyl fluoride	2.9	29	1.6
Water gas	6.0	70	0.5

Appendix N

DIFFERENCES BETWEEN UNITED KINGDOM AND UNITED STATES EXPLOSIVES TERMINOLOGY

English is the language of both the United Kingdom and the United States. Over the course of years differences have developed between the usage of the language in the two countries. These differences are sometimes expressed by describing the usages as English English and American English respectively. Other English speaking countries and countries where English is widely used tend to follow one or other of these two, sometimes with minor variants of their own. The text of this book follows United Kingdom usage.

In explosives literature, the differences in grammar and spelling do not usually cause any great difficulties or result in ambiguities, though it is best for any given publication to be consistent in this respect. In terminology, however, there are differences in the words used to denote various explosives and devices, which can lead to confusion and misunderstanding unless their existence is appreciated. A comprehensive list of such differences would include many, such as technical mining terms, which would seldom, if ever, be encountered by the explosion investigator. There are, however, a number of widely used explosives terms which are different in the two usages. A selection of those most likely to be encountered by the explosion investigator is as follows:

Explosive or device	United Kingdom	United States
EXPLOSIVES:		
Industrial blasting explosives:		
Explosive containing essentially nitroglycerine and inert absorbent such as kieselguhr	Dynamite	Straight dynamite
Explosive based on nitroglycerine and nitrocellulose	Blasting gelatine	Gelatin dynamite
Explosive based on nitroglycerine, nitrocellulose and ammonium nitrate	Ammon dynamite *or* ammon gelignite *or* special gelatine	Ammonia dynamite special gelatin

259

Explosive or device	United Kingdom	United States
Explosive of any kind authorised for use in coal mines	Permitted explosive	Permissable explosive
Explosive based on ammonium nitrate and fuel	Blasting agent	Blasting agent

1. These definitions are a simplification of a complex semantic situation. While they broadly represent current practice individual manufacturers use their own variations.
2. In the United States the term dynamite is sometimes loosely used to denote any type of high explosive used in blasting operations.
3. In each type there are many explosives each with their own manufacturer's name which may or may not incorporate the type name.
4. In each type the individual explosives contain a variety of minor ingredients in addition to the major ones on which they are based.

Other explosives:

Explosive formulated from potassium nitrate, carbon and sulphur	Gunpowder *or* Black powder	Black powder

EXPLOSIVE DEVICES:

Igniters

Electrically operated device containing a small charge of gunpowder	Gunpowder igniter *or* powder fuse	Electric squib
Igniter, usually operated by percussion, fitted into the base of cartridges for weapons and actuator devices	Cap	Primer

Detonators:

Detonators for use with blasting explosives operated by flame (*e.g.* safety fuse)	Plain detonators	Blasting caps *or* fuse blasting caps
Detonators for use with blasting explosives operated by electricity	Electric detonators	Electric blasting caps *or* EB caps
Detonators for use with blasting explosives operated by electricity and having built-in delays in steps of $\frac{1}{2}$ seconds	Delay detonators	Delay blasting caps

Explosive or device	United Kingdom	United States
Detonators for use with blasting explosives operated by electricity and having built-in steps of few milliseconds	Short delay detonators	Millisecond delay blasting caps
Wires forming part of an electric detonator	Lead wires	Leg wires

Fuses:

Fuse containing a core of detonating explosive, usually PETN	Detonating fuse, often called Cordtex after a widely used proprietary product	Detonating cord, often called Prima-cord after a widely used proprietary product

Other devices:

Component containing the propellent in a cartridge for weapons	Cartridge case	Shell

EQUIPMENT:

Portable device for generating electricity for operating electric detonators	Exploder	Blasting machine

EXPLOSIVE PROPERTIES:

The energy liberated by an explosive	Power *or* bulk strength *or* weight strength	Strength *or* grade strength *or* cartridge strength *or* field execution value (other terms are also in use)

TECHNIQUES:

The process of setting off charges of blasting explosives	Firing *or* the term shooting is used in some applications	Shooting

OTHER SUBJECTS:

Hydrocarbon fraction used to operate internal combustion engines	Petrol	Gasoline *or* gas

Confusion can occur with the second United States term since it is also used in both usages to denote a gaseous substance.

REFERENCES

References in the form of the number of a year A.D. in brackets denote that the matter referred to will be found in the annual report of Her Majesty's Inspectors of Explosives for that year.

References in the form of a roman numeral in brackets denote that the matter referred to will be found in the special report of Her Majesty's Inspectors of Explosives of that number.

Case histories quoted without a reference are from the author's personal experience.

All other references are numbered and are as follows:

1. E. B. Hensel, *J. For. Sci. Soc.*, 5, 1965, p. 65.
2. E. I. du Pont de Nemours and Co., *Blaster's Handbook*, 1968.
3. Nobel's Explosives Company Ltd., *Blasting Practice*, 1971.
4. T. Urbanski, *Chemistry and Technology of Explosives*, 1964-7.
5. Rev. R. Lancaster, *Fireworks Principles and Practice*, 1972.
6. S. Fordham, *High Explosives and Propellents*, 1966.
7. J. Calzia, *Les Substances Explosives et Leur Nuisances*, 1969.
8. H. Ellern, *Military and Civilian Pyrotechnics*, 1968.
9. M. A. Cook, *Science of High Explosives*.
10. B. T. Federoff *et al.*, *Encyclopedia of Explosives and Related Items*, 1960.
11. T. C. Brodie, *Bombs and Bombings*, 1972.
12. R. A. Durfer, *Bombs, Explosives and Incendiary Devices*, 1961.
13. R. R. Lenz, *Explosives and Bomb Disposal Guide*.
14. J. F. Stoffel, *Explosives and Home Made Bombs*.
15. W. Powell, *The Anarchist Cookbook*, 1971.
16. A. C. Doyle, *A Study in Scarlet*, 1887.
17. S. A. Granstrom (Trans. Roy. Inst. Tech., Stockholm), 1956.
18. Lord Penney, D. E. J. Samuels and G. C. Scorgie, *Phil. Trans. Roy. Soc.*, A 266, 1970.
19. R. J. Mainstone, *Building Research Station Current Paper 26/71*, 1971.
20. V. J. Clancey, *Canadian Aeronautics and Space Journal*, 1968, p. 337.
21. E. Newton, *Canadian Aeronautics and Space Journal*, 1968, p. 385.
22. H. P. Tardiff and T. S. Stirling, *J. For. Sci.*, 12, 1967, p. 247.
23. C. S. Robinson, *Explosions; Their Anatomy and Destructiveness*, 1944.
24. M. Kornhauser, *Structural Effects of Impact*, 1964.

25. T. D. Northwood, R. Crawford and A. T. Edwards, *The Engineer*, 1963, p. 973.
26. R. Jenkins and H. J. Yallop, *Explosivstoffe*, No. 6, 1970, p. 139.
27. N.R.A. of America, *American Rifleman*, May 1970.
28. K. Gugan, *Private communication*.
29. D. P. Lidstone, *Explosivstoffe*, No. 9, 1969, p. 193.
30. A. Marshall, *Explosives*, 1972. p. 468.
31. A. R. Martin and H. J. Yallop, *J. Appl. Chem.*, 9, 1959, p. 310.
32. R. J. Grogan and K. H. Marshall, *The Criminologist*, No. 26, 1972.
33. R. W. Wright, *Space Technology Laboratory*, STL 372–30, 1965.
34. S. J. Board, R. B. Duffey, C. L. Farmer and D. H. Poole, *Nuclear Sci. and Eng.*, 52, 1973, p. 433.
35. A. C. Doyle, *A Scandal in Bohemia*.
36. R. C. Selkirk and D. F. Nelson, *J. For. Sci. Soc.*, 1968, p. 12.
37. R. W. Van Dolah, F. C. Gibson and J. N. Murphy, *US Bureau of Mines Report*, 6746.
38. G. F. Kinney, *Explosive Shocks in Air*, 1962.
39. Th. M. Groothuizen, E. W. Lindeijer and H. J. Pasman, *Explosivstoffe*, 1970, p. 97.
40. A. J. Tulis and T. A. Erikson, *Recent Developments in Shock Tube Research*, 1973, p. 508.
41. A. H. Gill, *J. Ind. and Eng. Chem*, 15, 1923, p. 140.
42. J. R. Ward, R. K. Pahel and K. J. White, *Chem. Abs.*, 80, 1974, 49927y.
43. Institute of Makers of Explosives (New York), *Safety Guide for the Prevention of Radio Frequency Radiation Hazards*, 1971.
44. R. G. Hall, Private communication.
45. H. G. Tanner, *J. Chem. Ed.*, 36, 1959, p. 58.
46. U.S. Atomic Energy Commission, *The Effects of Nuclear Weapons*, 1962.
47. H.M.S.O., Report on the Accident to Comet Series 4B G-ARCO which occurred in the Mediterranean near Rhodes on 12 October 1967.
48. Capt. W. E. Parry, *Journal of a Second Voyage*, 1825.
49. H. J. Yallop, *The Investigation into the Causes of the Explosion at Ronan Point 16 May 1968*, R.A.R.D.E. Report 3/69.
50. W. E. Ayrton, *J. Inst. Elect. Eng.*, 21, 1892, p. 404.
51. A. R. Martin and H. J. Yallop, *Trans. Farad. Soc.*, 1958, p. 252.

INDEX